3

631.504 SMT

D0119680

LEARNING.
•••••••••••services

Duchy College Rosewarne
Dartington

This resource is to be returned on or before the last date
stamped below. To renew items please contact the Centre

Seven Day Loan

2 8 SEP 2011		
- 5 DEC 2013		
1 2 DEC 2013		
2 3 FEB 2015		
- 2 MAR 2015		

Sattler · Wistinghausen

Bio-Dynamic Farming Practice

Bio-Dynamic Farming Practice

Friedrich Sattler

Eckard v. Wistinghausen

Translated from the German by A.R. Meuss

85 diagrams
36 colour plates
82 tables

BDAA

©1989 by Eugen Ulmer GmbH & Co. Stuttgart, Germany.

ISBM 0 9518976 0 8

First edition 1992

Translation © A.R. Meuss 1992

Diagrams: Rainer Benz, Stuttgart

Printed by Cambridge University Press,
University Printing House, Shaftesbury Road, Cambridge CB2 2BS

Computer generated diagrams and text formatting,
Index software origination, Colour film separations by
Michael Davighi Associates, Elton House, Powell Street, Hockley,
Birmingham B1 3DH

Published in English by the
Bio-Dynamic Agricultural Association,
Goethean House, Woodman Lane, Clent, Stourbridge,
West Midlands DY9 9PX

Preface

Most people are by now aware of the fact that the environment has been used and abused by the human race and is very much at risk. This means that everything possible must now be done to retain and restore what after all is the basis of human life on earth.

Biodynamic agriculture, based on a course given by Rudolf Steiner in 1924, has now existed for over sixty years. The method has been further developed and applied in practice and has proved successful. It is not enough to write theoretical treatieses on the problems of our time, and in our view it is vital to put ideas into practice so that they become realities. This book is an attempt to present the knowledge and experience gained in the practice of biodynamic agriculture. Since experience tends to be as wide-ranging and different as are the individuals that gain it, the contents of this book are of necessity a selection presented from the point of view of its authors. No claim can be made for completeness.

As a practical farmer responsible for sixty head of cattle, fifty hectares of land and training a number of young people, I thought at first that it would be impossible to write a book about the knowledge and experience I have gained with the biodynamic method. However, my publisher, Roland Ulmer, and Professor H.H. Koepf insisted that I make the effort, and I am grateful for this, having gained a great deal in the doing of it.

If readers find even a few ideas and practical applications that serve them as well, then the difficulties and problems I encountered in many a hard night's work will be amply rewarded.

I'd like to say a special thank-you to my parents who brought me up to revere and honour God and the world of nature and to respect human labour. They have also given me a practical education in the ways of biodynamic agriculture, which they practised. I also owe much to my teachers in this field – Ludwig Piening, Immanuel Voegele and Erhard Bartsch – and to Lore and Hanns Voith, whose foresight and initiative made it possible for us to farm Talhof biodynamically.

Many friends have given their help and advice to make this book possible. It is not possible to mention them all by name but I would like to say 'Thank you and God bless you' to them all. The help given by my good friend Krafft von Heynitz does merit special mention, however, for he has always gone immediately and in detail through every draft and made the necessary corrections. Marlene Grimm assisted with the organizing, revision and typing of the manuscript, and this gave me some valuable breathing space in the period just before Christmas.

Last but not least, my warmest thanks to everybody who has worked with me over the years on the farm.

Without my wife's steady, quiet support and understanding, always at hand and prepared to help, our 33 years of work at the Talhof farm would not have been possible, nor could this book have been written. To her, therefore, my deepest and most loving gratitude.

Fritz Sattler
Talhof near Heidenheim, Germany

Working in collaboration with such an experienced practitioner, I am grateful to have been allowed to have a part in the writing of this work. My special thanks go to my father and teacher in farming practice, A. Chr. von Wistinghausen, holder of a diploma in agriculture, Mr Martin Schmidt who showed me how effective anthroposophy can be in working with plants, and Professor H. H. Koepf who introduced me to the scientific work. Let their names stand for the many to whom I'd wish to express my gratitude. I am indebted to my brother, Dr Christian von Wistinghausen, for suggesting that I collaborate in the work.

Eckard von Wistinghausen
Darmstadt, Germany

Acknowledgements
The authors are indebted to the following individuals for assistance in producing the manuscript:

U. Abele, Darmstadt
D. Bauer, Bad Vilbel
E. Becker, Bad Vilbel
E. Breda, Darmstadt
R. Dietrich, Witten-Annen
J. Fetscher, Dortmund
G. Graf Finkenstein, Dueren
M. Grimm, Darmstadt
H. Heilmann, Weckelweiler
K. von Heynitz, Pforzheim
P. Jacoby, Witzhalden
M. Klett, Bad Vilbel
H. H.Koepf, Forest Row
H. Pfeiffer, Heidenheim
K. Roggenkamp, Bad Wurzach

G. W.Schmidt, Friesenhofen
W. Seidl, Heidenheim
H. Spiess, Bad Vilbel
K.M. Thun, Dexbach
M. Thun, Dexbach
K. Tress, Bichishausen
A.Chr. von Wistinghausen, Schafhausen
Chr. von Wistinghausen, Maeusdorf

We are also most grateful to Mr Rainer Benz, Stuttgart, who produced the drawings in this work from our sketches or from the literature and was responsible for the graphic design. The plants used in the special preparations have been drawn by our friend Wolfgang Scheibe, Vogelsberg.

Contents

Every idea which
does not become your
ideal, slays a force in
your soul; every idea
which becomes your
ideal, creates within
you life-forces.
Rudolf Steiner,
*Knowledge of Higher
Worlds and its
Attainment,* 1909.

Frequently used abbreviations

AA   = agricultural area (Switzerland)
AL   = agricultural land
CAL = calcium ammonium lactate solubility
CU   = large animal (cattle) unit
DCY = direct cost-free yield
DM   = dry matter
GM   = gross margin
h   = hour

kSE = kilo starch equivalent
LW   = live weight
MFA = main fodder-growing area
NEL = net energy lactation, measure used to evaluate feedstuffs for milk production in cows
p.t.o. = power take-off
RCU = roughage-eating large animal unit
SE   = starch equivalent
SI   = soil index
TGW = thousand grain weight

The idea of the farm as an individual entity

At Whitsun 1924 Rudolf Steiner, PhD, the founder of anthroposophy, gave a course of eight lectures on agriculture at Koberwitz near Breslau (today the Polish Wroclaw). This was at the request of farmers and horticulturalists. Basing himself on insights won through spiritual science into the life of the earth and the world of nature, he presented the principles for a more far-sighted approach to horticulture and agriculture and practical suggestions for their implementation. A number of those who attended the lectures took this up immediately and there and then established a group to test the method that has since come to be known as biodynamic agriculture. In the sixty years that have passed, many people in many different countries around the globe have worked to refine and develop a method that has proved eminently practicable. Many of the questions that are raised today with reference to the environment, quality of produce and energy management have found an answer in biodynamic agriculture, though there is of course room for consolidation and further development.

Rudolf Steiner's concept of farm management was based on a picture of the farm as a largely self-contained integral whole. This may seem surprising when one considers the commonly accepted structure of agriculture today. In Steiner's day, family farms and even some larger establishments did still come close to his concept. Since then, however, most conventionally farmed holdings have become specialised in line with business and labour management criteria. Steiner's concept of a sound, integral unit or organism evolved on the basis of local conditions has been developed out of spiritual scientific findings concerning the interaction of energies and forces in the natural world. It is becoming increasingly meaningful today. Taking up the best tradition of sound farming practice adapted to local conditions, modern management skills, methods of cultivation and feeding, the benefits of technology, etc. are utilised to evolve an up-to-date unit that is also ecologically sound.

Local conditions are the prime criteria, with economic, ecological and social requirements taken into account. The aim is to utilise the farm's own resources to achieve sustained fertility and a sound system. Humus replacement is a good starting point; it depends on a combination of animal keeping, utilisation of animal manure and crop rotation.

Livestock numbers should be such that the manure they produce will maintain and enhance soil fertility. The right number and kind of animals needs to be determined in relation to site and climatic conditions. Experience has shown that on most

Rudolf Steiner, born in Kraljevec (Austria) on 27 February 1861, died in Dornach (Switzerland) on 30 March 1925.

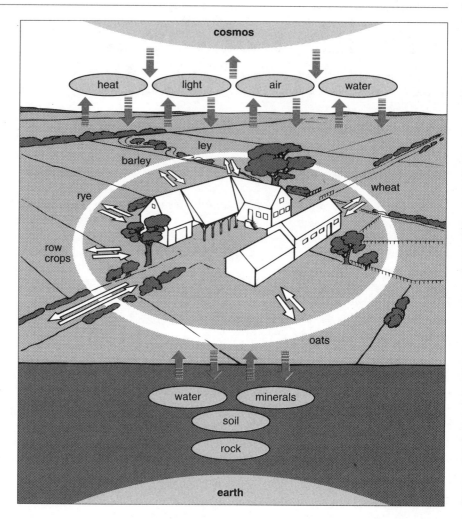

Fig. 1. The farm

farms, stock equivalent to one large cattle unit (500–600 kg live weight) per hectare of agricultural land is about right. The farm needs to be able to produce all the feed the animals require. To be economically viable and for the sake of animal health, all animal feed should be grown on the farm itself. Biotopes and economic conditions vary, and biodynamic farms therefore vary enormously in this respect. A good variety of fodder plants grown as part of the crop rotation system also helps to improve the soil, apart from anything else because they include leguminous plants and grasses. There is no conflict of interest with the need for land required to grow the cereal and root crops and pulses that are of major importance for the population as a whole. The land will give good, reliable yields of high-quality produce.

Seed production requires special care to ensure good, high-quality yields for as long as possible without deterioration. The only breeding stock to be bought in should be sires (to avoid inbreeding); the rest should come from the farm's own breeding programme. The life environment of plants, and to some extent also of animals and humans, consists of rock formations and soil, the landscape in which the farm lies, and the surrounding cosmos with sun, moon, planets and fixed stars. The aspects and constellations of heavenly bodies and their rhythms influence the conditions in which plants and animals live and grow. One important task is to learn all we can about their effects at sowing, planting, cultivation and harvesting times and on animal keeping and breeding. This knowledge is then put into practice.

Another important aspect is the intensive use of biodynamic preparations. These are applied to the soil, to plants and in the preparation of manure and compost. They are produced on the farm or in cooperatives, i.e. a number of farms working together.

To look after a farm and give it the right form is a task that has real meaning and challenges all the human faculties of the community involved in the work. Links with the social and cultural environment are many and varied. The tasks of agriculture also include the following:

– producing high-quality food entirely out of the potential of individual holdings
– maintaining and enhancing the landscape and its natural and cultural potential
– training young people and introducing them to the concept of work as something that has meaning and serves the common weal
– taking part in experimental and research work for the further development of an agriculture that is attuned to the natural world
– nurturing cultural life on the farm in cooperation with the social life of the region.

Farms where Rudolf Steiner's concept of agricultural holdings as individual and essentially self-contained units are realised are able to make a real contribution to finding the answers to questions concerning human life in the present time and in the future.

Farm profiles

The farm profiles given below in form of basic statistics are intended to show the different routes taken to achieve a common goal under different site conditions, the goal being to make the holding into an individual, largely self-sustaining unit.

The first four (unnumbered) farms no longer exist in that form today.

They did however hold special significance for the development, spread and reputation of biodynamic work, and are part of its history, as are the individuals who ran them:
Ernst Stegemann, Klostergut Marienstein; Immanuel Voegele, Rittergut Pilgramshain; Erhard Bartsch, Gut Marienhoehe; Benno von Heynitz, Rittergut Heynitz.

Klostergut Marienstein in Noerten-Hardenberg

Farmed biodynamically from 1925; conversion started in 1922, following directions given by Rudolf Steiner

Soil: 27 % marsh (river Leine), 28 % alluvial, 24 % sloping ground with loam, 21 % steep weathered rock slopes

Altitude: 127.5–188 metres above sea level   Av. annual rainfall 515 mm
Total area: 153.5 ha, incl. 150 ha AL
Ratio of arable to grass 1:0.06
CU/ha AL: 0.58, incl. 0.34 RCU

Cropping sequence

1. rye, winter barley
   IC: black medick/white melilot
   IC: vetches/field peas/beans
   sugar beet
   peas/oats
   wheat

2. potatoes
   wheat
   oats/beans
   clover
   rye
   IC: black medick/white melilot

Stock (total of 87.6 CU)

15 horses
 2 draught-oxen
 1 breeding bull
40 dairy cows

28 young stock
16 pigs
poultry

For abbreviations see pages 10 and 34

Farmed biodynamically from 1927; conversion that year.

Soil: granite residual, sL–lC
Altitude: 255 metres above sea level   Av. annual rainfall 595 mm
Total area: 303.75 ha, incl. 225.75 ha AL
Ratio of arable to grass 1:0.16
CU/ha AL: 0.57

Gut Pilgramsheim, Silesia

Cropping sequence

Row crops (1/3 potatoes, 1/3 beet, 1/3 red clover)
Summer grazing (2/5 spring barley, 3/5 oats)
Winter grazing (1/2 rye, 9/20 wheat, 1/20 winter barley)

Stock (total of 129 CU)

23 horses	2 breeding bulls	5 breeding sows
4 foals	47 dairy cows	30 fattening pigs
24 oxen	73 young stock	22 piglets

Farmed biodynamically from 1931; conversion started in 1928

Soil: end moraine, sandy soil, lime-poor
Altitude: 96 metres above sea level   Av. annual rainfall 423 mm
Total area: 105 ha, incl. 75 ha AL
Ratio of arable to grass 1:0.25
CU/ha AL: 0.50, incl. 0.39 RCU

Gut Marienhoehe in Bad Saarow

Cropping sequence

1. potatoes
   oats/legumes
   IC: lupins/vetches/field peas
   rye
   IC: serradella

2. serradella or lupins
   (for seed)
   rye
   IC: lupins
   summer grazing (oats)

3. root crops
   spring barley undersown with clover
   clover
   rye/spelt
   IC: lupins
   oats

Stock (total of 37.4 CU)

5 horses	1 breeding bull
2 draught-oxen	12 young stock
22 dairy cows	

Rittergueter Heynitz & Wunschwitz in Saxony, management by Lommatz

Farmed biodynamically from 1933; conversion started 1930 with 11.1 ha, 1931: 95.81 ha, 1932: 223.51 ha

Soil: sL
Altitude: 250–300 metres above sea level Av. annual rainfall 500 mm
Total area: 358.29 ha, incl. 285.29 ha AL
Ratio of arable to grass 1:0.14
CU/ha AL: 0.88

Cropping sequence

Heynitz

red clover
oats
root crops with farmyard manure
wheat, barley
rye
legumes, mixed
wheat
potatoes with farmyard manure
wheat undersown with clover

Wunschwitz

red clover
root crops with farmyard manure
wheat, oats with beans
winter barley, wheat
potatoes with farmyard manure
wheat
rye, oats with undersown with clover

Stock (total of 202 CU)

23 horses
20 draught-oxen
 2 breeding bulls
80 dairy cows
50 young stock

 10 calves
200 ewes
 50 yearlings
100 lambs
 60 fattening pigs

Apart from the individuals mentioned by name and their holdings, there are many other farms and farmers who have been and still are contributing to the development of biodynamic agriculture. Almar von Wistinghausen's book *Erinnerungen an den Anfang der biologisch-dynamischen Wirtschaftsweise* (the early days of biodynamic farming – a memoir; not available in English) may be of interest in this respect.

The farm profiles that follow are of farms that have been farmed biodynamically for some time, are still continuing in this way and are actively involved in development work.

The reference numbers used in the text refer to these farm profiles.

Farm in Swabian Alb (1)

Farmed biodynamically from 1929
All biodynamic preparations are produced on the farm

Soil basis: Upper Jurassic residual. Rendzina (humus carbonate). Terra fusca
Soil index: 16-59 500–560 metres above sea level
Av. annual temperature 5.7 °C Av. annual rainfall 780 mm
52 ha AL Ratio of arable to grass 1:1.1
CU/ha: 1.0 Main feed growing area: 0.75 ha/RCU

Labour force
Manager: 0.8 units   Regular staff: 0 units
Trainees, apprentices: 4
5.6 workers/100 ha   207 kW (276 hp)/100 ha

Cropping sequence	Intercropping (U = undersown, S = stubble sown)	solid/liquid manure t/m³ per ha
1. ley		
2. ley		35 t composted manure + 22.5 m³ dung liquor
3. potatoes, maize	U: white clover	18.0 m³ dung liquor
4. naked barley	U: red clover ley	
5. red clover ley		20 t composted manure + 10.0 m³ dung liquor
6. spring wheat	S: rape/mustard	20.0 m³ dung liquor
7. oats	U: ley	
8. ley		
9. ley		20 t composted manure + 20.0 m³ dung liquor
10. winter wheat	S: rape/mustard	15 t composted manure + 10.0 m³ dung liquor
11. peas	shed peas	
12. oats	S: oil radish	10.0 m³ dung liquor
13. oats/legume green mixture	U: ley	

Special crops: none.

Bought-in fertilizer: none.

Bought-in feed: For rearing young bulls: linseed meal, dried sugar beet chips, oats (if own production falls short). For laying hens: fish meal 4 kg/year/hen. Skimmed milk if not available on farm. In dry years, hay and feed grain for dairy cows.

Cattle: spotted mountain breed   26 dairy cows
1 breeding bull   32 replacements
Management: summer: grazing all day; winter: short stands, daily exercise.
Young stock: summer: grazing all day; winter: deep litter loose housing with yard.

Chickens: 80 leghorn
Management: free range, 25 m²/hen (changed annually); own natural breeding programme.
51 CU cattle   1 CU poultry   total of 52 CU.

Manure treatment: composted manure.

Marketing: 80% farmgate sales, 20% general market.

Comments: none.

Farm in Swabian Alb (2)

Farmed biodynamically from 1955
All biodynamic preparations are produced on the farm

Soil basis: Upper Jurassic residual.
Soil index: 32.   730 metres above sea level
Av. annual temperature 6.5 °C   Av. annual rainfall 800 mm
29.7 ha AL   Ratio of arable to grass 1:3
CU/ha: 1.1   Main feed growing area: 0.62 ha/RCU
Labour force: Manager: 1 unit   Regular staff: 0 units
Trainees, apprentices: 2–3
8 workers/100 ha   230 kW (307 hp)/100 ha

Cropping sequence	Intercropping (U = undersown, S = stubble sown)	solid/liquid manure t/m³ per ha
ley		12 t composted manure
ley		
ley		12 t composted manure
row crops		35 t composted manure
cereal	U: black medick	
clover		12 t composted manure
clover		
cereal		
row crops (field beans/sunflowers)		35 t composted manure
cereal	U: black medick S: rape	
cereal		12 t composted manure

Special crops: 0.2 ha strawberries, 1 ha field-grown vegetables

Bought-in fertilizer: pigs bristles c. 40 DM/ha; calcified seaweed 10 DM/ha

Bought-in feed: In dry years, small amount of hay: 90 DM/cow

Cattle: 15 dairy cows
                                                   22 replacements
Management: tethered housing, cows in pasture from 10 May to 25 October; young stock in pasture from 1 May to 1 November; in winter daily exercise in yard.

Horses: 1

Chickens: 100 laying hens
Management: flock houses, 0.6 ha open run

30 CU cattle   1 CU poultry   total of 32 CU.
  1 CU horse

Manure treatment: 70% of manure is composted with added earth. Every field has an application of compost every two years. Dung liquor is applied to cereals, beet and leys.

Marketing: 100% farmgate sales; milk 100% general market.

Comments: Own seed grown for cereals, red clover, sainfoin and lentils since 1981.

Farmed biodynamically from 1957
All biodynamic preparations are produced on the farm

Soil basis: arable: diluvial mineral soils, $^1/_3$ S, $^2/_3$ lS–sL; grassland: low moor
Soil index: 22–56   1–3 metres above sea level
Av. annual temperature 8.2 °C   Av. annual rainfall 741 mm
86.5 ha AL   Ratio of arable to grass 1:1.04
CU/ha: 1.24   Main feed growing area: 0.6 ha/RCU
Labour force:
Manager: 1 unit   Regular staff: 1 unit
Trainees, apprentices: 8
6.9 workers/100 ha   155 kW (211 hp)/100 ha

Cropping sequence	Intercropping (U = undersown, S = stubble sown)	solid/liquid manure t/m³ per ha
1. ley		
2. ley		15 t composted manure
3. row crops		20 t composted manure + dung liquor
4. oats, peas, some beans	U: red clover ley	
5. wheat		20 m³ dung liquor
6. $^1/_2$ rye	U: $^1/_2$ ley	
$^1/_2$ spelt	S: $^1/_2$ vetches & rye	
7. roots & tubers		30 t composted manure + dung liquor
8. rye		U: ley

Special crops: none

Bought-in fertilizer: small amounts of calcified seaweed and basalt rock dust

Bought-in feed: none

Cattle: German red pied   50–52 dairy cows   15 year-old bulls
　　　　1 breeding bull   60 replacements

Management: 6 summer months - strip grazing
　　　　　　　　　6 winter months - 1–2 hours daily in the yard

Pigs: Angler saddleback   3 breeding sows
　　　　　　　　　　　c. 40 fattening pigs
Management/feeding: row crops (roots, potatoes), coarse cereal meal; whey
and skimmed milk as protein suplement

Horses: 3

96 CU cattle   c. 7.4 CU pigs   total of 107.2 CU.
3.6 CU horses

Manure treatment: meadows and pastures: compost (up to 9 months old)
from cleared ditches (moorland) + 30% manure with 150 kg/ha of calcified
seaweed; application of 6 - 8 t/ha
Farmyard manure has daily addition of birch pit concentrate and a mixture of
12 parts old compost, 5 parts basalt rock dust and 2 parts calcified seaweed.

Marketing: farm shop and 2 shops in Hamburg.

Comments: All milk is sold direct, either fresh or processed. Bread grain is made into bread for wages, the rest sold direct. Beef and pork meat and meat products are processed in the farm's own slaughterhouse and supplied to two 'green' shops in Hamburg. The farm also has its own school shop in Hamburg. Two women help with processing milk and vegetables and farmgate sales.

Farm in south of Black Forest (4)

Farmed biodynamically from 1957
All biodynamic preparations are produced on the farm

Soil basis: Lower Triassic
Soil index: 18–32   760 metres above sea level
Av. annual temperature 7 °C   Av. annual rainfall 1000 mm
30.5 ha AL   Ratio of arable to grass 1:1.5
CU/ha: 0.9   Main feed growing area: 0.75 ha/RCU
Labour force:
Manager: 1 unit   Regular staff: 0.5 units
Trainees, apprentices: 1
6 workers/100 ha   200 kW (267 hp)/100 ha

Cropping sequence	Intercropping	solid/liquid manure t/m³ per ha	
1. ley			
2. ley		12	1.2
3. ley		12	1.2
4. ley		20	1.2
5. winter wheat		25	3.5
6. oats/barley			
7. winter rye			
8. green fodder mixture oats/peas/vetches		25	3.5
9. winter wheat		25	3.5
10. summer grazing, sown	U: ley		

Special crops: none

Bought-in fertilizer: hyperphosphate 1,500 kg/year

Bought-in feed: feed grain 2 t/year; feed for dairy cattle if required

Cattle: German red pied   15 dairy cows
1 breeding bull   15 replacements
Management: medium stand with solid manure composted
whole-day grazing in summer

Pigs: 5 breeding sows
1 boar   4 fattening pigs
Management: loose boxes with straw litter

Chickens: 120 brown hybrid
Management: flock houses with open run

23.0 CU cattle   2.8 CU pigs
                         1.2 CU poultry   total of 27.0 CU.

Manure treatment: composted manure, with 50 kg/ha hyperphosphate per year.
Marketing: 40% farmgate sales, 60% general market.
Comments: Sainfoin grown regularly, from farm-grown seed

Farmed biodynamically from 1963
Horn manure preparation only produced on the farm

Soil basis: lean clay keuper, moor, gypsum keuper, small amount alluvial, small proportion of loess
Soil index: 20–60, av. 43   420 metres above sea level
Av. annual temperature 7.8 °C   Av. annual rainfall 750 mm
21.5 ha AL   Ratio of arable to grass 1:0.48
CU/ha: 1.5   Main feed growing area: 0.4 ha/RCU
Labour force:
Manager: 1 unit   Regular staff: 1.5 units
Trainees, apprentices: none
11.6 workers/100 ha AL   417 kW (567 hp)/100 ha AL

Farm in Hohenlohe region (5)

Cropping sequence	Intercropping (U = undersown, S = stubble sown)	solid/liquid manure t/m³ per ha
1. ley		compost
2. ley		compost
3. winter wheat		composted manure.
4. potatoes or vegetables		composted manure and possibly dung liquor
5. winter wheat	S: legume mixture	composted manure and possibly dung liquor
	S: with phacelia and mustard	
6. oats/peas mixture or winter barley or spring barley	S: legumes	
7. winter wheat	U: ley	

Special crops: none

Bought-in fertilizer: annually 1 t coarse linseed meal, 0.2 t Oşcorna drill fertilizer, 2 t pigs bristles, 1.7 t rock phosphate

Bought-in feed: 4 t sugar beet chips, 5 t piglet nuts, 2 t feed for breeding sows

Cattle: flecked and German   21 dairy cows
            black pied   own replacements

Management: all year round in tethered housing (medium stand)

Pigs: German landrace, Schwaebisch-Hall breed
                                    7 breeding sows
                                    0 fattening pigs
Management: Danish system with solid dung
28.5 CU cattle   4 CU pigs
                                    total of 32.5 CU.

Manure treatment: solid dung is composted

Marketing: 13% farmgate sales, 62% Demeter processor/dealer, 25% general market.

Comments: Av. size of fields is 1 ha. Farm was resettled in 1960. Bentonite and Agriben are used to treat dung. Buying-in of manure to be reduced in future by increasing stock numbers and percentage of clover in cropping sequence. 120 piglets sold annually. Cereals go partly to wholesalers and are partly sold direct as flour (6 t) or bread (2,400 kg). Beetroot grown on contract for Eden. Milk goes to a dairy and is processed into Demeter products.

Farm in Oxenfurth district (6)

Farmed biodynamically from 1965
All biodynamic preparations produced on the farm

Soil basis: 95% loess loam, 5% lean clay keuper
Soil index: av. 60   325 metres above sea level
Av. annual temperature 8.2 °C   Av. annual rainfall 500 mm
23.4 ha AL   Ratio of arable to grass 1:0.08
CU/ha: 1.13   Main feed growing area: 0.40 ha/RCU
Labour force:
Manager: 1 unit   Regular staff: 1.5 units
Trainees, apprentices: 2, one of them for indoors
12.8 workers/100 ha AL   531 kW (722 hp)/100 ha AL

Cropping sequence	Intercropping (U = undersown, S = stubble sown)	solid/liquid manure t/m³ per ha

1. lucerne/grass
2. lucerne/grass
3. winter wheat
 	
4. oats
 	
5. root crops: beets or
   turnips,carrots
 	
6. winter wheat
 	
7. rye or carrots or Landsberg
   mixture and green maize
 	
8. spring barley or mixture of
   oats & barley
	S: peas, field beans
	oil radish
	U: red clover
	
	(S: Landsberg mixture)
	
	U: lucerne/grass
		50 t fresh manure
		(top dressing)
		beets or turnips: 15 m³
		dung liquor
		carrots: no fertilizer
		25 t composted manure
		+ 12 m³ dung liquor
		rye: 10 t composted
		manure and 6 m³
		dung liquor

Special crops: beetroot and carrots

Bought-in fertilizer: 8 t basalt rock dust annually

Bought-in feed: 200 kg/year Schaette Ursonne mineral mixture; 150 kg/year mineral mixture for cattle; 200 kg/year mineral mixture for pigs; 14,600 l skimmed milk/year for pigs.

Cattle: spotted mountain breed   15 dairy cows
                                         own replacements
Management: all year round in tethered housing (medium stand); dung removal by hand. Female replacements in deep litter loose housing.

Pigs: Angler saddleback   2 breeding sows
                                  60 fattening pigs sold annually,
                                  equals 30 fattening places
Management: fattening pigs in pens, dung removal by hand. Breeding sows have daily exercise. Breeding sows served by boar from neighbourhood.

Chickens: 30 leghorn
Management: Each hen has 6 m² run. No breeding programme.
23 CU cattle   3.5 CU pigs   total of 26.5 CU.

Manure treatment: Solid dung is composted. Alternating tank for dung liquor.

Marketing: 10% farmgate sales, 75% Demeter processor/dealer, 15% general market.

Comments: Arable land relatively difficult, with soil types differing within plots: mild loams that are easy to work but tend to puddle, with high proportion of silt, and clayey loams. Lucerne/grass mixture made up as follows: 73% Old Franconian lucerne, 10% clover-type plants (black medick, red, Alsike, white clover), 12% grasses (timothy, meadow fescue, perennial ryegrass, false oatgrass, cocksfoot, yellow oatgrass, smooth-stalked meadow grass) and 5% herbs (caraway, chicory, wild parsley, burnet).

Farmed biodynamically from 1969
All biodynamic preparations produced on the farm

**Farm in
Cologne-Aachen
bay (7)**

Soil basis: para-brown on loess
Soil index: 90   c. 150 metres above sea level
Av. annual temperature 8.5 °C   Av. annual rainfall 600 mm
105 ha AL   Ratio of arable to grass 1:0.17
CU/ha: c. 0.7   Main feed growing area: 0.48 ha/RCU
Labour force:
Manager: 1 unit   Regular staff: 3 units
Trainees, apprentices: 4
5.7 workers/100 ha AL   220 kW (300 hp)/100 ha AL

Cropping sequence	Intercropping (U = undersown, S = stubble sown)	solid/liquid manure t/m³ per ha

1. red clover/grass
2. red clover/grass
3. 50% rape,
   50% vegetables
   –beetroot or similar
4. winter wheat
5. winter rye
6. row crops (sugar beet,
   carrots, potatoes)
7. spring wheat
8. rye or oats
	
	U: white clover
	
	U: red clover/grass
		composted manure
		
		composted manure

(catch crops undersown where circumstances permit)

Special crops: none

Bought-in fertilizer: none

Bought-in feed: small amounts of calcified seaweed

Cattle: German red pied   40–50 dairy cows
1 breeding bull   own replacements
Management: deep litter loose housing, half-day grazing in summer

Pigs: Angler saddleback   1–2 breeding sows
                            25 fattening pigs
Management: usual system for fattening pigs. Breeding sows and boar on solid dung, no yard.

Sheep: coarse-wool sheep (planned) (Pomeranian land race)

Chickens: 50 laying hens
Management: flock houses with c. 15 m² open run/animal. Partly own breeding programme.
c. 70 CU cattle   c. 9 CU pigs   (c. 1) CU sheep
                   c. 1 CU poultry   total of c. 80 CU.

Manure treatment: dung from deep litter housing is composted.

Marketing: 10% farmgate sales, 90% Demeter processor/dealer (rape)

Comments: 1 seasonal worker employed. Sale of piglets c. 20 a year. An application of cowpat preparation is made in 1st year of red clover/grass. 30 ha of woodland.

Farm at edge of Wetterau (8)

Farmed biodynamically from 1970
All biodynamic preparations produced on the farm

Soil basis: river valley loam (86 ha), mainly para-brown
Soil index: 25–75, av. 55   102–142 metres above sea level

Av. annual temperature 8.5 °C   Av. annual rainfall 550 mm
142 ha AL   Ratio of arable to grass 1:0.24
CU/ha: 1.1   Main feed growing area: 0.41 ha/RCU
Labour force:
Manager: 5 units   Regular staff: 0 units
Trainees, apprentices: 9
6.3 workers/100 ha LA   176 kW (239 hp)/100 ha

Cropping sequence	Intercropping (U = undersown, S = stubble sown)	solid/liquid manure t/m³ per ha
1. wheat	S: pea mixture	
2. row crops		manure
3. wheat	S: oil radish	
4. oats		
5. clover		
6. wheat		
7. row crops (carrots, beetroot, potatoes, mangels, cabbage, vegetables)		manure
8. wheat		
9. rye	S: phacelia	
10. oats/beans		
11. lucerne		
12. lucerne		

Special crops: 8 ha fruit and vegetables

Bought-in fertilizer: lime

Bought-in feed: small amounts of crushed seashells

Cattle: German black pied   65 dairy cows
1 breeding bull   own replacements
Management: deep litter loose housing, half-day grazing in summer, daily exercise in winter

Pigs: 5 fattening pigs
Management: daily exercise

Horses: Hessian warm-blooded

Chickens: 900 Rhode Island
Management: wooden houses with 10 m² open run/animal. No breeding programme.
Other poultry: 20 geese.

150 CU cattle   1 CU pigs
2.4 CU horses   11 CU poultry   total of c. 154.4 CU.

Manure treatment: dung from deep litter and solid dung housing is composted for pastures

Marketing: 10% farmgate sales, 70% Demeter processor/dealer, 20% general market

Comments: communal farm.

The soil - basis of all agriculture

The solid earth is the basis of all physical existence on this planet. The different life forms use its mineral constituents to create their physical bodies. Human beings, who are able to stand and walk erect, receive both internal and external support from it.

The way human beings relate to the mineral, plant and animal worlds has changed in the course of history. A long time ago, people were hunters and food gatherers and their lives were bound up with the life of nature; they gathered the fruits they found growing wild without imposing changes on their environment. In the same way, the herdsmen of old merely cared for their animals.

The human race only began to connect more strongly with the earth when people started to live in settlements and work the soil. Hoe culture and later tillage changed virgin soil into fertile cultivated land, and breeding produced cultivated crops from wild plants.

Hand in hand with this went the progressive evolution of human consciousness. It is still possible to follow this to some extent by carefully observing the inner development of a young child all the way to a mature human being with life experience. Initially human beings felt themselves to be part of the organism of nature (as children still do) and kept their own vital processes attuned to this. As epoch followed epoch, they separated more and more from the world of nature (youth) until today they approach it with the strict logic of modern scientific thinking (adulthood), wanting to understand it in terms of physics and chemistry. The vast knowledge acquired in these sciences serves to improve living conditions and make life easier for people.

Only too often, however, individuals or groups benefit from this to the detriment of the common weal. Yet it is one of man's primary responsibilities to ensure that all life forms on earth are able to live and prosper. The task begins with the development and care of the soil, of plants and animals, and culminates in the creation of social structures that make it possible for the whole world population to live fully in accord with human dignity both now and in times to come.

Farmers get to know their fields with their essential characteristics as they work in them, particularly with tillage and on regular walks of inspection. They know where plants thrive particularly well in dry or in wet years, where they regularly fail to thrive, where the soil dries off fairly quickly in spring and where the wet spots are. They take account of local conditions and decide what measures should be taken and when. Again and again the unforeseen will arise and create problems that have to be dealt with, the weather being an example. Farmers thus live with the conditions nature provides and seek to improve them by tillage, use of fertilizers, planting and plant cultivation, landscaping work such as the planting and maintenance of hedges, and care of stretches of water. Human work transforms a natural site into one that is developed and cultivated and bears fruit to feed both animals and humans. The soil provides the basis for plant growth and hence for food and feed production. Its fertility depends on the conditions that have created it and the care it has been given.

The surface of the earth is covered with a thin skin (ranging from a few millimetres to several metres in thickness) which we call 'soil'; this lies between the bedrock and the atmosphere and usually has a protective plant cover. The soil, and therefore plants, animals and man, can only survive on earth in places where heat, light, air, water and rock material are available, and an equilibrium is maintained that lies within extremely narrow limits.

If we look at the earth as a whole – the polar regions with their ice-caps, the temperate regions which are our own latitudes, the dry desert regions and finally the tropical rain forests –

we realize how well balanced conditions are in Central Europe. The great ocean currents have a major effect on climatic conditions. One example is the Gulf Stream, which helps to maintain a balanced climate well into the European continent.

Geological background to rock and soil composition

The earth's surface has been and still is undergoing changes that proceed on a time scale of long epochs. The outermost layer, the crust, is about 50 –60 km thick and covers the less rigid and more pliable mantle.

The areas now occupied by continents once were oceans inhabited by many life forms. Vast masses of animal organisms sank to the bottom, their shells forming a calcareous sediment. The dead wood of virgin forests has been transformed into brown lignite and black bituminous coal. Life processes have thus played a part in the generation of the dead minerals and rocks of today. Mountain ranges arose through flow processes and folding of the still pliable rock masses. Ice ages, water, heat, cold and wind caused weathering, erosion and mixing. Sedimentary rocks make up about 70 % of the earth's surface in the form of limestone, sand, mudstone and metamorphic transition rocks such as shale and gneiss. On the other hand, 95 % of the earth's crust are plutonic (deep-seated) rocks such as granite and younger basalt.

Soil-forming rocks include the following:
– Loose sediments: river deposits, boulder clay, sand, gravel, wind-borne sediment (loess), clay.
– Consolidated sediments: limestone, sandstone, mudstone.

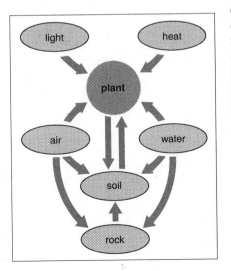

Fig 2.
Soil is formed under conditions of equlilibrium.

Soil type	Particle size	
stones	> 20 mm	progressive
gravel	2–20 mm	weathering,
sand	0.06–2 mm	enlargement of
silt	0.002–0.06 mm	surface area,
clay	< 0.002 mm	solubilization

– Metamorphic rocks: schist, gneiss.
– Plutonic rocks: granite, basalt, diorite.

The above is just a basic list.

All kinds of terrain are familiar to us – mountain ranges, valleys, highlands and lowlands. It needs the plant world, however, to create the variety and beauty we enjoy in the countryside, with woods, grassland and arable fields.

Weathering and the formation of new clay minerals

Rocks show great variation in weathering properties, depending on their structure, density and mineral composition. In the mountains, rocks are exposed to extreme changes in temperature. They expand if heated and contract on cooling, and this creates tensions in the surface. Water penetrates into the cracks that develop and splits the rock as it freezes. The detritus is carried away in streams and rivers, ground to a powder and deposited as sand and clay in the valleys.

Minerals such as the feldspars (silicates rich in potassium, sodium or calcium), mica, augite, hornblende and above all carbonates and oxides are subject to chemical weathering; the elements potassium, sodium, calcium, magnesium and phosphorus are leached out in the process. Organic acids and microorganisms continue the process until highly structured rock has been converted to weathered mineral substance. This forms the main part of the soil and gives it texture. The mineral elements are then taken up into the vital processes of the soil and of plants.

Table 1 illustrates progressive weathering. It gives the particle sizes for different soil textures or types.

With clay, the particle size is 0.002 mm or less. The basic material from which clay is formed has been produced by attrition and erosion. It combines to form colloidal material (colloid = fine particles suspended in a gel-like medium) with different swelling capacity and ability to absorb and hold water (ability to attract

	swelling capacity	water retention capacity	adsorption capacity
kaolinite	minimal	low	low
illite	low	low	medium
montmorillonite	high	high	high

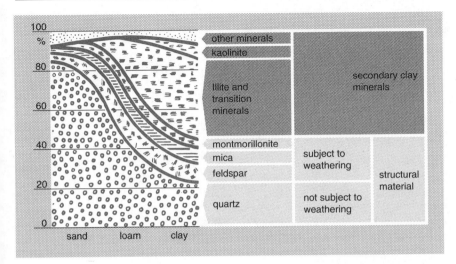

Fig 3. Mineral
composition of sand,
loam and clay
(adapted from
Schroeder 1978)

ions). Table 2 gives some examples.

Weathering, separation into different fractions during transport and new clay formation change the soil type and therefore also the mineral composition (Fig. 3).

The soil type is always based on a mixture of three different particle sizes – sand, silt and clay.

Soil composition and humification

Weathering causes rocks to break down. Plant roots penetrating into cracks contribute to the process. The aerial parts of plants on the other hand cover the ground and later contribute to it as they die and rot down.

In the soil, and plants are an integral part of it, destructive and creative processes run side by side:
– Weathering of rocks to produce the basic material for new minerals
– Dissolution of organic matter to produce humus material and contribute to the growth and development of plants, generating vegetable matter.

Inorganic and organic processes are intermixed, with one changing to the other.

Figure 4 shows the composition of a 'humus horizon' (Schroeder 1978).

Solids only make up 50 % of the volume, the rest being pores filled with water or air, depending on size. The greater part of the solid phase consists of mineral matter, the composition of which depends on the original rock material. Organic matter makes up the smaller part but has a major effect on soil characteristics. If we take grassland soil as an example, 5 % by weight of its organic matter are organisms. The relative proportions vary considerably according to season. This means that if the topsoil is 20 cm thick, 1 hectare will contain 7.5 tonnes of organisms, more or less equivalent to 13 cows or 15 cattle units. The question arises as to how it is possible for 13 'cows' to live in the soil when the feed grown on that one hectare will only be enough for 2 or 3 cows. These are not cows, however, nor are they animals or organisms that can be considered in isolation from their biotope, for they and the biotope form an integral whole. As Rudolf Steiner said in 1924, 'It is important always to think on a large scale when considering living things – which are of prime

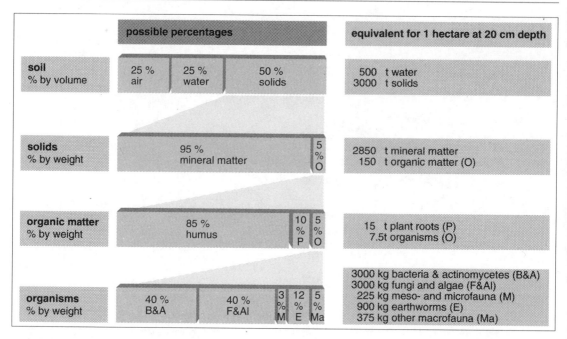

	possible percentages			equivalent for 1 hectare at 20 cm depth
soil % by volume	25 % air	25 % water	50 % solids	500 t water 3000 t solids
solids % by weight	95 % mineral matter		5 % O	2850 t mineral matter 150 t organic matter (O)
organic matter % by weight	85 % humus		10 5 % % P O	15 t plant roots (P) 7.5 t organisms (O)
organisms % by weight	40 % B&A	40 % F&Al	3 12 5 % % % M E Ma	3000 kg bacteria & actinomycetes (B&A) 3000 kg fungi and algae (F&Al) 225 kg meso- and microfauna (M) 900 kg earthworms (E) 375 kg other macrofauna (Ma)

Fig 4. Composition of humus horizon in fertile meadowland (Schroeder 1978)

significance in agriculture – and as far as possible avoid looking at these small organisms in isolation.' What are these organisms? Apart from small burrowing mammals such as moles, mice, hamsters, rabbits, etc., and reptiles such as lizards and snakes, the *macro-* and *mesofauna* of the soil includes the large group of arthropods (about 800,000 species, including insects and insect larvae, ants, springtails, centipedes, millipedes, woodlice, spiders, mites), worms (earthworms, pot-worms [enchytraeids], nematodes, flatworms [Turbellaria]) and slugs and snails.

The *microfauna* includes the unicellular animals (Flagellata, Rhizopoda, Ciliata, etc.). These are between 0.005 and 0.05 mm in size. They are to be found in soil water and also in sea water.

Bacteria and *actinomycetes* make up about 40 % of soil organisms. It is difficult to say whether these microorganisms belong to the animal or the plant world. Their size is in the region of 0.001 mm, and relative to their volume the surface area is

large (1 g = c. 6 m²). Oxygen consumption (oxygen requirement) is one or two litres per 10 g of microbe substance per hour. Their vital functions are highly specialized, involving a tremendous variety of physiological processes, including nitrogen fixation and the oxidation and reduction of nitrogen, sulphur, iron and other compounds. Some of these organisms are aerobic (living on free oxygen derived from the air), others anaerobic (requiring the absence of free oxygen). Actinomycetes are fungus-like filamentous bacteria that break down woody material such as cellulose, lignins and chitin and produce humins. The characteristic smell of woodland soil, sometimes also to be noted in the compost heap, is due to these bacteria.

Fungi and *algae* are a large group of more plant-like organisms. The mostly colourless or white hyphae of fungi and the green strands of algae are to be found everywhere in the soil, and these organisms play an important role in the decomposition, dissolution and synthesis of soils. Toadstools and mushrooms are the part that is visible above ground of larger fungi; they also grow on higher plants. Algae are more closely related to plants; they form a slimy green layer on wet ground.

The above is just a rough outline (for more detailed information, see Trolldenier 1971), yet even so it seems difficult to keep track, as soil organisms are so many and varied. Would it be possible to find an underlying principle? Let us consider the decay of autumn leaves:

A leaf that falls to the ground is wetted and becomes overgrown with algae and fungi. Holes appear, first in the lamina and later also the veins of the leaf. This is where insect larvae and springtails have been feeding, using their highly developed masticatory organs. The residual material is usually taken below ground by worms (earthworms being the most familiar of these) (Willmann 1976), thoroughly mixed with earth by the peristaltic movements in their intestines, and excreted as stabilized crumb. Occasionally rolled-up leaves can be seen sticking up into the air from worm burrows before they are gradually pulled down. In the intestinal canal and the mucilage that lines the burrows, microorganisms initiate an intense decomposition process in which the plant residues are reduced to their constituents. With the aid of enzymes, pieces of plant matter are broken down on the microbial surfaces and new forms of matter synthesized. Quite specific conditions are required by individual species of microorganisms – water with salts in solution, the presence or absence of air, acidity levels, specific chemical elements, organic and inorganic matter that will decompose, temperature conditions, etc. The organisms multiply rapidly under the

Soil organisms do not constitute the life of the soil; they are the actual organs of a living organism.

right conditions, doubling their population in less than 30 minutes. When conditions are not right they form cysts, spores and other resting forms that allow them to survive for long periods even under extreme conditions.

The process of decay may be compared with that of digestion in humans and higher animals. Table 3 shows such a comparison (v. Wistinghausen 1978).

It is evident, if we look at this, that soil organisms do not exist as individual plants and animals but are an integral part of a greater organism, depending on one another. Their metabolic products and their dead bodies provide food for others. We are now able to appreciate why it is possible for organisms equivalent to the weight of 13 cows to live in one hectare of soil. They are subject to an underlying principle:

Soil organisms do not constitute the life of the soil; they are the actual organs of a living organism.

The digestive process breaks down organic matter into its constituents – sugars, amino acids, phenols and soluble salts. These can only combine to form humins under aerobic conditions in a neutral environment (c. pH 7). Oxidation and the synthesis of cyclic compounds are assisted by the enzymes of microorganisms (Scheffer & Schachtschabel 1966). A tremendous variety of compounds is produced, not all of them chemically identifiable.

As the colour gradually darkens from yellow to brown and finally

Soil	Man and animals
Dropped leaves are moistened. First stage of decomposition through fungi and bacteria.	Food is mixed with saliva.
Leaves chopped up as insects eat them (masticatory organs).	Food is chewed (teeth).
Partly decomposed leaves eaten by worms, kneaded with earth (peristalsis) and excreted as crumb aggregates.	Food mixture is swallowed and passes through gastrointestinal canal (intestinal perstalsis).
Intense activity of microorganisms in worms' intestines, faeces and mucus-lined earth passages.	Intense microbial activity in gastrointestinal canal.
Continued chemical and enzymatic decomposition reduces material to basic components – amino acids, carbohydrates, fats and a whole range of chemical elements.	
Humin synthesis, with all basic components fully incorporated owing to microbial and chemical activity.	Synthesis of body substance.
Minimal losses through release of gases such as CO_2, N_2 and leaching of Ca, K, NO_3, etc.	Elimination of undigested material and body substance.
Energy that becomes available is used in synthesis (e.g. humus production, N fixation).	Energy becomes activity.

Table 3. Comparison of decay of organic matter in the soil and human and animal digestion.

black, the humins grow more stable, with their carbon/nitrogen (C/N) ratio within increasingly narrower limits. They are in the colloidal state in the soil, a state which may be defined as an unstable equilibrium between fluid and solid, rather like a jelly.

Under the anaerobic conditions caused by wet, for example, conversion takes a different course and putrefaction results. Hydrogen sulphide (recognizable in soil from the blue-black colour and the smell) and methane are produced. Or the material turns peaty, sphagnum moss grows and moorland may develop. Conversion to peat is equivalent to a withdrawal from the living process of soil formation; it usually occurs in cool, damp climates, but the result does add life to the appearance of a landscape.

Close intermingling of organic and mineral matter, brought about mainly by earthworms, causes clay minerals and humins to combine and form clay-humus complexes. The surfaces of these have strong binding properties, allowing the attachment and reay exchange of mineral elements such as Ca, K, Mg and Na.

Soil formation and soil types

Soil forms from the surface downwards. With hard rocks like granite or magnesian limestone the process is extremely slow; with loose sediments like sand, loess or boulder clay it is faster. First of all lichens begin to colonize rock. They are followed by higher plants which penetrate more deeply with their roots as weathering progresses. Humus forms at the same time, and enables plants to thrive even more. Damp weather conditions or destructive interventions cause salting in the soil, with the result that clay and humus colloids are leached out. The salts collect in the subsoil, making it compact, so that water cannot drain away. This reduces the volume of aerated soil in which roots can spread, so that plants then fail to thrive.

Soils may develop to their full potential, or they may degenerate due to leaching, compaction and poor drainage. Soil development through the millenia has resulted in characteristic soil horizons. Figure 5 shows the development of horizons in diagrammatic form. Many different factors are involved, producing a wide range of soil types.

The shallow soils found in mountain areas, on hilltops and slopes are known as 'rendzina' on calcareous and 'ranker' on clay and other non-calcareous parent material profile 2 in Fig. 5). Brown earths are residual soils of weathered material in erosion-protected sites (profile 3 in Fig. 5).

Deep layers of humic black earth (chernozem) form on loess in 'boerde' regions (fertile plains bounded by hills) and large basins where the climate is humid continental, mainly in the east of Europe.

Loess is deposited in wide plains and to the east of raised ground in Central Europe; in relatively moist conditions the movement of clay particles results in para-brown earths or,

Fig. 5. Stages of soil evolution determine natural growth and stature of plants.

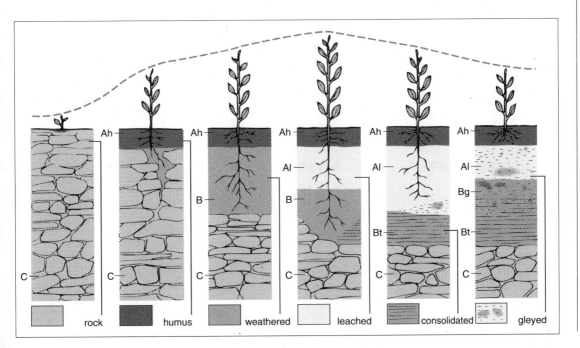

rock   humus   weathered   leached   consolidated   gleyed

on sand, in poor leached soils (podzols) that show an ashy-coloured horizon just below the surface and below this a dense dark brown horizon. In either case, gleying may result in surface-water gley (profile 6 in Fig. 5). Gley forms at ground water level, in low-lying areas and in river valleys and may finally cause peat bogs to develop. Clay (pelosol) develops at a very slow pace in regions where there are clay rocks, e.g. Keuper (West European Upper Triassic).

It is the task of farmers to transform their land into arable soil. This will obviously require different methods in different sites. Sandy soil in a warm climate will clearly react differently from clay that is subject to ground water action.

Soil fertility

Soil, plants and animals are organs of the farm organism, with the soil as the very basis of existence in agriculture. Soil fertility is the prime requirement for success in farming. A cow that has become infertile can be replaced from young stock, the soil cannot. It is a sensitive system and human intervention and unusual climatic effects can enhance it or cause lasting damage. Errors made with tillage or crop rotation may cause problems that persist for years. The processes that occur in the soil are reflected in plant growth and yields, in animal health and in the final instance also in the quality of produce for human consumption. The factors

Table 4. Finger test for soil type (adapted from Schlichting and Blume 1960)

Consistency	soil type	symbol	elutriable particles (%) < 0.01 mm	group
Cannot be moulded and shows no cohesion	sand	S	< 10	light
Leaves slight film on hands when rubbed	slightly loamy sand	Sl	10–13	light
and is cohesive	loamy sand	lS	14–18	medium
Moulds easily to pencil thickness, but not to half that thickness	very sandy loam	SL	19–23	medium
Moulds easily to threads half the thickness of a pencil; gritty between thumb and index finger	sandy loam	sL	24–29	medium
Little or no grittiness; gives dull surface on rubbing	loam	L	30–44	heavy
Polished surface on rubbing; no grittiness between teeth	clay loam	lC	45–60	heavy
Soft as butter	clay	C	> 60	heavy

that contribute to soil fertility (soil type, humus content and quality, soil tructure, soil depth and root space, water, air and temperature conditions, minerals, acidity) are closely interactive and interdependent.

The individual factors are briefly discussed below, to enable us to work with them effectively.

Soil types

The soil type varies with the degree of weathering and the nature of the parent material. Table 4 gives details of the finger test that enables any practical farmer to get an idea of the soil type. It consists in taking a small amount of soil, moistening it in the hand (using saliva when out in the field) and kneading it until it is pliable.

Textural classification is based on workability, i.e. light land is a sandy soil that is easy to work, whereas clayey soils rate as heavy land that is difficult to work ('minute' or 'hour' soils, as there is only a limited time when the moisture content is ideal for working).

Humus

All fertility factors are influenced by the organic matter in the soil, which may be decomposing (unstable humus) or in the process of synthesizing humates (stable humus).

In mineral soils, the humus content is between 1 and 10 %. Arable land usually has a lower humus content than grassland because of mechanical mixing and higher chemical conversion rates.

Depending on the conditions under which it has formed, humus is differentiated into different types:
– mull: soil fauna active in aerobic conditions

Humus always improves the balance in soil formation.

– moder: reduced soil activity in litter composed of pine needles or woody material that does not break down easily
– raw humus: produced in the presence of moisture under anaerobic conditions
– peat: in very wet areas where the organic matter does not decompose
Mull gives a soil structure; it develops in arable and grassland.

Humus always improves the balance in soil formation, making sand less freely draining whilst improving drainage from clays. Sandy loams such as loess tend to puddle; humus creates a stable crumb structure. The proportion of clay and humus determines the ion exchange capacity (metal ions) of soils. The ions attach themselves to the surfaces of the smallest soil particles, partly penetrating their outer layers; ion exchange takes place between soil and soil solution. Drainage water cannot leach them out in this case, and they remain accessible to plant roots.

Soil structure

How does the soil look on ploughing? Does it form long glossy slices, does it break down into individual particles that will rapidly form a dense layer, or is the result a loose, crumby texture? The latter is known as 'good tilth', with the soil in friable condition soon after being worked.

Clayey soil with little humus tends to have a dispersed structure; there are no discrete structural units (peds), the soil is dense and impermeable. Sandy soils generally have single grain structure, units being determined by the size and shape of the sand grains. Water and minerals dissolved in it tend to be transported to lower layers. Real structure in soil results from aggregation of structural elements. Material that is capable of swelling will do so when wet and shrink on drying. The fissures caused by shrinkage may go deep, causing prismatic soil structures to develop. Shrinkage in all directions results in smaller units known as 'blocks'. In clayey soils, blocky structures are angular, with shiny surfaces. In dry conditions they may harden and become impenetrable to roots. Moisture will soften them. High proportions of silt result in a subangular blocky structure with less angular particles that break up easily when moistened.

With tillage, the weight and drag of tractor wheels may result in platy structures in the subsoil that are difficult for roots to penetrate. The same structure develops when particles come to lie horizontally in para-brown earth.

Organic matter will change the above structures, which are essen-tially due to physical laws. The activity of soil organisms results in thorough mixing of organic and mineral matter. Structural soil elements such as quartz sand and mineral elements that have not weathered down are brought together with clay particles and humus material. The resulting complexes provide the biotope for organisms that produce mucus or fungal hyphae, enhancing cohesion. The resulting crumb structure is the ideal soil. Sekera refers to this as 'live incorporation'. The crumbs have good relative proportions of large pores (holding air and permitting water movement), medium-sized pores (for water storage and movement), fine pores (holding water) and micropores (fixing water).

This is the type of crumb needed for a stable soil structure that is not destroyed by precipitations. It is however extremely sensitive to cultivation errors.

Frost-induced tilth results when ice expands and breaks up larger soil units. It does not equal the quality of crumb structure but if cultivated with care in spring can prepare the way for the live incorporation that produces a genuine good tilth.

Fig. 6. Soil structures (diagrams from Schroeder 1978)

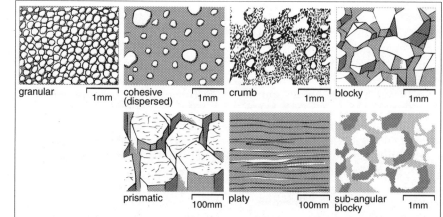

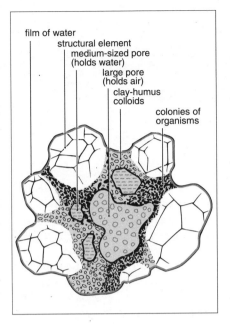

film of water
structural element
medium-sized pore
(holds water)
large pore
(holds air)
clay-humus
colloids
colonies of
organisms

Root space and penetrability

The root space is the depth to which roots can penetrate. Soils with ample root space develop on loose sediments such as loess, boulder clay and river deposits (alluvium), on lower slopes where material eroded higher up has settled (colluvium) and on deeply weathered solid rock. Shallow soils with reduced root space are found on solid rock where soil development is in its early stages and on upper slopes liable to erosion. The problem is that they do not hold water well and therefore dry out quickly during periods of low rainfall.

Root space may be limited due to:
– high water levels: ground-water gley
– water-logging for limited periods: surface-water gley
– deep pan: platy structure, iron and humus deposits in podzol.

The last of these may also be due to 'ploughpan' or inexpert plough-ing-in of stable or green manure.

Penetrability may be reduced when dense clayey aggregates resist root pressure. Shallow soils where roots cannot penetrate to any depth are generally used as grassland or woodland. In grassland, the matted root layer creates a topsoil with high humus content. Continuous plant cover protects the – sensitive – soil.

Water and air

The amount of water and air in a soil is directly related to local climate. Rain penetrates into large soil pores (> 0.05 mm), displacing air; it then drains down to deeper layers, at the same time penetrating into medium pores (0.05–0.01 mm) and micropores (0.01–0.002 mm). It moves slowly through medium pores but is held in micropores due to capillary attraction. Water runs off puddled soil surfaces, carrying soil particles away with it, so that erosion occurs. Water losses due to this and to evaporation are prevented by shallow hoeing or light harrowing to break the surface crust.

Some of the water in the soil drains to lower levels whilst some is fixed. A small proportion remains as available water. Water held in micropores is fixed by the power of adsorption and roots cannot absorb it. Extremely dry soil binds water with a suction pressure of 10,000 at, whilst the roots of plants grown as agricultural crops can at most exert a suction pressure of 10 at.

Soil water is not the same as rain or spring water. It contains mineral salts in solution and is in solution equilibrium with the sorbents that fix and allow exchange of salts.

Waterlogged soil contains no air, which means that its organs – roots and soil organisms – are unable to breathe. When rainwater disperses

See also page 109.

Fig. 7.
Crumb structure
(diagram from
Sekera 1958)

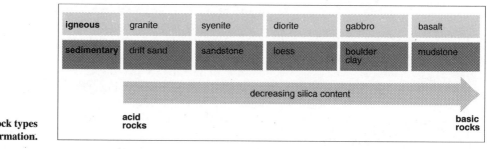

Fig. 8. Rock types and soil formation.

through the soil or drains to lower levels, the large pores in the soil fill with air. Roots and aerobic organisms take up the oxygen and release carbon dioxide. In dense and encrusted soils the exchange of air with the atmosphere cannot take place, carbon dioxide accumulates and inhibits respiration in the soil and consequently also chemical reactions. The water and air levels in soil must be in good balance.

Soil temperature

Warmth is needed for the germination and growth of plants and to maintain the activity of soil organisms. Dark soils absorb more heat than light-coloured ones. Moist soil takes longer to heat up but then holds the heat better (1 litre of water needs four or five times as much heat to raise its temperature by 1 °C as is needed to do the same with 1 kg of soil or rock). Surface evaporation is a vaporization process that involves heat loss. Loose soil and mulches are poor heat conductors, resulting in major surface temperature fluctuations.

Soil warming is assisted by warm air, dark-coloured soil and moisture in the soil.

The risk of frost damage arises with clear night skies, dry air, calm air, in valley areas subject to the inflow of cold air, in places where hedges, buildings, etc. impede the movement of air, on dry sandy soils, loose top layers of soil, mulches, and on wet ground.

Plant cover prevents extreme temperature changes in the topsoil. Hedges planted in the right way can deflect currents of cold air. Mulches should be removed from sites where frost may occur during the winter months and are always best applied in spring.

Soil with good structure, humus content and moisture retention will warm up more quickly in spring and dry off sooner, so that tillage can start earlier.

pH and minerals

The pH gives the ratio of acidity (hydrogen ions) to alkalinity (hydroxide ions). pH determinations in soil samples always give the mean value for the soil mixture concerned.

The mineral content and availability depend on the parent material. Rocks are classified as acid and basic. Figure 8 shows some examples that demonstrate the trend.

Limestones consist essentially of calcium carbonate, which places them at the basic extreme of the range.

Soils are mixtures of different materials, e.g. unweathered rock particles, clay minerals, humic acids, humates, fixed and dissolved salts and oxides and soil organisms. Functioning as an integral whole, soil is able to release acids and alkalis to compensate fluctuations in pH (buffering). If rain introduces acid pollution for an extended period of time, the soil will release alkalis to counteract the acid.

When the soil's buffering capacity has been exhausted, the acids are washed down to lower levels and the soil grows acid. As a result, conditions deteriorate and soil organisms and plants are unable to thrive. Figure 9 illustrates the close connection between pH and soil forming processes on the one hand and the solubility and hence availability of minerals on the other. Conditions are clearly best in both cases in the pH 5 –7.5 range. If the pH is much below this, the acidity proves toxic for soil organisms and roots; if it is much above 7.5, alkalinity presents the same problem.

Mineral availability depends on the interaction of
– weathering intensity; this decreases as the pH increases,
– decomposition of organic matter; this is optimal at pH 7.5, which offers the best conditions for soil organisms,
– leaching; this tends to be less at higher pH levels.

Phosphorus is fixed by the iron and aluminium released in an acid medium, and by calcium in an alkaline medium. Potassium becomes more soluble as the pH increases, with optimum solubility at pH 7.5. Magnesium availability is reduced in an acid and increased in a more alkaline medium. Decomposition of organic material, mineral synthesis and the development of soil structure all depend on these and other factors.

It is evident from the above that the ideal pH varies with different soil types and different land use.

Arable soil requires high pH levels

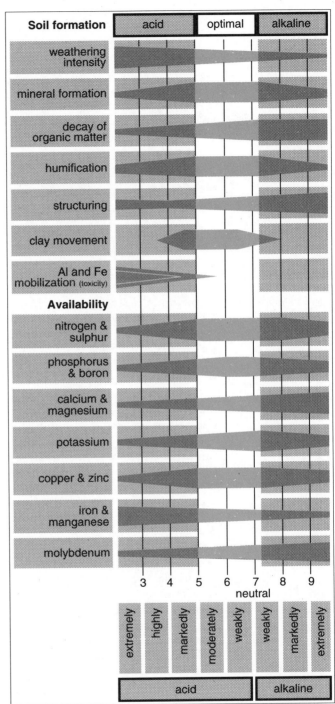

Fig. 9. Relationship between pH and soil formation. Band width = intensity (diagram from Schroeder 1978)

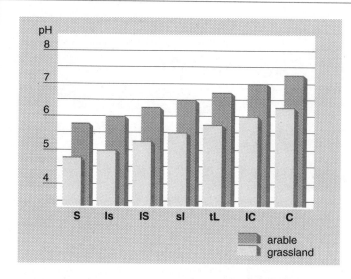

conditions such as climate, parent material, soil type and also growth and yield potential. Laboratory tests provide useful information for specific areas.

Soil samples are taken from a number of sites evenly distributed over the field in question, going to a depth of 20 or 30 cm, depending on depth of tilling. The nature of the terrain, consistency of the soil and agricultural use should as far as possible be the same for the field sampled. Mix thoroughly, dry, sieve to remove particles greater than 2 mm, and analyse for the following parameters:

pH = degree of acidity
C = carbon, as % of air-dried soil
N = nitrogen, as % of air-dried soil
C/N ratio
P = phosphorus (x 2.29 = P_2O_5 as P_2O_5 in mg/100 g air-dried soil
K = potassium (x 1.205 = K_2O in mg/100 g of air-dried soil
Mg = magnesium, in mg/100 g of air-dried soil
T = exchange capacity, in meq/100 g of soil
FC = field capacity, in % by vol. of water.

Goerbing's spade test is useful in determining the condition of the soil:

The specially designed spade has a flat 30 x 18 cm blade. It is pushed down into the soil at right angles to the furrow by moving it to and fro without applying pressure. The soil behind the blade is then removed with an ordinary spade. The special spade is used to make a second cut at a distance of about 7 cm from the first. The section of soil is carefully lifted out and broken up using a claw hoe. The following are noted:

– non-crumb aggregates and large clods,
– consolidation due to poor tillage (ploughpan),

Fig. 10. Optimal pH ranges for different soil types – arable and grassland.

to maintain a stable structure. In long-term grassland, lower pH levels will enhance weathering intensity, for the risk of leaching is nil or only minimal in humic soils with a high root content.

Sandy soils naturally contain fewer minerals and are especially low in trace elements, above all boron and manganese. A reduced pH is said to intensify weathering in this case. Clayey soils on the other hand tend to lose structure; free calcium will enhance aggregate stability. Thus the optimal pH is 5–5.5 for sandy soils and above 7 for clay.

Rocks should normally provide adequate amounts of minerals for healthy plant growth as they weather. If weathering is extreme minerals may be leached out, producing an acid soil; conversely inadequate weathering will produce calcareous soils. In either case, supplements have to be added to stimulate soil processes.

Soil tests

The proper assessment of soils requires detailed knowledge of local

– nature and intensity of root growth: regularity, direction (?horizontal), convolutions, branching,
– waterlogging.

Further information on soil structure and consistency is obtained from the way the clod breaks up when thrown off the spade.

Table 5. System for determining soil index (Scheffer & Schachtschabel 1982)

Soil type	Origin	Structural Stage						
		1	2	3	4	5	6	7
S	D	–	41–34	33–27	26–21	20–16	15–12	11–7
	Al	–	44–37	36–30	29–24	23–19	18–14	13–9
	W	–	41–34	33–27	26–21	20–16	15–12	11–7
Sl (S/lS)	D	–	51–43	42–35	34–28	27–22	21–17	16–11
	Al	–	53–46	45–38	37–31	30–24	23–19	18–13
	W	–	49–43	42–36	35–29	28–23	22–18	17–12
lS	D	68–60	59–51	50–44	43–37	36–30	29–23	22–16
	Loe	71–63	62–54	53–46	45–39	38–32	31–25	24–18
	Al	71–63	62–54	53–46	45–39	38–32	31–25	24–18
	W	–	57–51	50–44	43–37	36–30	29–24	23–17
	Wr	–	–	47–41	40–34	33–27	26–20	19–12
SL (lS/sL)	D	75–68	67–60	59–52	51–45	44–38	37–31	30–23
	Loe	81–73	72–64	63–55	54–47	46–40	39–33	32–25
	Al	80–72	71–63	62–55	54–47	46–40	39–33	32–25
	W	75–68	67–60	59–52	51–44	43–37	36–30	29–22
	Wr	–	–	55–48	47–40	39–32	31–24	23–16
sL	D	84–76	75–68	67–70	59–53	52–46	45–39	38–30
	Loe	92–83	82–74	73–65	64–56	55–48	47–41	40–32
	Al	90–81	80–72	71–64	63–56	55–48	47–41	40–32
	W	85–77	76–68	67–59	58–51	50–44	43–36	35–27
	Wr	–	–	64–55	54–45	44–36	35–27	26–18
L	D	90–82	81–74	73–66	65–58	57–50	49–43	42–34
	Loe	100–92	91–83	82–74	73–65	64–56	55–46	45–36
	Al	100–90	89–80	79–71	70–62	61–54	53–45	44–35
	W	91–83	82–74	73–65	64–56	55–47	46–39	38–30
	Wr	–	–	70–61	60–51	50–41	40–30	29–19
LC	D	87–79	78–70	69–62	61–54	53–46	45–38	37–28
	Al	91–83	82–74	73–65	64–57	56–49	48–40	39–29
	W	87–79	78–70	69–61	60–52	51–43	42–34	33–24
	Wr	–	–	67–58	57–48	47–38	37–28	27–17
C	D	–	71–64	63–56	55–48	47–40	39–30	29–18
	Al	–	74–66	65–58	57–50	49–41	40–31	30–18
	W	–	71–63	62–54	53–45	44–36	35–26	25–14
	Wr	–	–	59–51	50–42	41–33	32–24	23–14
Mo		–	54–46	45–37	36–29	28–22	21–16	15–10

Origin:
D = superficial glacial deposits
Al = alluvial river deposits
Loe = loess (wind-borne sediment)

W = weathering of local rock
Wr = weathering of local rock, high percentage rock material in soil (> 10 %)
For soil types, see page 34.

Soil index and stages

The parent material from which soil has formed, the soil type and moisture level serve as the basis for determining the soil index (Table 5).

Scheffer and Schachtschabel (1982) define the following stages:

Stage 1: Good crumb structure, subsoil well aerated, gradual transition from crumb to subsoil (usually containing $CaCO_3$); no rust stains; no signs of acidification.

Stage 3: Crumb contains less organic matter than in stage 1, transition to subsoil more abrupt; subsoil frequently shows pale spots and greyish colour; greater depth of decalcification, incipient acidification and first signs of displacement.

Stage 5: Crumb clearly distinct; zone of impoverishment; first signs of subsoil consolidation and of rust stains; usually marked degree of acidification.

Stage 7: Crumb clearly distinct; more or less marked zone of bleaching; normally considerable subsoil consolidation and rust stains; plough-pan and iron pan are common with sandy soils.

These stages are indicators of soil development. Moisture conditions may make soil improvement work necessary. Ground-water soils are normally used for permanent grassland. Waterlogged ground can be improved by drainage. Both the depth and width of the drainage channels are important (the deeper they are, the greater is the area drained). Clayey soils drain more slowly, and the channels should be closer together than in soils with a higher proportion of sand. Drainage is particularly important for improving soil aeration.

Interpretation of laboratory reports

The pH (degree of acidity) must be regulated, as fertility can only be expected in soils with pH 5–7, depending on soil type and use. The natural buffering system of the soil helps to maintain the balance. Climatic factors such as high rainfall levels and acid pollution (mainly sulphuric and sulphurous acids) exhaust the soil's buffering capacity.

The application of stable manure

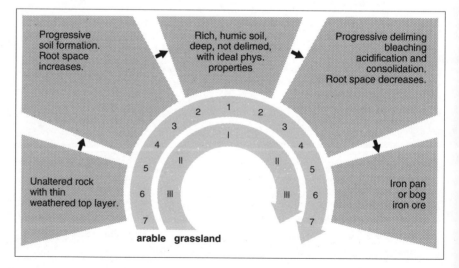

Fig. 11. Soil stages (Görtz, in Scheffer & Schachtschabel 1982)

and compost and careful humus production and management by growing legumes for a number of years will balance the pH by increasing the buffering capacity of the soil. In cases of extreme acidity due to pollution, lime has to be applied, with larger amounts required for clayey than for sandy soils.

Carbon and nitrogen levels indicate the proportion of organic matter and its condition (% C x 2 = % organic matter; % C x 1.72 = % humus). Organic matter undergoes progressive changes from fresh material (low N) to stable humic acids (high N), so that its composition is always changing. This is indicated by the C/N ratio. Carbon is the vehicle for plant structure; it is released during decomposition and partly given off in the process of respiration. Nitrogen is part of the protein structure of organisms and also forms protein-like compounds in humus. Organisms then reduce it to its mineral form so that it is available to plants. A low C/N ratio indicates that nitrogen is mostly fixed, a high one that more nitrogen is needed for the decomposition of organic matter. The optimum C/N ratio is 10 (10 parts of carbon to one of nitrogen); at this level mineralization should be ideal. A low C/N ratio indicates either intense conversion in progress or that no fertilizer has been applied for some time. A high figure suggests inhibition of conversion, usually in conjunction with a low pH.

Phosphorus and potassium are essential for plant growth. The laboratory report usually also gives solubility levels – e.g. CAL (calcium ammonium lactate) solubility.

Calcium ammonium lactate solubility relates to the level of availability; it does not give information on the total amount present, some of

Soil analysis can be helpful in deciding on specific measures.

it not yet weathered. Active soils have higher weathering activity than dead soils with low conversion rates. If the concentration of a nutrient in the soil is 10 mg/100 g of air-dried soil, this is equivalent to 150 kg/ha at a depth of 20 cm.

In Central Europe, the mean concentrations of soluble minerals are

600–2,400 kg of P/ha
6,000–99,000 kg of K/ha
1,500–15,000 kg of Mg/ha.

The figures given in the analysis relate to the elementary or fixed form of elements and need to be recalculated to allow comparison:

$P \times 2.29 = P_2O_5$
$K \times 1.205 = K_2O$

Soil analysis can be helpful in deciding on specific measures that will prevent deficiency states.

Phosphorus deficiency may occur with a 10 mg concentration of P_2O_{5CAL}/100 g in lifeless clayey soils, compared to a 3 mg concentration in humic soils.

Excessively high or low potassium levels cause clay minerals to degenerate and crystallize, so that the colloidal state is lost. Excessively high levels are subject to leaching, excessively low levels cause clay expansion and finally degeneration.

Excessively high potassium levels will also increase leaching of magnesium and calcium. The resulting imbalances have a detrimental effect on stock, e.g. calcium deficiency in cows (milk fever).

It is therefore also advisable to add

% C x 2 = % of organic matter;
% C x 1.72 = % of humus.

Table 6.
Field capacity
relative to soil type
in % by volume.

	S	Sl	lS	SL	sL	L	LC	C
Field capacity minus	10	15	20	25	30	35	40	45
'dead water' =	3	4	6	7	10	15	23	32
available storage								
capacity	7	11	14	18	20	20	17	13

magnesium whenever it becomes absolutely necessary to apply potassium.

Potassium deficiency may occur in heavy alluvial soils and in sandy soils with poor exchangeable base capacity.

The *exchangeable base capacity* (T factor) indicates the exchangeability of minerals (potassium, calcium, magnesium and sodium) in the soil. When dissolved, these minerals are attached to clay minerals and humus material (base exchange) and cannot be leached out. Plant roots are however capable of dissolving them and absorbing them either directly or from soil water.

Fertile soils with high interior surface areas (high humus and clay levels) therefore have a high exchangeable base capacity.

The *field capacity* (FC) indicates the water retention capacity of a soil. The permanent wilting percentage, also known as 'dead water', has to be deducted from this. It refers to water

that is irreversibly fixed in the soil and therefore not available to plants. In reality, however, life is particularly intense in this 'dead water'.

Table 6 shows the average field capacities for different soils. The figures are given as per cent by volume in litre/m^2 or mm of rainfall at a depth of 10 cm.

The main purpose of soil testing is to monitor the efficiency of agricultural methods applied. In conventional agriculture, soil tests have encouraged the idea of nutrient supplementation, often resulting in financially nonviable applications (Scheffer & Schachtschabel 1982).

In essence, agricultural methods should enhance soil vitality to the point where decomposition (decay of vegetable matter, weathering, mineralization) and synthesis (humification, clay formation, plant growth) are in balance, and enhancement of both processes develops a natural site into a cultivated site that will give high yields.

Tillage

The three elements of husbandry – tillage, crop rotation and the application of manures and compost – are highly interactive. They are more likely to create favourable growing conditions if the given characteristics of the soil in a particular field are taken into account when developing it beyond its natural potential to make it into good arable soil.

The aim of tillage is 'biological enhancement' (Koepf et al.), i.e. to improve the balance of decomposition and synthesis, or of humification and mineralization and enhance productivity. It serves to improve the physical texture of the soil, stimulate the whole range of biological and chemical processes and create the conditions for good tilth. In the final instance it is the biological activity of a soil that determines soil structure and its permanence and resistance to unfavourable influences such as heavy precipitation, the weight of machinery, and so on.

Tillage stimulates microbial activity and therefore humus decomposition and also causes temporary loss of soil structure as the natural soil stratification is destroyed. At the same time the chaos created in a previously well-ordered system offers potential for heat, light, air and cosmic forces to intervene and establish new conditions. The weather is an agent capable of enhancing tillage effects. This is particularly important with heavy soils. Frost causes soil water to expand and break down large aggregates. Alternate wetting and drying of the land creates a layer of fine friable soil in heavy, plastic soils with high clay content (plastosols).

On the other hand, very heavy rain leaches nutrients and colloids from cultivated fields, causes soils with high silt content to puddle and leads to erosion, which is also caused by wind. This kind of damage can be prevented by working the soil at the right time and not too frequently, creating the right surface profile, sowing catch crops to provide quick ground cover after working the stubble and applying adequate amounts of organic matter (manure, compost) to stabilize the soil structure.

Tillage, crop rotation and the application of manure and compost are thus closely interrelated. These three basic functions of the farm organism combine to maintain and improve soil fertility and increase and safeguard good yields.

In the cycle of the year, the emphasis is on spring and autumn where tillage is concerned.

1) Spring: As the soil begins to warm up, the soil becomes active. Seed germinates, established plants begin to put out new growth. The earth is breathing out, plants grow and come to physical expression in form until they flower. Oxygen requirement

Tillage operations are greatly dependent on the time of the year.

is high, so that soil organisms and plant roots need a good, loose crumb structure. Mineralization, i.e. release of minerals from organic and inorganic soil elements as soil life becomes active, runs parallel to creation of soil structure and to plant growth.

Cultivations: As far as possible avoid using heavy machinery on the land. Shallow tillage is needed to create a permeable skin and interrupt capillary activity. The prime requirement is to keep the winter moisture in the soil.

2) Summer: Soil activity slows down everywhere except in fields where row crops continue to require cultivation. Plants begin to

ripen, buds and then seeds form. The soil enters into a rest phase. The earth has breathed out completely and is fully open to light and heat.

Cultivations: When cereal crops have been harvested, the soil should be worked immediately to prevent further drying out. It is advisable to work it more deeply if compacted or if there is a lot of couch grass. The dryness of the soil makes this a good time for such a measure. A sowing of deep-rooted green manure plants will stabilize the loosened soil.

3) Autumn: Soil activity is again increasing as dead leaves and harvest residues decompose and con-

Fig. 12. Factors influencing soil fertility

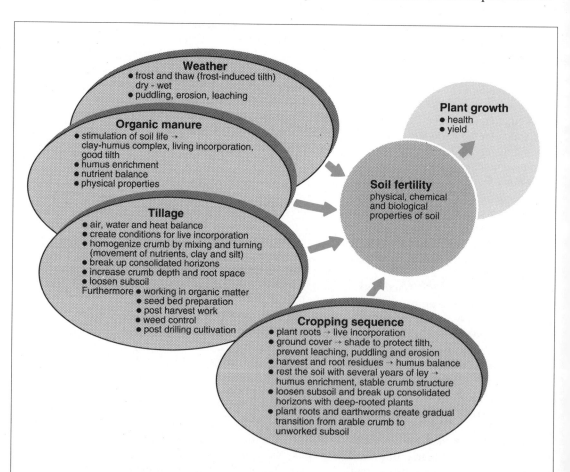

vert to humus. The earth is now breathing in. Minerals in solution (e.g. potassium, calcium and above all nitrates) are leached from highly permeable soil and go down to lower soil levels. Catch crops grown in late summer help to prevent this.

Cultivations: Shallow ploughing-in of material from undersown and intercrops to avoid excessive activity resulting in humus decomposition. Best time for working the subsoil – deep work with chisel plough or with a mould-board plough (winter furrow).

4) Winter: The growing period has come to an end. The earth has breathed in and is open to cosmic influences; frost and snow, weathering and clay formation occur. Frost helps to break down aggregates and create the conditions for live incorporation to produce good tilth in spring.
   Cultivations: Field work ceases during winter.

Tillage should be as infrequent as possible. This will minimize the compaction caused by machinery and give the soil adequate opportunity to develop structure and build up humus. The timing of individual tillage operations depends on moisture levels in the soil. Ploughing or deep work with a cultivator on very moist or even wet ground will bring wet sticky lumps to the surface that harden on drying and are difficult to break down again. Drag from the wheels also causes compaction. The result is considerable damage to soil structure that still makes itself felt years later with poor crops and reduced yields. The rule, now as in the past, is:

Leave the soil for nature to work on rather than risk long-term damage

Leave the soil for nature to work on rather than risk long-term damage by bringing on machinery and tilling too early.

by bringing on machinery and tilling too early.

The moisture content of soil can be estimated by kneading some of it into a ball. The spade test should always be done; it is most helpful in determining the moisture level and structure of a soil when considering the choice and use of suitable implements, taking into account the site, season and crop.

The effect of precipitations, or the ratio of precipitation to evaporation, indicates the depth to which soil may be turned. The limiting depth is the point where synthesis and decomposition of mineral and organic matter are in balance. The aim is neither to bring too much unenlivened subsoil to the surface, nor to let unused nutrients be lost.

Tillage to loosen and improve soil may go much deeper when it is necessary to counteract potential podzolization or damage done by faulty tillage (zones of compaction—plough-pan).

In general, the following applies:
– The lighter the soil, the drier and warmer the climate, the deeper the soil may be worked; or, conversely:
– the heavier the soil and the damper and colder the climate, the more shallow the tillage.

In Germany, for example, potential tillage depths range from 10–20 cm in alpine regions to 30–40 cm in the dry region of the Palatinate.

Basic tillage

Basic tillage includes deep loosening of soil, turning and mixing.

The depth to which soil is worked has an effect on root space. The zone worked contains the main mass of plant roots and also the major proportion of available minerals, so that the depth of working is an essential factor for healthy plant growth. The soil should therefore be worked deeply once a year.

The main implement is the plough; it turns the soil ideally by 135 degrees, causing stubble to lie against the side of the furrow, bringing minerals and clay and silt particles up to the top and burying weed seed. Fairly large air spaces are produced that assist drainage of surplus water and aeration of the soil. Many soil organisms will be destroyed by deep turning and the mixing of levels, but rapidly multiply again when conditions are favourable. Activity will in fact be higher than prior to ploughing.

Heavy soils, and above all 'minute' and 'hour' soils (see page 33), need to be ploughed before winter sets in so that the frost can break down larger aggregates and the crumb will settle in time for preparing the seed bed in spring. Rolling with ring, star, Cambridge or Croskill rolls is a poor second best compared to the natural settling process. The resulting mechanical consolidation only goes to a depth of 15 cm, or 20 cm with a subsoil packer. Slight levelling before winter may sometimes be advisable; otherwise the few centimetres of fine tilth are taken to the bottom of the furrow when tilling in spring, and the coarser aggregates on the ridges are exposed.

Light soils can also be ploughed in spring. The intense loosening effect does however cause considerable loss of moisture; if there is a dry period in early summer, the lost water will no longer be available to plants.

If the ratio of width to depth of furrow is 1:1, the surface will be more of the loose-bed type; if it is 1.4:1, the surface has more profile. Fast tractor speeds cause clods to collapse and lose form, often lying at a right angle to the furrow. 5.4 km/h is the normal speed for careful work. Soils that tend to puddle or are subject to capping need to be piled in well-shaped 'dams' to retard compaction and minimize erosion. Tractor wheels should not be wider than the furrow, to avoid compacting the freshly ploughed soil.

A steady increase in the depth of root space is desirable where conditions permit. The best time for this

Fig. 13. Relationship between width and depth of furrow and width of tractor wheel.

width = depth of furrow

wrong

wrong

Rain factor	Depth of furrow in cm	
150–141	17	
140–131	18	Example:
130–121	19	$\dfrac{875 \text{ mm}}{6\,°C} = 146 = 17 \text{ cm}$
120–111	20	
110–101	21	
100–91	23	
90–81	25	
80–71	27	
70–61	30	
60–51	35	
50–46	40	
45–41	45	

Table 7. Lang's rain factor and optimum depth of crumb.

For normal soils, the optimum depth of crumb is indicated in the table.

is when a ley of several years' standing is ploughed in, with farmyard manure worked in at the same time. The effective depth of arable soil will thus be increased as part of the rotation system, with new unenlivened subsoil incorporated in the root space at regular intervals and enlivened by mixing it in with the biologically active crumb.

Ploughed soil can be mixed with a grubber, cultivator, spoon or spring-tined harrow. A heavy grubber may be used for basic tillage after harvesting roots in dry weather.

Lang's rain factor is useful for determining tillage depth (see box at bottom of page).

Soil cultivation

Stubble cleaning

The aims are as follows, particularly when dealing with stubble after cereal crops:
– mixing in harvest residues (or mulches) superficially to achieve optimum decay under limited oxygen supply

– stopping capillary activity to reduce evaporation
– maintaining good tilth
– preparing good conditions for the germination of weed and dropped cereal seeds which are then destroyed in a further operation.

Any implement that effects superficial mixing or cuts, loosens and shallow turns may be used to turn in stubble.

Disc and skim coulters, disc harrows and rotary spade harrow (Scandinavian) can also be used on heavy soils if moisture conditions are right. They permit intense shallow mixing. Rotary cultivators and p.t.o.-driven implements will cause compaction and cohesion of aggregates if the soil is too wet. Rotary cultivators in particular tend to be problematical as the rotating blades destroy the soil structure, leaving a fine, loose surface layer but beneath it a consolidated layer caused by pressure and drag from the blades. The upward movement of capillary water is interrupted, with structural development above it inhibited. Heavy precipitation then compacts and consoli-

$$\frac{\text{annual rainfall in mm}}{\text{mean annual temperature in °C}} = \text{Lang's rain factor}$$

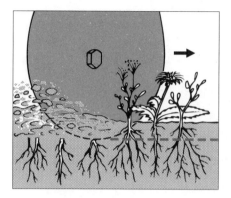

Fig. 14. Post harvest cultivation with disc harrow

Table 8. Suitability of implements for different aspects of stubble cleaning operation (v. Boguslawski 1981)

dates structureless surface material. The use of rotary cultivators should thus be limited to summertime stubble cleaning before growing catch crops (*Saemavator* cultivator); it is definitely not advisable for autumn and spring cleaning. They may also be used to work in dung either before or after ploughing a furrow.

The depth to which organic material should be buried depends on climate and soil type. Too much air will cause 'combustion'; too little, putrefaction and peat formation. Shallow burying is thus indicated in damp and cool climates and for heavy soils, deeper burying in dry and warm climates and for light soils.

To deal with severe fouling and for autumn seed bed preparation, it may be advisable to reverse the usual sequence (shallow burial followed by deep turning).

Seed bed preparation

Cultivation operations to prepare a seed bed aim to produce a level bed, reasonably firm but not too dense, so that seed is supplied with water from below and seedling roots can penetrate easily. A crumby surface layer is needed to provide adequate warmth and access for air, and to stop capillary activity and minimize water loss through evaporation.

Different crops have different requirements in this respect. Soil pores should be limited in size for winter cereals, since they are responsible for major temperature fluctuations and for plants being forced up by frost. Sugar beet needs a crumb structure that is firm but not too firm, covered by a layer of fine crumb that will not puddle. It is important to firm the soil after ploughing, e.g. using a crumb packer. If the seed bed horizon is uneven, capillary activity is interrupted in parts, resulting in

implement	purpose		
	germination of weeds and shatted seed	putting in catch crop	working in organic matter
1. stubble plough	+	++	−
2. disc stubble cleaner	++	+	+
3. disc harrow	++	++	+
4. rotary spade harrow	++	+	+
5. rotary cultivator	++	++	++
6. fine field cultivator	++	+	−
7. heavy cultivator	+	++	++
8. heavy rotary cultivator	++	++	++

++ suited and well suited   + less suitable   − not suitable

delayed and irregular germination. If the soil is liable to puddle and encrust, the seed bed must be sufficiently coarse to prevent serious interference with germination but should offer more resistance to puddling.

Prior to spring sowing, the soil is generally levelled and crumb created by using a planker. The soil dries off quickly on the surface and warms up. Seed bed preparation creates ideal conditions for the germination of numerous weeds. A further harrowing operation or cultivation will remove these.

Implements that create surface crumb and a more consolidated horizon below (zig-zag drag harrow, fine field cultivator, rollers) can be combined, reducing the operations required for seed bed preparation to two or even one; this also reduces the number of wheel tracks. Weed control is less efficient, however, so that combinations can only be used in special circumstances.

Soil that has firmed up much during the winter needs to be loosened with implements that work to a greater depth (e.g. *Kultiegge* cultivator harrow). Suitable tyres or cage wheels help to reduce wheel pressure when the ground is still wet.

potatoes s barley rape (maize)	loose-structured, well-aerated soil
w rye w barley w wheat sugar beet red clover	firm soil
oats fodder beet	both loose-structured and firm soil

Table 9.
Seed bed
requirements

Table 10.
Implements used to
prepare seed beds
(von Boguslawski
1981)

Implement	Design and function
Trailed behind the plough	
crumb packer (furrow press)	wedge-shaped steel rings 70–90 cm in diameter mounted on a bar at 15–18 cm intervals; pack soil down to 8–20 cm, depending on weight and soil condition.
Norwegian roller harrow	2 or 3 bars with a staggered system of 5 or 6 pointed stars, 25–30 cm diameter; compress upper crumb layer, crumb structure.
packer combinations	crumb packer + Norwegian roller, to pack crumb structure.
tined implements	
field harrow (light, medium, heavy)	16–18 cm tines fitted about 25 cm apart in staggered rows, scratch lines in soil 4–6 cm apart. Large soil aggregates break under impact, working at a speed of 8 km/h or more, mainly on light and medium soils.
zig-zag drag harrow	stronger, curved tines widening into a spoon-shape at the end. For puddled, crusted and heavy soils.
spring-tined harrow (finishing harrow)	4 or 5 rows of small spring-mounted sickle-shaped tines. Scratch lines in soil about 5 cm apart. Suitable for all soils, crumb structure.

Implement	Design and function
angled tine harrow	recent design based on spring-tined harrow; angled blades adjustable for depth, supported on rotary harrows; particularly suitable to prepare seed bed for beet.
chain harrow (flexible harrow)	Flexible links permit harrow to follow surface irregularities. Weed control in cereal and potato crops.
fine field cultivator	goes deeper, therefore used for potatoes and to a limited extent for maize.
harrows with elements at an angle to line of forward travel	
rotary spade harrow disc harow	mainly to prepare seed bed for autumn sowing; increasingly replaced by p.t.o.-driven implements
multitiller	new design for preparing seed bed in heavy soils; two staggered rows of rotor stars, with spiral spring tines between.
p.t.o.-driven harrows	
reciprocating harrow	2–4 bars of tines 20–30 cm in length moving to and fro in opposite directions. Soil is well broken up by impact and levelled, tractor lines are removed.
tumble harrow	tumble bearings cause elements fitted with two tines each to move to and fro. Limited usefulness on heavy soils.
rotary harrow	interlocking rotating tined elements; intensity depends on rotary and forward speeds.
tined rotary cultivator	in very wet soils, the knife disc can be replaced with a tined disc to prevent slip formation.
clod crushers (crumbling rollers)	
angled bar type toothed type wire roller type helical bar type	used in seed bed combinations; consolidation and crumb structure of top layer; regulate working depth of basic implements; used according to soil type.
rolls	
flat roll rough roll ring roll Norwegian roll Cambridge roll Croskill roll	little used on arable land – boggy soil } firming seed bed, working to a depth of 5–15 cm, rings with rib on axle rolling seed bed star-shaped rings for beet and alternating smooth and star-shaped rings fine seeds. smooth and cam discs connected by wedge-shaped elements
floats, scrubbers	range of designs. Levelling rough furrows in spring helps crumb structure, drying and warming up and encourages weeds to germinate.

Post drilling cultivations

Subsoiling

Post drilling cultivations encourage plant growth by breaking up crusts and restoring the integrity of frost-lifted soil. All kinds of rolls with rough surfaces and sufficient weight to firm the soil are suitable. Weed control is another important aspect of post drilling cultivation. The table on page 52 shows the different implements, mainly light harrows, and their function. Hackstriegel (harrows with long spring-loaded tines developed by Raberwerk in Germany) and tractor hoes should also be mentioned. The Hackstriegel may also be used to prepare the seed bed. It needs to be driven at quite a high speed, 10–12 km/h, whereas 6–7 km/h is best with other harrows, which leave furrows if driven too fast, do not go deep enough and jump if the soil is encrusted.

A tractor hoe breaks up crusts so that air and precipitation are able to penetrate better; it also controls weeds without making it necessary to wait for cereal plants to be at a certain stage, which is the case with harrow and weed harrow. When plants are still young, hoeing is mainly done with angled and later with ducksfoot shares. Plain or concave discs protect seedlings and make it possible to work close to each row. The slightly loosened top layer of soil dries up quickly and prevents the germination of further weeds. It provides protective cover for the root space and prevents evaporation.

Rotary hoes and cultivators have only limited use in weed control, for two reasons,

– they leave a wide unworked strip next to plant rows, and
– they create the ideal seed bed for weeds, which will germinate and quickly foul the land.

Ploughing of wet soil will create ploughpan horizons beneath the tilled land and it may be necessary to stir the soil deeply with special implements such as a combination of plough body and subsoil tine. The operation should be immediately followed by drilling a mixture of deep-rooting plants (lucerne, lupins, peas, everlasting pea, vetches or tares, field or horse bean, *Phacelia* etc.), to prevent reconsolidation. Different plough depths will prevent plough pan.

The above implements are to be found on most farms, but there are also systems which have been specially designed for alternative agriculture.

The first of these is the Weichel unit system. The simple implements are easily combined and permit basic tillage as well as the superficial incorporation of organic material and seed bed preparation to be done in a few, and occasionally even just one operation. The main implements achieve shallow turning, deep loosening and rolling.

The principle is as follows:
1) Deep loosening, in one or several layers with one implement, which may be done under growing crops, e.g. a mixed fodder crop grown for several years.
2) Surface mixing with rotary harrow, with a combination roll fitted to follow.

A combination of implements makes it possible to reduce the number of operations to a minimum and may be expected to give long rest periods for the development of a good crumb structure.

A special method is Kemink's ridge cultivation. This increases the

Double tyres or cage wheels will effectively reduce pressure on the soil.

Continuous study and observation, re-examining the existing methods and principles, will develop the right intuition for what needs to be done.

soil surface and improves aeration to enhance the thermal balance, which results in more rapid restoration of natural tilth. After stubble cleaning and weed control – on weed-free soils only a single operation is required – the loosened top layer is formed into ridges. Weichel has developed a special ridging implement for the purpose that can be combined with other implements. Later on the ridges may be changed by enlarging them or moving them sideways before they are finally levelled prior to drilling in autumn or spring.

In conclusion it should be stressed that tillage operations and the implements used depend on soil conditions, manuring status, the requirements of particular crops, the weather, the season and above all the farmer's skill and experience.

Ongoing study, observation and re-examination of the principles that have been evolved, will develop the right intuition for what needs to be done.

Radioactive pollution

The Chernobyl disaster in 1986 has shown that increased radioactive fallout calls for additional cultivation and possibly also fertilization. A living, fertile soil will, as always, be the best insurance.

The half-life of I^{131} (radioactive iodine) is so short that only plants directly exposed to it when they are ready for harvest cannot be used. They have to be ploughed under or composted. Sr^{90} (strontium) behaves very much like calcium in the soil and has a long half-life; liming may be necessary in extreme cases to achieve optimum pH for agricultural land. $Cs^{134/137}$ (caesium) is exchangeably fixed in the soil in a way similar to potassium. Low potassium levels should therefore be corrected by cautious applications of potash-magnesia fertilizer. High field capacity (see page 44) is equally important, as it reduces caesium uptake in plants. If necessary, an application of bentonite will improve the T factor.

According to the present state of knowledge, biodynamic preparations will not reduce or remove radioactive pollution; however, intensified application is important in so far as soil vitalization and greater plant vitality will always have a positive effect.

Manures and manuring

The essence of manuring

Permanent natural soil fertility depends on four elements working in harmony:
- the soil and its natural flora and fauna
- a plant world where many different species and varieties share in the rhythms of the seasons
- animals with different needs for husbandry and feeding and with specific excretions
- and human beings who bring all this together in such a way that a self-sustaining unique individual whole is brought to life and can continue to live.

Tillage, manuring and crop rotation are key factors in achieving this goal.

Manuring means reintroducing materials of mineral, vegetable and animal origin and their inherent forces into the farm cycle, so that the soil becomes an organ that is full of life within the total organism.

The humus and nitrogen content provides a measure of the degree to which a soil is able to serve as a basis for healthy plant growth. Livestock also have special needs for space and suitable fodder plants. The well-being of a farm organism is deeply dependent on the right balance between domestic animals and the crops that are grown (Steiner, *Agriculture*, lecture two).

The cow has always been the symbol of fertility. In a soil that has life in it, root residues and stubble from fodder plants (grasses, leguminous plants and herbs) grown in a cropping sequence that effectively builds up soil combine with properly prepared and applied cow manure to effect the slow but steady improvement in soil fertility that will guarantee productivity.

Cow dung, vegetable matter, added soil and proper management are the foundation of manure production.

Farmyard manure

The first things a trained observer takes note of when entering an animal house between feeding times are lighting and cleanliness; the first deep breath taken will tell what the dung is like and what the animals' state of health is. The smell of the dung also provides information on fodder quality and whether the animals are able to process their fodder in the right way.

A pungent odour of ammonia or stinking dung indicates that the protein composition of the fodder or the combination of feeds does not meet the animal's needs. Other possible reasons are the wrong type of hou-

Cow dung and leys for several years will give long-term improvement in soil fertility.

sing, errors of husbandry and lack of care.

Having spent some time in the animal house or among the animals resting in a pasture, the sensitive observer will above all note whether the animals show contentment or unease. When the inward gaze of a cow that is quietly chewing the cud comes to life for just a moment as interest is shown in the observer, then to be calmly concentrated again on the inner process of digestion, the person knows that when he now walks through the fields of the farm he can expect to find balanced, healthy crops growing. Similar experiences, though adapted to the specific nature of the animal in question, can be gained with pigs, sheep and horses, if we are sufficiently attentive.

The quality of the dung as part of the total organism will reflect the harmony or lack of harmony to be found on the whole farm. Every animal includes something of its inner qualities, its character and state of well-being in its excretions, and cow dung has specially balanced, universal qualities that are suited to all conditions.

In cool, damp sites, and to prepare the soil for plants in special need of warmth, dung from horses, sheep or goats may be added as a supplement. Pig dung is more suitable for dry, warm and hot sites. In any site where spring is slow and late, and for all flowering plants (rape, peas, lupins, etc.), the addition of poultry dung to cow dung has great potential.

The percentage compositions given for different types of dung in Table 11 are of course only mean values, but they do give some indication of the qualities of different animals. Looking at the middle and lower part of the table, it is immediately apparent that the relative proportions of cow dung components are remarkably similar to the requirements of wheat, rye and barley. A 5:1 ratio of K_2O to MgO is ideal for both the soil and the blood of dairy cows.

It is evident from these brief details that every farm should have not only dairy cattle and their offspring but

Table 11. Mean concentration of constituents of farmyard manure in per cent (from *Faustzahlen* 1980)

Fresh (long) dung	N	P_2O_5	K_2O	CaO	MgO	org.m.	H_2O	C:N
cattle	0.40	0.20	0.50	0.45	0.10	20.3	77.3	25
horses	0.60	0.28	0.53	0.25	0.14	25.4	71.3	21
sheep	0.80	0.23	0.67	0.33	0.18	31.8	64.3	20
pigs	0.55	0.75	0.50	0.40	0.20	18.0	80.0	16
poultry	1.70	1.60	0.90	2.00	0.20	0.3	56.0	0.1

Ratio	N	:	P_2O_5	:	K_2O	:	MgO	K_2O	:	MgO
cattle	100		50		125		25	5		1
horses	100		48		88		23	3.8		1
sheep	100		29		84		22	3.7		1
pigs	100		136		91		36	2.5		1
poultry	100		94		53		12	4.5		1

Fertilizer requirement (relative to N = 100)					
w wheat	100	50	110	at 5 t/ha yield
w rye	100	60	125	at 4 t/ha yield
w barley	100	60	115	at 5 t/ha yield

Type of housing	straw requirement		short dung t/year	liquid manure* m³/month
	kg/day	t/year		
tethered housing solids, medium-length standing	4–6	1.5–2.2	9.0–11.0	–
tethered housing solids, short standing	2–3	0.7–1.1	9.0–11.0	–
tethered housing liquids	0–2	0–0.7	–	1.4–1.7
open space loose housing with litter	10–12	3.7–4.4	16.5–20.0	–
open space loose housing, concrete run	8–10	2.9–3.7	13.0–15.0	–
cubicle solids	0.5–1	0.2–0.3	5.5–6.5	–
cubicle liquids	0.2–1	0.1–0.3	–	1.4–1.7

* no water added

also such other domestic species as local conditions and crops require. It is not a question of numbers, but of continuously adding the available horse, pig, sheep or poultry dung to the daily volume of cow dung, or also processing them separately for special crops.

For mixed farming on average soil and in an average climate, the dung produced by 1 CU/ha is normally sufficient, if used in combination with leguminous crops and green manuring, to vitalize the soil to the point where production quality and quantity will sustain a balanced farm organism.

If local conditions are less good and the aim is to avoid buying in fertilizer and foodstuffs, the area used for growing the main fodder plants for the same number of animals will have to be somewhat larger, which will of course mean a reduction in the volume of saleable produce. If conditions are good or even ideal, product sales will progressively increase as the number of livestock increases and the area used to grow fodder stays the same; alternatively, sales remain the same, with the number of animals reduced and larger areas available for saleable crops. In the first case, fertility may be expected to increase progressively, in the second to remain the same.

Table 12. Cows (per CU) kept indoors year-round.* Daily faeces and urine production per RCU: c. 25 kg faeces, 15 litres urine, or 45–55 litres of mixed faeces and urine.

*Appropriate deductions to be made for days in pasture.

Table 13. Heifers kept indoors year-round.* Figures per CU (2.5 animals) and day and year respectively; 30 months rearing.

Type of housing	straw requirement		short dung t/year	liquid manure* m³/month
	kg/day	t/year		
tethered housing solids, medium-length standing	5.6–8.5	2.0–3.0	12.5–15.5	–
tethered housing solids, short standing	2.8–4.2	1.0–1.5	12.5–15.5	–
open space loose housing solids	14–17	5.0–6.2	23.0–28.0	–
cubicle solids	0.7–1.4	0.3–0.5	7.5–9.0	–
housing with liquid manure	0	0	–	1.9–2.3

Factor for 27-month rearing period: 0.9
Factor for 33-month rearing period: 1.1
Factor for 36-month rearing period: 1.2

* no water added

Type of housing	straw requirement		short dung t/year	liquid manure* m³/month
	kg/day	t/year		
tethered house solids, short standing	2.5–3.5	0.9–1.3	9.0–11.0	–
open space loose housing with litter	12–15	4.3–5.3	16.5–20.0	–
liquid manure	–	–	–	1.3–1.7

* no water added

**Table 14.
Beef cattle, kept
indoors year-round.
Figures per CU (1.8
animals), sold at 18
months, 125-550 kg
liveweight.**

**Table 15.
Sheep, pigs, poultry.**

Tables 12–15 show straw requirements and farmyard manure production for the most important farm animals kept by different methods (KTBL *Datensammlung* 1981).

Taking account of losses in collecting, processing and storing dung, annual farmyard manure production for one CU/ha is 6–8 tonnes. If one adds crop residues, the organic matter resulting from green manuring, nitrogen fixed by soil organisms and the dung liquor, this is sufficient for good long-term yields to be achieved for the given site. The basic rule in processing manure is:

Biodynamic compost preparations should be added at the earliest possible stage, so that chemical conversion is channelled in the right

Type of animal and dung		straw requirement			liquid manure* m³/month
		kg/day	short dung t/year (t/stated period)		
ewe with lambs deep litter loose housing for 145 days		0.5–1.0	0.07–0.15	0.5–0.8	–
sow with litter,	solid dung	2.5	0.9	3.5–4.0	–
	liquid manure	0	0	–	0.4–0.5
gilt, 240 days	solid dung	1.0	(0.24)	(1.1)	–
	liquid manure	–	–	–	0.15
fattening pig, per 140-day period	solid dung	0.5	(0.07)	(0.35)	–
	solid dung	1.0	(0.14)	(0.35)	–
	solid dung	1.5	(0.21)	(0.42)	–
	liquid manure	–	–	–	0.15
100 laying hens in cages: 175 g fresh dung/animal per day				6.4 t long dung	
60 g dried dung**/animal per day				4.0 t short dung	
				2.2 t dried dung	
floor husbandry			1.0	2.6	
1000 broilers (day 2–45) floor husbandry (20 g dried dung/animal per day)**			(1.0)	(1.8)	

* no water added
** dried dung = artificially dried, 80% dry matter (0.8 t/m³)

direction. They are added immediately on stacking the daily manure quota in the composting site, with one portion to every 2 or 3 tonnes of long dung. Once all six preparations have been added, you start again from the beginning.

If manure has to be put in a temporary heap by the animal houses, it is important to make sure that the preparations are added to newly produced manure within three days. If the heap is too small for correct spacing of preparations (1-metre intervals are required), only camomile and nettle are used to begin with, adding yarrow, oak bark and dandelion two or three days later.

Another method that has proved useful is to pour a bucketful of birch pit concentrate (see page 68) over the dung or into the liquid manure channel before cleaning out. The quantity is sufficient for 30 cattle units. In this way regulating principles are brought to bear on the conversion and transformation processes from the very beginning, with losses kept to a minimum.

Solid dung

Composted manure
Straw makes the best litter both for the animals and for quality of manure. Once composted, this manure can be used in many different ways and to excellent effect.

On many biodynamic farms fresh manure goes straight from the dung

Fig. 15.
Various methods of processing and applying farmyard manure

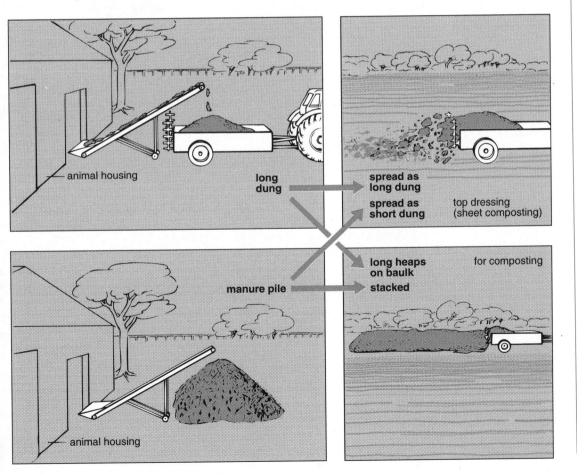

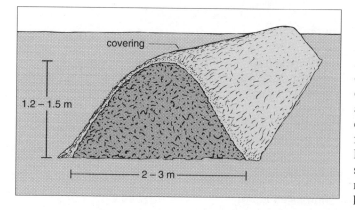

covering

1.2 – 1.5 m

2 – 3 m

**Fig. 16. Compost
heap design**

Piped water must be available to moisten daily quantities of farmyard manure with a high straw content. Another possibilty is to use liquid drained from the heap or, even better, dung liquor. Moistening the heap and if necessary also treading it down prevents overheating. If the farmyard manure has a relatively low litter content, a rotary or lateral spreader will be most suitable, as the material will be piled loosely and the heap well aerated.

Residues from the last heap act as starters for the new one, which is then rapidly colonized by micro-organisms to initiate decomposition. If it is more labour-saving to make the compost heap on the baulk of the field, up to 15% of mature compost may be added as a starter. Turves make another useful addition, as do calcified seaweed (10 kg/m³), basalt rock dust (5 kg/m³) bentonite (3 kg/m³) and other organic conditioners.

During conversion and on sites where phosphorus levels are low, the addition of attrital rock phosphate (20–75 kg/ha = 5–20 kg P_2O_5 annually) to the farmyard manure will stimulate phosphorus processes to such good effect that even when analysis shows available P_2O_5 levels to be low, plants and animals do not develop deficiency syndromes. It is usually possible to discontinue this after some years, as soil life and root activity will have intensified sufficiently to provide plants with the necessary phosphorus.

removal system or electric trolley on to a litter cart and is immediately set up in compost heaps in specially chosen sites or on the baulk of the field for which it is destined. Compost sites need to be chosen with care. Shade from trees and shrubs is an advantage, but the roots should not be able to reach the heap, as run-off from the heap can be harmful to them, particularly in the case of fruit trees. The elder (*Sambucus nigra*) is the one tree that flourishes under these conditions and creates exactly the right environment if planted around the composting site.

Vehicular access is important in all weathers. Liquid draining from the heap after heavy rains should be channelled for collection in a pit. Seepage to deeper soil horizons is generally prevented by the mucilage contained in dung, even on sandy soil. Application of a thin layer of bentonite also helps in this respect.*

A clamp 1.5–3 metres wide and 1–1.6 metres high has proved highly suitable for composting. Surface area is minimal and the angle of the slope is ideal for letting rain water run off.

Manure distributors or tipper lorries may be used to set up the compost heaps. If supplements have to be mixed in to enhance humification and fertilizer quality, distributors are the only choice.

As the heap is progressively built, each of the five solid biodynamic compost preparations in turn is added to 2–3 tonnes of long dung, placing it at the centre of the section that has been added to the heap. Cover the heap with a thin layer of soil (up to 1 cm) and add the valerian preparation by making a hole down to the centre

* see also page 76

of the heap at 1.5 metre intervals and pouring in one or two litres of diluted and stirred valerian preparation from a watering can. Tread on the holes to close them, then fit a rose to the can and pour c. 2 litres/cubic metre over the heap. Finally give the heap a good covering of old grass, straw, or even peat, so that neither substance nor energy is lost and the inside stays warm. At the same time it allows the 'inhalation' of subtle influences from the earthly and cosmic environment.

If manure is temporarily stacked by the animal houses before a heap is built, care must be taken that it does not heat up to any great extent, which happens if the surface area is too small. A fresh layer needs to be added daily if at all possible and good compost soil scattered thinly over it. After two or three weeks the manure is taken to the composting site and the heap is built as described above. This method makes it easier to control decomposition from the beginning. Add the solid preparations again after six months, and repeat the valerian treatment just before the composted manure is ready for use. This is usually after the heap has gone through the full cycle of a year. Turning the heap with a fore-end loader and manure distributor after three or four months of rotting down will reduce the time to six or eight months. While turning, it is possible to add straw or other bulky material if the mixture is too wet, or to mix in moist fresh dung or moisten with dung liquor if it is too dry.

Farmers need to develop real feeling and sensitivity in their work with manure. Rudolf Steiner was most emphatic on this point.

Deep litter and stacked manure

This also applies to dealing with

Fig. 17.
Loose housing with deep litter

deep litter manure. Dung from loose housing with litter (up to 15 kg of straw/CU per day) may be composted or brought out as it is. In either case, the rule is to apply the compost preparations as early as possible.

With a deep litter system, the litter is treated with the preparations a few days after cleaning out and then again at four or six week intervals. It will be perfectly evident the next time the house is cleaned out if litter has not been treated, for it will need a great deal more energy to loosen the litter with the front-end loader, and the dung will be greasy and malodorous. This kind of material cannot be applied as it is but has to be composted. It then needs great care and attention to ensure that initial heating is not excessive; wetting the heap and treading it down will prevent this.

Well cared-for dung from loose housing is loose and friable in texture and has a pleasant odour; it can be applied to the soil as it is.

The same applies to stacked manure, but stacking should only be done in exceptional situations. It is far from easy to avoid losses with this method and produce material that is well rotted down and able to vitalize the soil.

The composting process

The temperature of a compost heap provides a good indication of how the composting process is going. During the first week the temperature will normally rise to 50 or 60 °C, except in cases where the outside temperature is extremely low or the heap is too small. Thermophilic (warmth-loving) soil bacteria split off any readily available carbon and exhale it as carbon dioxide. Nitrogen may be lost in the form of ammonia during those early days. If the heap is too wet, decomposition does not get going and the temperature stays low. Air is needed in this case; it is supplied by mixing in dry material and making sure the heap is piled loosely. If the compost is too dry, the temperature will get too high and combustion will occur. In this case, the heap must be wetted and trodden to firm it.

The hot phase continues for one or two weeks. When the temperature falls the hyphae of the inkcap can be seen on the surface; this fungus produces white fruiting bodies that later turn bluish. The nitrogen remains in the heap. The temperature continues to decrease and then remains at about 30 °C for some time.

The heap is intensely colonized by organisms, mainly insects, the most important of these being the springtails (Collembola), a family of numerous species (for details, see Bockemuehl 1981).

These insects have powerful masticatory organs which they use to break down organic matter that does not decompose easily, thus speeding up the process. Earthworms make their appearance at almost the same time, above all the small red brandlings (*Eisenia foetida*). At night the worms can actually be seen to migrate from an old, largely rotted down heap to a new one, where they'll be breeding fast.

After six to nine months, decomposition will be more or less complete and the material stabilizes. Earthy humus begins to form, compost life quietens down and the temperature now equals the soil temperature. Different organisms then initiate a further decomposition process and later incorporation in the soil.

Essentially there are four phases in the humification process (adapted from Bockemuehl 1981):

1) *Heating up*. Initial heating process, establishment of a uniform heat organism, killing off micro-

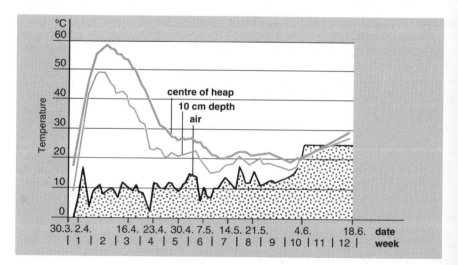

Fig. 18. Temperature changes during conversion of farmyard manure to compost (Bockemuehl 1981)

organisms, including pathogens. Initial odour disappears after one to three days.

2) *Air phase*. Gases evolve; the heap relates to the surrounding air; increasing microbial growth, transition to fungal growth; nitrogen largely in the form of ammonia, which is liable to escape.

3) *Progressive change*. Gradual decomposition, massive increase in soil fauna (springtails, followed by worms) which limit fungal growth. Nitrogen oxidized to nitrate.

4) *Structuring*. Differentiation and stabilization of matter; great variety of small animal species, with numbers of each limited. Uniform structuring of material to produce humus. Nitrogen largely taken up by organisms and incorporated in their protein.

Knowing these phases, it is possible to formulate possible uses for manure at different stages of maturity.

The solid excrement of cattle, horses, sheep and pigs differs in nature and consistency. The hard bean-like pellets of sheep dung, loose-structured dry horse dung, pappy cow dung and wet, often runny pigs' dung all reflect something of the nature of the species involved and at the same time their value as fertilizer for soil and plants.

Sheep and horse dung acts fast, with hot, burning qualities, and more or less tends to force growth; cow dung is cool, restrained and long-lasting; pig dung tends to be cold and slow.

Liquid manure

Dung liquor

This is produced at the same time as solid manure and has to be carefully processed to make it into life-enhanced fertilizer. Two separate pits are required, their combined capacity sufficient for a year's production.

Pit capacity in m^3 required per CU and year is 5.5 for cattle, 3.0 for horses, 3.7 for sheep and 7.3 for pigs.

To control fermentation, put well matured compost in a strip 50 cm wide and about 20 cm high down the middle of the pit. Add the five solid biodynamic compost preparations at one metre intervals. A single portion of each is sufficient for 1 m^3 of liquor. A pit that is 10 m long, 5 m wide and 5 m deep would therefore require ten holes to be made in the compost. Put five portions of one particular preparation into one hole at a time. To avoid nitrogen losses it is advisable to put a loose 25–45 cm layer of straw over the floor of the pit and make provision that fresh liquor does not run straight into the pit and cause the straw cover to break open. A good method is to put in a wooden box structure that stops about 50 cm short of the base (see diagram). In addition, tie the solid biodynamic preparations to a cross made from two wooden laths about 4 m in length (Fig. 19); this will float on top of the liquor under the straw cover.

When the pit is about a third full, add the biodynamic valerian preparation (2 cm^3/m^3, stirred for 15 minutes) and use the pump to agitate the whole for an hour.

When the pit is full, leave it for several weeks to complete fermentation. Finally add the valerian preparation once more, as described above. Soon after this, the resulting dark brown, almost odourless viscous liquid will be ready for use to stimulate both plant and soil life. For use on growing crops (e.g. cereals), the effect is enhanced if fresh nettles (*Urtica dioica*) are added. Nettles may also be used instead of straw to make a floating cover.

Addition of nettles will improve dung liquor.

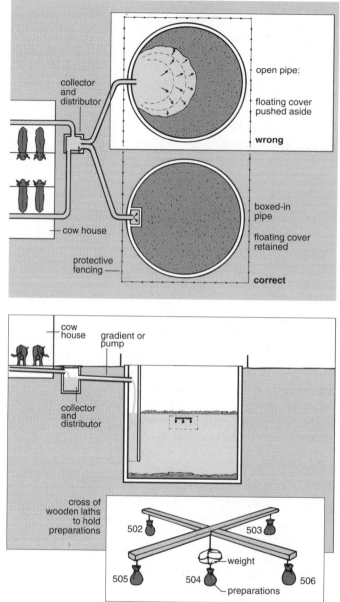

collector and distributor

open pipe:

floating cover pushed aside

wrong

cow house

boxed-in pipe

floating cover retained

protective fencing

correct

cow house   gradient or pump

collector and distributor

cross of wooden laths to hold preparations

502   503

505   504   506

weight

preparations

Fig. 19. Floating straw cover for pits containing dung liquor and liquid manure.

the bladder and kidney region and the sexual system of dairy cows that also influence the composition of the urine; this may well explain the beneficial effect of properly fermented dung liquor from cows.

Slurries

Litter-free animal keeping was initially developed in grassland areas in alpine regions. The original reason was that cereals are not grown in those areas (lack of straw). When it was realized how much labour can be saved by washing out cow houses, the method came to be widely used also on arable farms and for almost all types of animals. There are, however, a number of disadvantages and these are only mentioned briefly below as most farmers will be familiar with them.

– Bad smells in the animal houses and when manure is spread.
– Damage to extremities from grids and slatted floors.
– Psychological problems due to housing density and lack of straw.
– High nutrient losses with manure spread during non-growing season. This goes hand in hand with low nutrient utilization.
– Structural damage to soil.
– Scorch damage to green crops.
– Damage to roots through toxic conversion products.
– Meadows and pastures fouled with weeds.
– Valuable fodder plants and grasses crowded out.
– Loss of depth in sward.
– Grazing animals reluctant to feed after application of slurry because of smell and taste.

Housing with built-in facilities for washing out requires considerable financial investment; managers will therefore find it difficult to change back to clearing out solid dung in the

The vitalizing and stimulating effect of dung liquor is greater than the actual nutrient content suggests. This may be due to the presence of fine secretions from the animals' glandular system. A large number of hormone-controlled functions have been found to occur particularly in

animal, type of dung	dry matter %	kg/day	kg/year	per housing period days	kg
cattle, liquid	10	50	18 250	200	10 000
(cattle, 550 kg)	7.5	66.7	24 350	200	13 300
pigs, liquid	10	4.1	1 500	160	656
(mean for fattening period)	7.5	5.5	2 000	160	880
hens, liquid	20	0.17	62	365	62
	15	0.23	84	365	84
hens, dry	80	0.05	18	365	18
broilers, dry	80	0.02	6	53	1

Table 16. Dung produced per animal (Vetter und Klasink 1973).

old way when converting to ecologically more viable farming methods. When this is the case, it is most important to process the slurry so that the disadvantages are reduced to a minimum and the best possible use can be made of animal excretions in the animal - soil - plant - human being chain.

The first step is to get a clear picture of the volume of dung production and nutrient content, as shown in tables 16 and 17.

To minimize nutrient losses, slurry should never be applied in late autumn, early winter or on sloping ground when the soil is frozen, as this would reduce utilization by up to 80%. Adequate storage facilities will therefore be needed to collect liquid manure produced from September to March, i.e. a minimum of six months. For arable land, the best times for slurry application are prior to drilling and as a dressing for standing crops in spring; after the cereal harvest on to straw chaff, with catch or main crops to follow, in summer and autumn. The combination with straw and subsequent green manuring is to be specially recommended, as these are complementary with regard to the carbon/nitrogen ratio and assist humification.

On grassland and fodder crops

* Concentration of dry matter and nutrients varies according to amount of water added. Nutrient levels in liquid manures vary considerably due to consistency, composition and feeding (summer/winter).

	dil. cattle slurry 10% DM kg/m³	dil. pig slurry 10% DM kg/m³	dil. chicken slurry 15% DM kg/m³	dry chicken manure 80% DM kg/t
org. DM	73	74	98	570
N	4.7	6.7	10.7	38
K₂O	5.9	3.7	4.8	26
P₂O₅	2.4	5.8	9.5	39
CaO	2.5	4.5	16.0	52
MgO	0.6	0.8	0.9	6.6
Mn	0.02	0.03	0.06	0.24
Zn	0.02	0.04	0.05	0.24
Cu	0.005	0.028	0.009	0.04

Table 17. Nutrient levels in liquid manures and dry chicken dung, with mean concentrations of dry matter (DM) (Vetter und Klasink 1973)

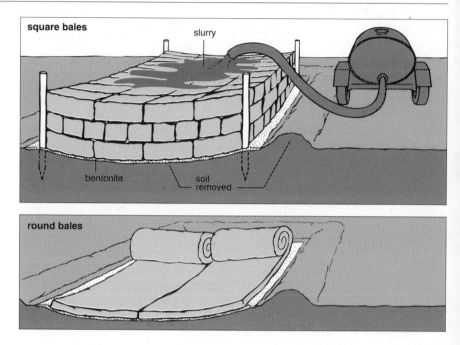

square bales

slurry

bentonite   soil
                   removed

round bales

Fig. 20. Compost
made from straw
and slurry.

application is best made at the beginning of the growing period and after
every cut or grazing period. A light
application may also be made after
the last cut or grazing period in autumn, this being a time when grasses
are still able to store reserves in the
roots. Spring growth will then be all
the more rapid.

Methods for processing liquid
manures so that they are available
when they can be most effectively
used and create no problems for soil
and plants are given below.

The first requirement for good
quality liquid manures is that feeds
and feed composition are of top
quality.

Apart from this, there are a number
of ways in which decomposition can
be effectively controlled:
– Biodynamic compost preparations
  prove effective if applied daily to
  grids and slatted floors as birch pit
  concentrate. This improves the
  odour and observations on cattle
  slurry have shown that this
  frequently improves flow

properties and dissolution of the
floating cover.
– Very fine rock dust (e.g. lava
  dusts, c. 200 g/CU and day) is also
  recommended.
– The addition of c. 2 kg of bentonite
  per m^3 slurry has a stabilizing
  effect. This clay mineral is rich in
  montmorillonite and has high
  swelling capacity and an internal
  surface area of 500–600 m^2 per
  gram.
– A further application of the
  biodynamic preparations in the silo
  is advisable.
– A storage time of at least three
  months has proved effective.
– Two storage vessels are efficient,
  with the liquid fermenting in one
  whilst the other is being filled.
Aeration with rotary aerators or
compressors serves to accelerate decomposition and further enhances
quality. Daily agitation (2–5 hours,
depending on appliance, silo content
and daily additions) largely removes
the characteristic smell and any compounds that are harmful to soil and

plants. Mucilage in the manure is also broken down, so that slurry from cattle runs off plants well and is quickly 'digested' by the soil. The result will be denser grassland growth with a higher proportion of clovers and herbs. Well prepared slurries may also be used as a dressing on growing arable crops.

Abele (1978) found in several years' trials that addition of the compost preparations to liquid manure from cows and pigs, together with aeration, resulted in extensive stabilization of odour, better tolerance in plants, increased root development and improved nutrient utilization.

In areas where straw is easily obtainable, compost heaps of baled straw may be made and soaked with liquid manure. In this way, the advantages of solid dung production can to some extent also be achieved in farms using slurry systems. Manure processed by this method can be used mainly on pasture (about every three years), on special crops, and in orchards and market gardens.

Manure supplements and improvers

Pigeons, chickens, pigs, sheep and horses are generally few in number on farms, if present at all. The volume of dung produced is therefore relatively low and is used to best effect by continuously adding it to the cow manure. Another useful method is to have a 'dung water barrel', which was a standard feature of every biodynamic farm in the early decades of the movement.

Put a few bucketfuls of pigeon or chicken droppings in a large barrel

Fig. 21. Dung water barrel.

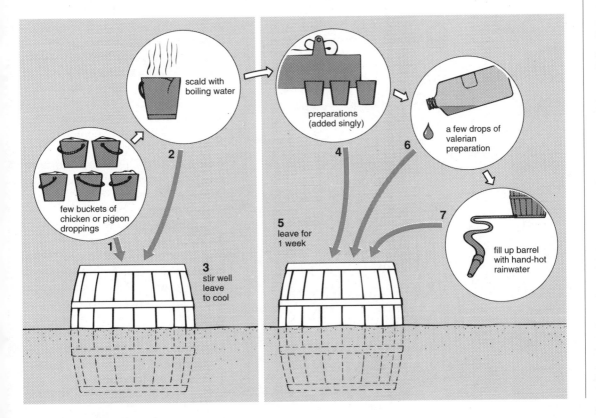

few buckets of chicken or pigeon droppings

1

scald with boiling water

2

3 stir well leave to cool

preparations (added singly)

4

5 leave for 1 week

6

a few drops of valerian preparation

7

fill up barrel with hand-hot rainwater

(300–400 litre capacity), add boiling water and stir well. When cold, add the solid biodynamic compost preparations and leave to act for a week. Add a few drops of the valerian preparation and fill to the brim with hand-hot rainwater. Once a day, before cleaning out the houses, give the mixture a thorough stir and apply to the dunging area or channel (approx. 1 litre per CU).

The same method may be used with pig, sheep and horse manure, except that warm rather than boiling water is used. Simple measures like these make it possible to use the dung in a way that gives the soil the full benefit of the special qualities of these animals and the dynamics of their forces.

The biodynamic compost preparations and mature cow manure are excellent farmyard manure improvers. M. K. Schwarz of Worpswede in Northern Germany developed a method in the early 1920s in which a birch-lined pit is used to produce a substance that will permit rapid and efficient utilization of these special properties. The method is as follows:

Dig a pit 60 cm wide and 30 cm deep, using the dug-up soil to raise the ground level around the edges. Line the pit completely with young birch saplings. The length will depend on the number of cattle units, with 0.5 m³ required for every ten units. Fill the pit with clean cow pats, which should be as dry as possible and free from straw and have been collected from pasture or cowhouse. Add a portion of each of the solid compost preparations in turn at 30 cm intervals. After ten days add the valerian solution. A loose lid placed at an angle allows air to enter and rainwater to run off. After about four weeks, a layer of bentonite (0.5 cm) may be added. Turn the mixture, using an old short-pronged dung fork, and add the biodynamic preparations again. After two or three months, the loose-structured dark-brown concentrate smelling of woodland humus is ready for use. Add it

 – to fresh manure in dunging or liquid manure channels before cleaning out,
 – to the mature compost at the bottom of the slurry pit before refilling,
 – once a week to loose-housing litter,
 – into the pre-collector of the liquid manure pit, and
 – when turning compost heaps.

A solution made with one part of the birch pit concentrate to six parts of hand-hot rainwater (stirred for ten minutes) is useful for treating seed, watering house plants and greenhouse crops, and many other purposes.

The birch pit is refilled as soon as any of the material has been used.

The same method may also be used with horse or sheep dung.

The birch pit product is a substrate

Fig. 22. Birch pit manure or concentrate

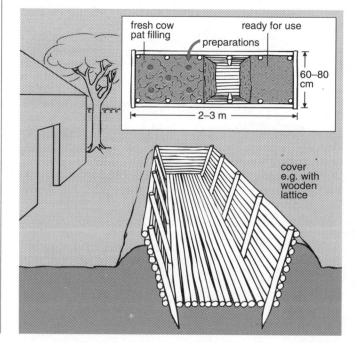

fresh cow pat filling   ready for use
         preparations

60–80 cm

2–3 m

cover e.g. with wooden lattice

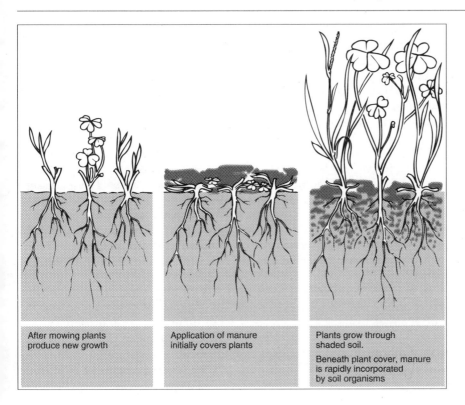

After mowing plants
produce new growth

Application of manure
initially covers plants

Plants grow through
shaded soil.

Beneath plant cover, manure
is rapidly incorporated
by soil organisms

**Fig. 23. Natural
incorporation of
composted manure.**

of great potency containing numerous organisms that promote humification. Used in addition to the standard application of biodynamic preparations it is an excellent starter to initiate the composting process.

Application

Fully matured composted manure is the ideal manure for practically every soil and crop (an exception, for instance, is stinging nettle, see page 193). It is best to apply compost to the soil surface during the period of active growth, when life is really active. In many areas little and often is better for soil and plant life than occasional large applications (Sauerlandt & Tietjen 1970). This has proved a useful rule for grassland and arable land. Distributors for finely particulate matter (e.g. a Weichel distributor) will distribute small amounts evenly over large areas (from 4 t/ha upwards). The more carefully this is done, the faster will the microfauna, worms and microorganisms be able to incorporate the manure in the life of the soil, with plant growth not inhibited by large lumps of material.

The use of fresh manure does mean that the soil receives larger amounts of organic matter and, as in the case of liquid manures, also more nutrients, but the lush growth one sees frequently does not come up to expectations. Dry matter yields prove disappointing; there may even be a reduction in yield, high nitrogen loss in gaseous form or through leaching, and serious problems with pests. Root life in the crumb and reduced or damaged root growth result from a combination of inadequately fermented liquid manure and unfavourable soil conditions. Long-term soil fertility is reduced as a result.

Yields that are the same or higher

than with compost are due to direct nutrient effects. Composted manure on the other hand has a much longer lasting effect on the soil, keeping it in good heart for years. Recent investigations by E. von Wisting-hausen (1984) have shown that despite losses due to composting, applications of composted manure gave approximately the same yields for farm-grown vegetable crops (spinach, dwarf beans and carrots) and perennial ryegrass as applications of fresh manure, but better quality produce. Fresh manure gave better yields and poorer quality in potatoes.

In active, loose-structured soil good results can be seen even with uncomposted manure. The safest way is to apply it in conjunction with straw or green manures, digging these in very shallowly at a time when temperatures are relatively high. Marked wetness or cold will reduce or prevent further conversion and frequently result in acid layers of undecayed matter, which cause fanginess in root crops and generally inhibit plant growth.

On farms where solid and liquid manure are processed separately, applications of composted manure are best supplemented with an application of well fermented dung liquor in the same period of active growth; this provides soil and plant life with the full range of dynamic effects that the animals are able to contribute.

With liquid manure applications, the amount of water added and the use of several separate applications are as important as choosing the right moment.

The details given above concerning

Table 18. Application of solid manure and dung liquor to different crops.

Crop	Time	Amount t, m³/10 ha	Method of application	Comments
1) Humified composted manure				
grassland	July–Aug. (March)	5–10 (4–6)	dressing	best annually (soil warms up quickly, protection from drying-out, e.g. paddock before first grazing)
ley, several years	July–Aug.	15–35*	natural incorporation, then plough under	in second year of maximum use
cereals –winter –spring	Feb.–March March–April	4–6 4–6	top dressing	needs distributor for finely particulate matter; poss. on to thin cover of snow; warms up quickly, protection from alternating frost and thaw and drying out
legumes	prev. year, late summer	8–10	work in lightly	encourages root development and root nodules

* Following crop cereals or rape at 15 t/ha, row crops if up to 35 t/ha.

Crop	Time	Amount t, m³/10 ha	Method of application	Comments
root crops	a) prev. year, late summer	15–35	work in for catch crops (see ley)	autumn manuring, do not plough in deeply
	b) spring	4–10	very shallowly	before or after drilling
2) Short dung				
grassland	Feb.–March	20	finely dispersed, only on open soil	to hasten first mowing; protects from late frost, dryness; soil warms up more quickly
ley, several years	July–Aug.	15–35	natural incorporation, not ploughed in too deeply	only on active soil before ploughing up
cereals	–	–	–	–
legumes	–	–	–	–
root crops	prev. year, late summer or autumn	20–45	work in shallowly	for catch crops: green rye, turnip rape, rape
3) Dung liquor, well fermented				
grassland	betw.1st & 2nd mowing or 1st & 2nd use as pasture	1.5–2.0		only if soil *slightly* moist
ley, several years	a) as for grassland			
	b) late summer	2–3	before ploughing up	with composted manure, natural incorporation
cereals			on to thawing snow cover, soil not frozen when growth stops, not if soil is dry	
–winter	February	1		
–summer	April–May	1		
row crops	May– June– July	2 per application	between rows of growing crop	

applications should never be taken as a fixed norm or even dogma. They merely present a number of aspects and practical experience. It is important not to be deceived by the short-term benefits that may well emerge on comparison of composted manure, liquid manure, or short and long dung.

In the long term consistent application of composted farmyard manure improves the performance, fertility and health of soil, plants and animals. Produce and its constituents

Table 19.
Relationship
between dilution and
yield (yields without
bought-in fodder)
(Bruenner &
Schoellhorn 1972)

70 farms divided into four groups according to frequency of application	Group 1 0–1.0	Group 2 1.01–1.50	Group 3 1.51–2.0	Group 4 2.01 or more
No. of applications p.a. (mean per group)	0.67	1.3	1.8	2.4
Dilution*	2.9	3.3	3.5	4.4
Slurry produced per ha fodder grown	41.9	73.3	102.1	127.3
Storage (days)	76	35.2	30.1	28
Fodder grown per CU (in 1/100 ha)	65	56	47	43
kg milk per ha fodder grown	3285	4155	5001	5706
kg starch equivalent per ha fodder grown	3026	3595	4245	4597

* Dilution 2.9 = 1 part faeces and urine + 1.9 parts of water

Table 20.
Application of well
processed and fully
fermented liquid
manure

Crop	Time	Amount* m³/ha	Method of application/comments
grassland	Feb.–March after mowing/ grazing early autumn	20–40 20–40 20 20	distribute evenly, soil moist if poss., but not wet, under cloud cover as above or on snow when soil not frozen
ley, several years	see above July–Aug.	40–60	natural incorporation before ploughing up, then plough in shallowly
cereals – winter	Jan.– March Sept.–Nov.	20–30 20–30	on snow when soil not frozen, or on frozen soil with no snow immediately after drilling, if soil
– summer		20–30	condition permits
row crops (beet, cabbage)	Aug.–Sept.	40–60 (20–25)	for catch crop or in early autumn; for potatoes in (); work in shallowly
maize	catch crop after drilling into growing crop	40–60 40–60 20–30	with adequate amounts of water for heavy, moist soil, under cloud cover
straw and green manure	Aug.–Sept.	40–60	work in shallowly

* The lower figures are for drift manure, the higher ones for floating slurry.

are of high quality providing the consumer with a sound basis for health and vigour in body, mind and spirit. This has been amply demonstrated in 56 years of practical experience on the Talhof farm in Southern Germany.

Compost

Apart from animal manures produced on the farm, all biodegradable material is also suitable for composting. The following are commonly available on farms:
– material excavated from ditches and ponds,
– material from cleansing cuts on pasture,
– weeds from arable land, e.g. couch grass roots),
– dead leaves and old grass from roadsides,
– twigs and thin branches and brushwood from woodland and orchards, unless suitable for burning to produce heat,
– pomace,
– bark and sawdust, providing they have not been treated with insecticides.

Mixing and setting up the heap is easy if one uses a dung distributor. When the vehicle is three quarters full add calcified seaweed, basalt or other volcanic rock dust, horn and bone meal, pigs bristles and also rock phosphate, as available and required; fill up to the top with fresh farmyard manure and set up as described for composting of manure. Care must be taken when applying the compost that compost made with grassland weeds is applied only to arable land, and compost made with weeds from arable land only to grassland. This avoids new weeds growing from seeds or surviving root elements.

In the garden, carefully mix weeds, harvest residues, vegetable and any kitchen refuse not suitable for feeding livestock in a proportion of 3:1 with fresh farmyard manure, adding calcified seaweed, basalt and other volcanic rock dust, organic starter materials such as horn and bone meal and birch pit concentrate. Make the heap about 1.2–1.5 metres wide and just under a metre high.

Fairly large amounts of fresh green plant material need to wilt a bit first. Add lime (quantity equivalent to putting a dusting of icing sugar on a cake) and leave to rot down in a separate heap, using the compost preparations as well, as always.

In autumn the heap made up of partly decayed matter collected over the growth period is turned. Depending on soil conditions, specific use, composition and maturity, add more of the mineral and organic matter listed above and mix thoroughly. Finally repeat treatment with the biodynamic preparations and cover with a layer of old grass or partly rotted straw. Compost needed for hotbeds and cold frames should be almost fully matured by autumn. Grass sod soil and sharp sand are useful additions in this case. This type of heap is sieved in autumn and covered to protect it from frost. However long the winter season, soil for the cold frame and hotbed will then be ready as needed.

For further details on producing garden compost see *Handbook on Composting and the Bio-Dynamic Preparations* by G. Corrin (1960) and *Grow a Garden and be Self-Sufficient* by E. Pfeiffer and E. Riese (1981).

Composts for special purposes may be produced as follows:
– excavated material from ditches and turves makes excellent grassland fertilizer,
– carrots and flax respond well to

All biodegradable waste should be composted.

fully humified pure horse dung,
- celeriac grows well with composted pig dung, and
- small doses of fully humified chicken droppings give good results with peas and beans, sunflowers and rape and also encourage seed development in fodder plants grown for seed.

Where the amounts of compostable material are relatively small, it is best to mix them into farmyard manure as they become available, before the manure is set up for composting.

Responsible farmers take care to make carefully planned use of all usable organic material, either feeding it to stock or processing it so that it will fertilize and enliven the soil.

Dressings and green manuring

Useful material for dressings includes long dung and also liquid manure, chopped straw, grass and other harvest residues. The material should not be stored under anaerobic conditions beforehand; it needs to be applied as thinly and evenly as possible, to make it easy for the soil fauna and flora to break down and incorporate in the soil. The method, also known as 'sheet composting', is particularly effective when used in fruit growing and vineyards and on grassland. The risk of damage from field voles needs to be taken into account, however.

The combination of top dressing and green manuring merits special mention. Ground cover crops not used for fodder will increase humus content and soil fertility if combined with a thin layer of finely chopped straw and an application of manure. It is important, however, to bury the

densely matted organic matter lightly when the weather is still reasonably warm. Shallow use of a paring plough may actually be too deep, disc harrow and rotary cultivators being the implements of choice. When it is time for drilling or planting, decay should have reached a point where it does not impede the new crop by depriving it of water or by creating an irregular soil structure.

Green manure plants which are killed by frost, like mustard and lupin, may be left to overwinter on light soils. The residues can be lightly covered with partly composted manure and ploughed in a bit deeper; this will do no harm to the following crop if done in good time. It is an excellent preparation for potatoes, for example.

Relatively large amounts of green manure material should be left to wilt slightly before they are lightly integrated. Care must be taken to see that the material decomposes and does not undergo anaerobic conversion at a deeper level, as this tends to reduce yields and creates serious weed problems.

A more effective method is to use stems and leaves for fodder, leaving only stubble and harvest residues; after an application of short dung the whole is incorporated at medium depth, e.g. with rotary stubble cleaner with trailed implements or a combination of rotovator and subsoiler.

The value of the fodder and the additional manure this produces would certainly be greater than the fertilizing effect of green material incorporated into the soil. All aspects of fodder crops that are also suitable for green manuring will therefore be fully considered in the section on intercropping in the chapter on fodder plants.

Fodder value and increased manure production for several years make use as fodder the better choice compared to green manuring.

Improvers and conditioners

Mineral improvers and conditioners

A number of improvers and conditioners are available to assist in the change-over to biodynamic farming and horticulture and later on to correct soil imbalances due to difficult weather conditions. They are widely used in horticulture and fruit growing, but less so in agriculture.

Rock dust or meal

These are primarily basalt rock dust or meal, a waste product from stone quarries such as those near the Kaiserstuhl mountain, Black Forest and Odenwald region in Germany. Chemical analysis has shown them to be rich in minerals and trace elements. Basalts are volcanic rocks and derive from the 'fire phase' of the earth's history; this gives them the capacity to benefit cold soils with high clay content (e.g. keuper [West European Upper Triassic]) which owe their essential characteristic to the 'water phase'. Here fire and water combine to give new life and vigour to worked-out, exhausted soils, as will soon be evident from healthy thriving plant growth.

Rock dust may be used in a number of ways:

– As a first step, basalt rock dust may be applied directly using a manure distributor (1 tonne/ha). There should be no wind and a respirator will be needed. The better method is to add the required amount of the dust to animal manure or compost and mix thoroughly. 1 tonne/ha is sufficient for 3 or 4 years, and the effect will be clearly evident.
– For intensive cultivation, e.g. tree fruit and soft fruit, use calcified seaweed and in addition approx. 0.2 tonnes/ha of basalt rock dust annually. This encourages steady progress in humus building and soil fertility.
– Farmers wishing to use this type of aid for extended periods may add the dust by the shovelful to the daily production of animal manure. It is not advisable to add rock dust to dung liquor or slurry pits as it will sink to the bottom and form a concrete layer that serves no purpose and is difficult to remove.
– The amount required for addition to the compost heap is 5–10 kg/m^3 of waste matter.

The recent trend has been to use lava rock dust instead. Application and effect are similar, though some of the constituents differ. One aspect to be considered is the difference between rock dust and meal. The choice will depend on soil consistency and the need for more rapid (dust) or sustained (meal) effect.

Small amounts added daily to farmyard manure for extended periods are preferable to larger amounts applied directly to the soil.

Clay minerals

Rock dust and meal assist clay formation in soil, manure and compost.
On the other hand some clay flours,
particularly those from the montmorillonite group, make the valuable
minerals much more rapidly available. These are the bentonites,
weathering products of volcanic tuffs
(Tertiary system), some of them
mined in Lower Bavaria, that owe
their name to Fort Benton in the
USA, the place where they were first
found.

Clay minerals are rapidly converted by soil organisms, so that soil
structure and water-holding capacity
improve. They are particularly useful
in light, sandy and dry soils, and in
this case it is not the quantity that
matters, as in the case of basalt dust,
but regular use – little and often.

- Add 1 or 2 kg/m³ to material for
  composting;
- may also be applied directly in
  gardens (0.2–0.4 tonnes/ha) but not
  on farmland;
- Abele (1976) reports that they may
  be added to good effect to dung
  liquor or slurries (200 g/m³).
- Fruit growers find high quality
  clay minerals indispensable. They
  are added to trunk washes and to
  mixtures used to spray the crowns
  in winter; they are also part of the
  popular SAB mixture* and make a
  excellent sticker (200 g to 100 ml
  of spray). Plenty of good reasons
  for making regular use of these
  helpful products.

Calcified seaweed

A major movement for organic
agriculture started in France after the
Second World War. It was named
after its founders Raoul Lemaire
(Professor of Plant Breeding and
Biology) and Jean Boucher (Professor of Soil Biology). The aim is to
farm organically, using a method that
is relatively easy to manage, with
sales guaranteed by contract, and the
system evidently works on quite an
extensive scale.

An important element in the
system is the use of seaweed manure
rich in calcium and magnesium. Vast
reefs and banks of the weed are to be
found along the coasts of Brittany
and Normandy and its use no doubt
goes back to a tradition among
Breton fishermen and farmers who
have always made use of this natural
resource. The material utilized is the
calcareous skeleton of the red or
coralline alga *Lithothamnium calcar-
eum*; this does not have the holdfasts
that green algae have and grows
directly on the sea bed, finding its
nourishment in the light-filled water
of its habitat. Today the algal
material is collected from small sea-
going vessels, carefully dried on land
to reduce the water content from 20
to 0.5% and finely ground. It soon
loses its lovely coral-red colour and
turns greyish white. Calcium and
magnesium are the main constituents,
but there are also numerous trace
elements, and a number of authors
also mention amino acids and growth
hormones. This substance, which in
terms of earth history is still very
young, thus has constituents that are
not to be found in calcium carbonate
fertilizers. Not surprising, then, that
the product soon came to be appre-
ciated in other countries as well. It is
marketed under the trade name
Algomin .

The experience of recent years has
shown the following:

- soil calcium levels increase quite
  rapidly with this material. For
  initial application over large areas,
  0.8–1 tonne/ha is recommended;
  later on the amount may be
  reduced;
- for intensive cultivation, especially

* SAB mixture:
wettable sulphur,
Algomin and
bentonite.

fruit growing, annual applications of 0.2–0.3 tonnes/ha will suffice;
– the algae cannot combine directly with nitrogen but must first be processed by microorganisms; they can therefore be added to animal manures and will accelerate humification;
– small amounts of calcified seaweed can be safely added to feeds for domestic animals;
– 3–5 kg/m³ will replace lime when composting vegetable residues;
– with the right kind of drying equipment the seaweed can be dried and used against insect pests on plants, as little as 30–50 kg/ha dusted on to potato plants will help prevent the blight caused by *Phytophthora infestans* and markedly inhibit larval development in Colorado beetle. The hygroscopic properties and blockage of respiratory passages deprive the insects of the basis for life.

Liquid conditioners

Seaweed preparations

From the red algae that provide calcified seaweed it is only a short step to leafy algae, which are also found on the Atlantic coasts of Europe. The main difference is that in this case we are using not the calcareous skeleton of dead but the leaf mass of living plants, mainly the brown alga *Ascophyllum nodosum* harvested in Norway. Again many trace elements and active principles have been found.

Algal concentrates are marketed under various trade names, e.g. Algifert, Polymaris and Oscorna Pflanzenstaerkung (Oscorna plant food). They have a positive effect on green plant leaves that is immediately obvious and encourage crop

Natural products can improve growth to a remarkable extent.

growth. The effect is quite different to that of nitrates; greedy feeders in field and garden crops and fruit crops, too, are strengthened by repeated applications of these products and positively thrive. Applications should be limited to three, however, or leaves and fruit begin to show hardening. 0.8–1% solutions are used, depending on the product.

Nettle tonic

The effect of nettle tonic on plant growth is less powerful than that of seaweed but extremely useful nevertheless; repeated application to crops is something not to be missed during the summer months. Stinging nettles (*Urtica dioica*) are widely available and easy to grow (see page 193). The vigorous, dark-green leaf growth shows that much chlorophyll is produced and the preferred site, waste places and rubbish dumps, indicates a capacity for readily converting waste matter and refuse into earth that smells good and is rich in humus. The plant is also rich in minerals and has a special affinity for iron, vitamins and plant hormones that can be utilized in the feeding of animals, especially young animals (e.g. chicks). Finally it is worth noting that the stinging hairs contain a compound of silica and calcium.

Cut the nettles when fully grown, prior to or at the beginning of the flowering stage, and combine in the ratio 1:10, i.e. 10 kg to 100 litres, with rain water in a tub or large barrel. Fermentation will take eight or ten days, ideally in a sunny position. Keep the container covered, not only on account of the smell but to protect domestic and other animals (e.g. hedgehogs) and young children. In the early stages, stir the mixture briefly in the mornings and evenings.

For horticultural purposes apply a 1:10 dilution using a watering can or sprayer when growth has been checked (by night frosts, drought, etc.), several times a week if required. It has also been found that 10% of nettle tonic may be usefully added to the water in which Preparation 501 is stirred (see page 90 ff.).

Where crops are thin, nettle tea made with boiling water may be used in early spring. The use of imported nettle powder should be regarded an emergency measure for city gardens.

A fresh cold-water nettle extract will cope with light aphid infestations on roses and beans. In warm weather the extract will be ready within 24 hours. Top up with fresh nettles and water throughout the summer months. When the first frosts come empty the contents on to the compost or manure heap and store the container in a safe place.

Wormwood and tansy

Wormwood (*Artemisia absinthium*) and tansy (*Chrysanthemum vulgare*) have a bitterness that makes plants unattractive to insects. They are used in powder form against carrot fly and as a spray by fruit growers. The effect is similar with both plants, which are part of the formula in all herbal products sold for the purpose.

Preparation is simple. Pour boiling water over three kilograms of the powdered material, leave to stand for a short time and make up to 100 litres with cold water. The addition of a sticker or wetter (bentonite, soft soap) is always advisable.

Equisetum liquor is highly effective in preventing fungus attacks.

Horsetail

The common horsetail (*Equisetum arvense*) plays a special role in bio-dynamic agriculture. Rudolf Steiner suggested the use of horsetail tea or liquor to combat fungus attacks. He based himself on the high silica content of the plant (combined with sulphur) and the particular growth and development dynamics of horse-tail which point to its actions. Growth dynamics are such that the leafy fronds are produced separately from the spore-bearing stems, a feature not shared by water and marsh horsetail. Every spring one can observe the brown sporangia breaking ground in sandy waste ground, on roadsides, railway embankments and in patches where drainage is poor in the fields, shedding their spores all around. They soon disappear again and the green fronds emerge from the rhizomes, growing on without reproductive organs.

Steiner was referring to this duality in development, with the 'fungal' element eliminated in advance through the development of spore-bearing stems.

The tea or liquor is sprayed as a preventive measure in very wet weather, which always means a high risk of fungal growth. It is best done in late autumn and early spring in all sites where harmful fungi are likely to appear. Examples of crops needing this treatment are winter barley, potatoes, fruit plantations and strawberries. A third, fourth and even fifth spraying operation may follow whilst crops are growing.

If preventive measures have proved inadequate, the following method, originally developed for ornamentals grown in hothouses, has proved effective with all types of crops:

On three consecutive days, always at exactly the same hour, spray the affected plants with the liquor. The fungus will disappear, providing there have no massive errors of cultivation.

The tea is easily made. Collect the green fronds in your own grounds in late summer when the silica content is highest and the fronds have grown really hard and firm. If the plant does not grow on your farm or it is too much of an effort to collect it, the herb can be bought. Boil approx. 300 g in five litres of water on a low flame for a whole hour before adding five times the amount of water. The tea may be used immediately as a spray or stored in a barrel. It will ferment in due course and turn into the liquor, which does not affect its usefulness.

Do not add horsetail when stirring Preparations 500 and 501. On the other hand both farmers and gardeners often mix nettle and horsetail liquor, which, of course, is only possible in the summer months. This is not advisable with all types of crops, e.g. strawberries. Nettle liquor strengthens cereal crops affected by fungus.

SPS and Bio-S

These two products increase resistance to fungal attack and virus disease; they were specially devel-oped for organic growers.

SPS – Schumachers Pflanzensaft (Schumacher's plant extract) – is a clear liquid concentrate of wild herb extracts; possible uses in greenhouses and out of doors include the treatment of asters (wilt) or strawberries (grey mould). Rooting is encouraged in seedlings and cuttings dipped in the solution, and sensitive crops like celeriac in seed boxes thrive better if watered with it.

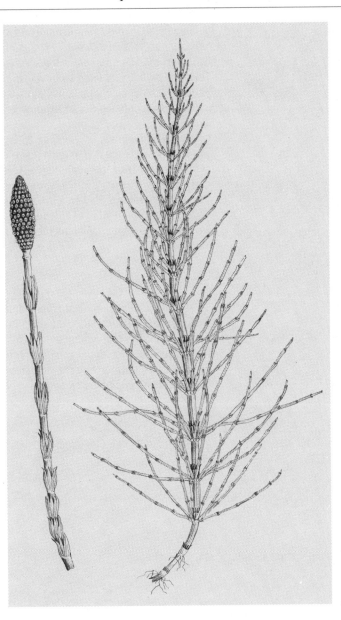

Trade names include Ledaxmikrob and Oscorna Wurzelstaerkung (rooting compound). Application is as a 2% solution.

Bio-S was developed in the 1950s by Inspector Salzmann for fruit growing in the harsh climate of the Swabian Alb in Germany. It contains a number of herbal extracts combined with sulphur. Bio-S is used as

Fig. 24.
**Common horsetail
(Equisetum
arvense).**

Timely application increases the chances of success.

a universal remedy against fungal attack, generally in 0.5–1% solution. It is applied to vegetables (tomatoes), tree and soft fruit; used in good time it will also prove effective against late blight in potatoes and mildew on cereals.

Again it is most important to be economical in use, for especially with crops like strawberries the sulphur content can affect the flavour. German Trade names include Ledax-san and Oscorna Pilz-vorbeugung (Oscorna fungus prevention)

Waterglass

In recent years it has been found that waterglass (sodium silicate) may be used to good effect when the season no longer permits the use of sulphur preparations. Some thought was then given to the properties of this highly alkaline silicate and further uses were explored. In the past, house-wives used it to store eggs for the winter, a method that has fallen into disuse.

Waterglass is not adequate as a seed dressing for winter cereals but has proved very helpful with flowers and ornamentals, though care must be taken not to spray too often (unprepossessing grey coating), and on fruit and vegetables. In a warm climate, concentrations higher than 1% may cause scorching, but potatoes can be safely sprayed with 2 or 3% solutions. 0.5% added to trunk washes acts as a sticker. Extreme caution is required close to buildings and with special types of glass (windows, glasses) as the resulting grey coating cannot be removed. Waterglass may be obtained from chemists and druggists.

1

Care given to the soil and the use of humus-building cropping sequences improve soil structure and fertility. 1: Upper Jurassic residual rendzina worked with cultivator/grubber and left in furrows instead of using winter furrow. Long-term leys increase the humus level (2) and prevent puddling even with heavy precipitation. 3 and 4: Even a thin layer of humus prevents erosion on the edges of a gravel pit.

5

6

7

Manure treated with the biodynamic preparations is left to mature in carefully covered heaps (5, 8, 9). Horn silica sprayed in the morning (6) encourages vegetative growth; sprayed in the afternoon before harvesting it helps the final ripening process, the development of valuable constituents and the keeping quality of the product.

8

9

Working with special dynamics and rhythms

People do not usually find it difficult today to understand the biological interactions involved in agriculture, but problems do arise when it comes to the financially viable realization of ecological principles. Anything connected with the dynamics that are operative in the world of nature, and particularly in practical farming, tends to meet with a total lack of understanding.

This is really surprising in the age of nuclear physics, nuclear fission and fusion, atom bombs and atomic energy produced for what are termed 'peaceful' uses. Surely everyone knows that tiny particles of matter hold tremendous energies, so that a single gram may contain something like 25 thousand million kWh, a figure well beyond our range of imagination.

Figures of far greater magnitude are juggled with the help of electronic brains by people who are working with vast, barely controllable energies. These derive from the sphere of magnetism, electricity and radioactivity, which Rudolf Steiner called 'subnatural'.

Equally dynamic forces come from 'supernatural' spheres; they are the dynamics of life, soul and spirit. 'The dynamics of earth and cosmos that I spoke of are acting through the physical substances in the soil in the realm of agriculture. And we shall only be able to go on to all kinds of practical aspects if we first consider in some detail the question as to how the forces we have spoken of take effect through the physical substances in the soil.' (Steiner 1924).

He then went on to show how a study of protein can show its constituents – carbon (C), nitrogen (N), oxygen (O), hydrogen (H) and sulphur (S) or phosphorus (P) – to be the vehicles for those forces.

The power of the spirit acts through carbon to create form, the power of the soul element through nitrogen to develop sentient response and sensitivity. Oxygen is the mediator of the life principle, and sulphur finally conveys the dynamics of loosing and binding (i.e. of chemistry). Sulphur (from the Latin for sun-bearer) is a bonding element that is almost always present, often only as a mere trace. Phosphorus (from the Greek for light-bearer) frequently takes over the role of sulphur.

It should be noted that in the DNA 'ladder', the basic functional unit in all living matter (C, N, O, H and P are the elements of which deoxyribonucleic acid, DNA, is composed), the rungs of the 'ladder' are held together by hydrogen bonds (secondary valences); these bonds are relatively easily undone during chromosome division, to join up again later.

A look at the living world around us soon makes it obvious that life only springs from life. Anything that

DNA is regarded as the carrier of genetic material

is dead cannot produce life. On the other hand, dead matter is continuously discharged from the life process. The secret of life cannot be found in the world of matter. It is however possible to deduce that the earth's minerals, which are the physical building stones for all life forms here on earth, have their origin in a principle that is living, ensouled and essentially non-physical.

It matters therefore, whether the nitrogen used to stimulate plant life derives from ensouled life forms or from non-living physical and chemical processes, for it is involved in all life processes. Animal manure will stimulate the life processes in soil and plants in quite a different way than mineral fertilizers do.

The biodynamic compost and spray preparations derive entirely from the sphere of life and are incorporated the rhythm of the seasons. Beat is part of the world of mechanics and materialism; rhythm on the other hand belongs to the sphere of life and spirit. Beat means repetition of the same at regular intervals, rhythm the recurrence of similar events at similar intervals.

The earth interacts with sun, moon, planets and fixed stars. The rhythms of the seasons reflect the relationship between sun and earth against the background of the zodiac. Every farmer knows that farm operations depend on the position of the sun in the zodiac. No one in the northern hemisphere would sow oats for grain

Fig. 25. Winter and spring cereal crops in relation to the cycle of the seasons.

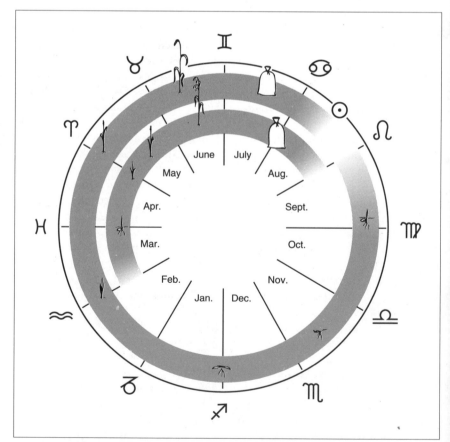

while the sun is in Leo (11 August – 15 September), nor winter wheat while it is in Taurus (14 May – 19 June).

The moon is the heavenly body that is closest to the earth. It, too, has an effect on all life processes, which may be more or less obvious. Many rhythms influenced by the moon or reflecting its rhythms have been identified. Thus R. Dierks (1983) writes:

'There is no longer any reason to doubt the effect of the biodynamic preparations and the influence of rhythms even if the mode of action has not yet been explained. Numerous trials have given conclusive proof that the action consists in enhancement of specific vital processes.'

Biodynamic compost preparations

In his *Agriculture* course, Rudolf Steiner established the principle of manuring to be as follows: 'The purpose of manuring must be to vitalize the soil.' He went on to describe the production and actions of a number of plant preparations. Added to manure in the right way, these will stimulate vitalizing and harmonizing processes in the soil.

The preparations are listed below (the figures given in parentheses have come from the early days and are commonly used in English-speaking countries today).

Yarrow flowers (*Achillea millefolium*) (502) are put in the bladder of a red deer stag, suspended in the sun throughout summer and buried in the earth during winter. The action addresses itself in a specific way to the relationship between nitrogen and potassium in the soil.

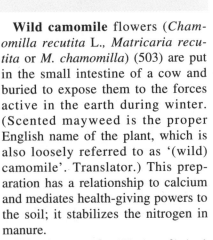

Fig. 26. Yarrow (*Achillea millefolium*).

Wild camomile flowers (*Chamomilla recutita* L., *Matricaria recutita* or *M. chamomilla*) (503) are put in the small intestine of a cow and buried to expose them to the forces active in the earth during winter. (Scented mayweed is the proper English name of the plant, which is also loosely referred to as '(wild) camomile'. Translator.) This preparation has a relationship to calcium and mediates health-giving powers to the soil; it stabilizes the nitrogen in manure.

Stinging nettle (*Urtica dioica*) (504) was considered irreplaceable

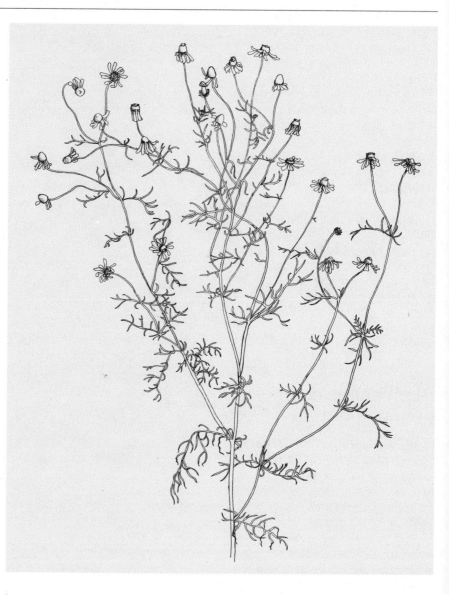

**Fig. 27.
Wild camomile
(Chamomilla
recutita).**

by Rudolf Steiner. Cut when in full flower – the first seeds may already have developed – leave to wilt slightly, place in a pit dug in the ground and press down lightly; leave for a full year to absorb the activities of all the seasons. The amount used is much greater than with the other compost preparations, at least five times as much, and may indeed be even more. This preparation will on the one hand support the activities of 502 and 503 and on the other confer on manure and soil the ability to deal with matter and forces rationally and attune themselves specifically to the crop grown at the time.

One can gain a certain insight into this activity by noting the preferred sites of these plants in the wild. Stinging nettle is mostly found in 'waste' places close to human habitations – the chaos of rubbish tips, decaying old buildings and the like.

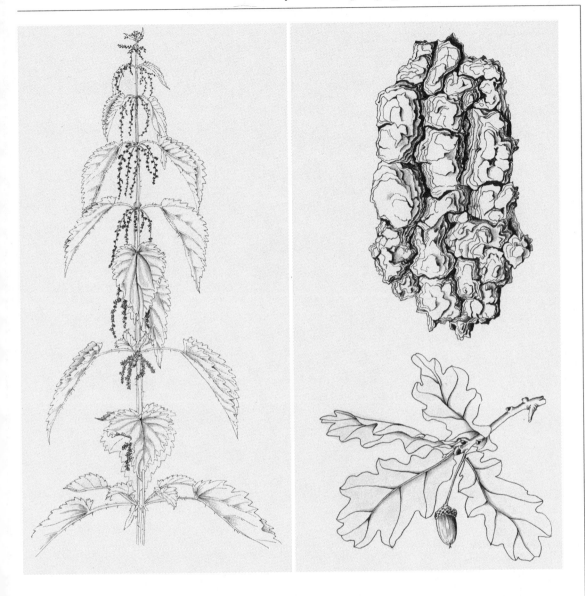

It disappears again after some time, leaving the soil 'in good order', well structured and rich in humus.

Similar help is given with understanding the **Oak bark** preparation (505) if one observes an English oak (*Quercus robur*) in an open field. The powerful upright trunk and the rounded crown extending well into space are in beautiful balance and harmony. The tree is particularly impressive in its leafless state during winter, with that balanced beauty evident in even the smallest branches.

The grated bark is put into the skull of a domestic animal (usually a cow), buried in a marshy place and left there during autumn and winter. By spring the substance has taken up qualities which it confers on the compost or manure to enable it to create soil conditions that will prevent and combat all plant diseases

Fig. 28. Stinging nettle (*Urtica dioica*).

Fig. 29. Leaf, fruit and bark of English oak (*Quercus robur*).

Fig. 30. Dandelion
**(*Taraxacum*
officinale).**

due to proliferating growth.

The right relationship between silica and potassium in the soil is encouraged by **dandelion** flowers (*Taraxacum officinale*) (506). These are wrapped in the mesentery of a cow and buried in the earth during winter.

A cold extract made from the flowers of **valerian** (*Valeriana officinalis*) (507) gives compost and manure the power to relate properly to phosphorus. Added to a manure or compost heap, the valerian preparation not only regulates phosphorus and temperature processes but also surrounds the heap with protective warmth. This quality can be put to good use for the prevention of late and early frost damage. If there is a serious risk of night frosts, spray the crops, e.g. flowering soft fruit plants or sensitive species such as beans, tomatoes, early potatoes and also basil, late in the evening with a valerian solution. As a rule there will be no damage with temperatures dropping to –3 or –4 °C; if they go down lower than that, damage cannot be prevented but can at least be minimized to some extent. If plants are covered with hoarfrost in the morning, a second application of valerian will often save the situation.

If valerian is sprayed on flowering plants (e.g. pulses, rape, linseed and mustard) and fodder crops grown for seed (e.g. sainfoin, phacelia and many others) when the shoots are c. 15–20 cm high and again just before they come into flower, the flowering process will be greatly stimulated. Crops will flower abundantly and at a good pace in sunny weather, ensuring a greatly enhanced yield.

The effect may be further enhanced by adding dung water made with chicken or pigeon droppings when making up the valerian solution.

The manufacture of these preparations calls for expert knowledge and great care, factors that have a major influence on their effectiveness. This is why details relating to method are not given here. The ideal place for producing the preparations is a farm.

Courses are available in which the necessary knowledge and skills can be acquired. Another widely used method is for the members of a cooperative or group to get together on one of the farms and produce the preparations under expert guidance. The preparations are then taken to the individual farms and buried in sites that are well apart.

It is advisable to use skulls and intestines for 503, 505 and 506 from animals from one's own farm if possible, as the quality of carcases, glands, membranes and organs is generally superior. Great care must also be taken when gathering, drying

and storing the plant material, which again should as far as possible be home-grown.

It is important to avoid pollution during drying and storage and also in the chosen site.

On the basis of many years' experience, the German Research Group for Biodynamic Farming Methods (Forschungsring fuer Biologisch-Dynamische Wirtschaftsweise) has published the following

**Fig. 31. Valerian
(Valeriana
officinalis).**

brief instructions for using and storing the compost preparations:

The six preparations are made from the medicinal plants yarrow, wild camomile, stinging nettle, oak bark, dandelion and valerian. They are added to compost, manure, dung liquor and slurries. To treat a compost heap, stacked manure or deep litter, use a stick to make 5 holes, each about 50 cm deep. The distance between holes should not be less than 50 cm nor more than 2 metres. Put 2 or 3 g (= a small teaspoonful) of the five solid preparations singly into consecutive holes, as shown in Fig. 32. The sequence does not matter that much, it is used for practical reasons.

The preparations are quite light in weight; to make sure that they go down to the bottom of their respective holes, mix each with a little dung or moist earth, shape into a small ball and drop this down the hole.

Close the holes up, so that the preparations are completely surrounded by manure. For the liquid valerian preparation you'll need hand-hot water which should be soft or have been left to stand for some time. Use 2–3 ml (a small teaspoonful) to 5 litres of water and stir for 15 minutes, reversing direction at intervals (clockwise until a vortex has formed, then anticlockwise, etc.). Spray the surface of the heap with the solution.

To treat dung liquor or slurry put the solid preparations into small bags made of fabric and weighed down with stones, and tie to a wooden cross or lath that will float on the liquor. Stir the valerian preparation as above and pour into the liquor.

With liquid manure, an additional measure is to make small balls of the preparations, as above, and throw these into the dung channel at weekly intervals.

To maintain their activity, store the preparations in glass, stoneware or porcelain containers standing in peat, each insulated by at least 7 cm of peat all around each container. Cover

**Fig. 32.
Adding biodynamic
preparations to a
compost heap**

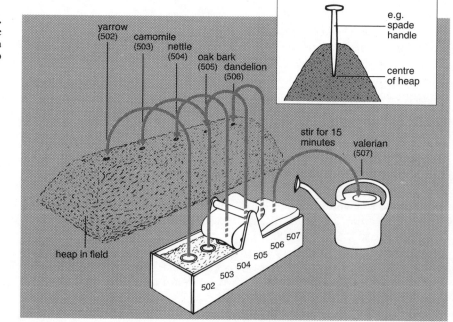

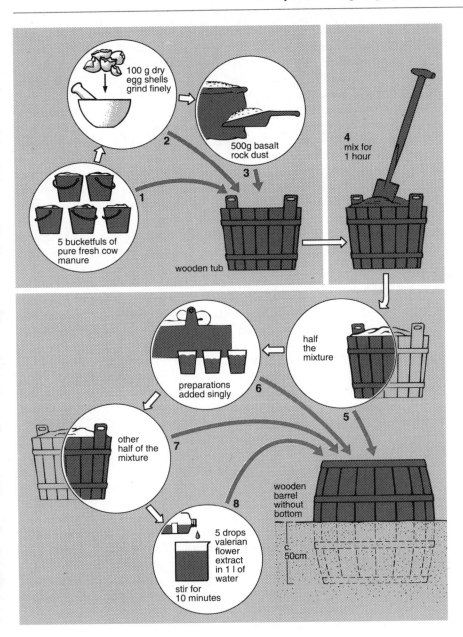

100 g dry egg shells grind finely

500g basalt rock dust

4 mix for 1 hour

1

2

3

5 bucketfuls of pure fresh cow manure

wooden tub

half the mixture

5

preparations added singly

6

other half of the mixture

7

8

5 drops valerian flower extract in 1 l of water

stir for 10 minutes

wooden barrel without bottom

50cm

Fig. 33. Making Maria Thun's cowpat preparation

with a peat-filled bag.

Maria Thun has developed a cow-pat preparation that stimulates soil life and the conversion of organic matter. It is intended to supplement rather than replace horn manure (500) and birch pit concentrate; add when ploughing in manure, compost or green manure, during all other ploughing operations, and on grass-land after grazing or mowing. This promotes the conversion of matter in the soil, improves soil structure and generally results in higher yields. It is reported to have given good results during conversion from conventional to biodynamic management. The same applies to its addition to fresh

Fig. 34.
Field sprays –
production, storage
and preparation
for use

manure for field dressing. The preparation is produced as follows:

Put five buckets of pure fresh cow manure in a wooden tub, add 100 g of dry, finely ground egg shells and 500 g of basalt meal and dig through and keep moving for 5 hours without break. Transfer half of this dynamized material to a barrel that has had its bottom removed and is buried to a depth of 40 or 50 cm in the ground. Add the compost preparations, each by itself, then the rest of the mixture and finally 5 drops of valerian preparation in a litre of water that has been stirred for ten minutes. Put a lid on the barrel.

After four weeks dig the material in the barrel over to mix it thoroughly. Another two weeks and it will be ready for use. 250 g of the material added to 40 or 50 litres of warm water and stirred for 15–20 minutes will be sufficient for one hectare of arable or grassland. The solution needs to be applied within three days, after that it loses its power. Maria Thun found that the best results were achieved by using a rhythm that involves spraying on three consecutive days.

Field sprays

In addition to the compost preparations, two field sprays are also used. Plants reflect the activities of earth and cosmos in the way they grow.

Horn manure (500) is designed to enhance the powers that come from the earth, **horn silica** (501) those that come from the cosmos. The specific powers of concentration that lie in the cow horn are utilized on the one hand to gather and concentrate the dynamics to be found in the earth in winter and on the other to let the

powers mediated by the cosmos via the earth in summer radiate into the rock crystal and be preserved in it.

It is possible to get an idea of the function of the cow horn in cases where some trauma has caused a cow to lose a horn. With the outer protection lost, one sees a stump of cancellous bone enveloped in delicate tissue with a rich blood supply. Bleeding tends to be prolonged and needs to be stopped as soon as possible. The horn acts as a sheath that gathers the streaming life blood together and sends it back into the organism of the animal.

To make horn manure, collect good quality, well formed manure from dairy cows in early autumn. As far as possible the animals should be fed on pasture supplemented with hay. Pack the horns well with the manure, making sure it goes right down into the tip. Bury in a pit in soil that has plenty of life in it and leave until spring. The horns are thus exposed to the powers of crystallization in the earth. When the horns are taken up, the contents will show if preparation has been successful. If it has, the greeny brown manure put in in autumn, with its strong smell, has turned into dark brown, almost black material with a pleasant odour of woodland earth. If damaged cow horns were used, or horns from oxen, bulls or heifers, one usually finds a stinking mass that is a poisonous green and quite useless.

The filled horns may be left in the ground until required, or their contents may be put in stone jars and stored in boxes, using 5–7 cm of peat to insulate them. Horns may be used up to four times. A good method of preserving their quality has been to put them in sacks of natural fibre (coarse mesh) once they have been dug up and emptied in spring or

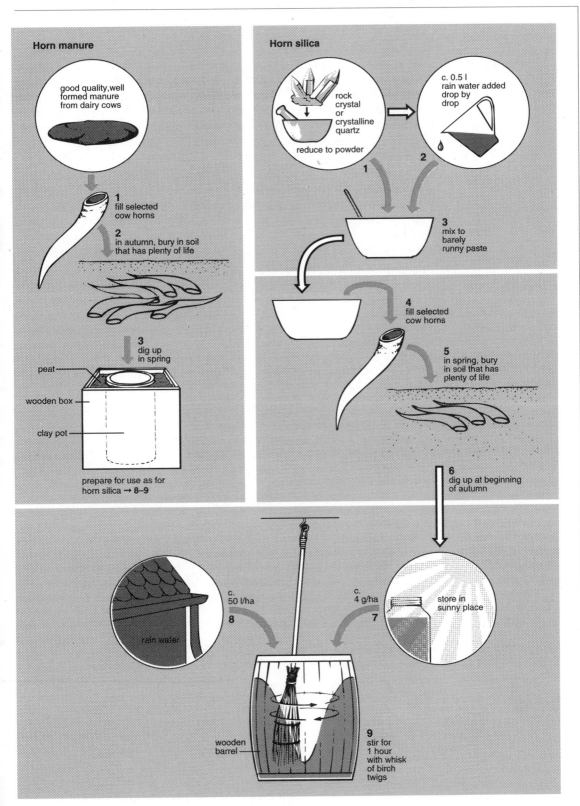

Horn manure

good quality, well formed manure from dairy cows

1 fill selected cow horns

2 in autumn, bury in soil that has plenty of life

3 dig up in spring

peat

wooden box

clay pot

prepare for use as for horn silica → 8–9

Horn silica

rock crystal or crystalline quartz

reduce to powder

c. 0.5 l rain water added drop by drop

1

2

3 mix to barely runny paste

4 fill selected cow horns

5 in spring, bury in soil that has plenty of life

6 dig up at beginning of autumn

c. 50 l/ha

8

rain water

c. 4 g/ha

7

store in sunny place

wooden barrel

9 stir for 1 hour with whisk of birch twigs

summer and store them in the cow house until re-used in autumn.

For the horn silica preparation, one needs particularly well-shaped horns from cows that have calved a number of times, though they should not be more than eight years old. Use very finely powdered rock crystal, crystalline quartz or even potash felspar. Add rainwater and mix to a paste that is barely runny. Fill the paste into the selected horns – as for horn manure, but in late spring – and bury in the ground so that it will be exposed to the cosmic summer dynamics in the earth. Choose a sunny site. When the horns are dug up in late autumn, keep the material in the horns or in a glass container kept in a sunny place.

Horn manure and horn silica hold the concentrated forces gathered through half a sun year. These need to be developed before use by stirring in rain water at body temperature for one hour. On average, the human pulse beats 4320 to 4380 times an hour (72–73 beats/min times

60). The sun also has 4380 'pulse beats' (182.5 days of 24 hours each = 4380). Reflecting on this without getting too much caught up in numbers, one can begin to realize that this is a case where machines cannot really take the place of human beings.

Nevertheless, stirring machines are available, and these can be helpful when converting to the biodynamic method. When one has worked with the preparations for some years, there will have been an inner conversion, too, and then the time needed for stirring by hand can usually be found.

40–60 litres of water and 250–300 g of horn manure or 4 g of horn silica will be required per hectare. Tall slender wooden vessels with a capacity of 200–500 litres are best suited to the purpose. Tie a whisk of birch twigs to a handle that is 3.5–4.5 metres in length and can be suspended from an overhead beam by a ring. It should be just a hand's breadth clear of the floor. Vigorous

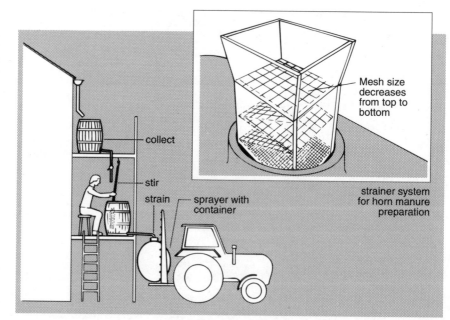

Fig. 35. Installation for stirring field sprays and transfer to sprayer.

collect

stir

strain — sprayer with container

Mesh size decreases from top to bottom

strainer system for horn manure preparation

stirring, starting at the periphery and moving inwards in concentric circles, creates a vortex that reaches almost to the bottom. Reverse direction and stir until an equally deep vortex is created, reverse again, and so on, for a whole hour without interruption.

The strained liquid must be applied immediately, using suitable sprayers. Tractor-mounted or back-pack sprayers may be used, and for the garden a small hand-sprayer will suffice, or even a hearthbrush. Every effort should be made to spray the preparations within two hours of stirring being completed; after this, activity is rapidly lost.

This is also why sprays cannot be made up in advance. If an interruption occurs during stirring, more of the biodynamic preparation has to be added, after which the mixture needs another full hour's stirring.

Horn manure

This preparation provides an immensely concentrated fertilizing power for the soil (Steiner 1924); root growth and primary shoot development are specifically enhanced.

Large droplets are required (remove helical element from spray head); they are applied to the soil during or shortly before preparing a seed bed, to grassland before active growth starts and later after cutting or grazing, combined with chain harrowing.

The earth breathes great breaths in the cycle of the year; it begins to breathe out in spring and breathe in again in autumn. The same happens on a smaller scale in the course of each day, with the earth beginning to exhale in the morning and inhale again in the evening. Afternoon and evening are therefore the right time for spraying horn manure. The soil will then take in its special dynamics as it breathes in at night.

The preparation may also be applied in conjunction with tillage

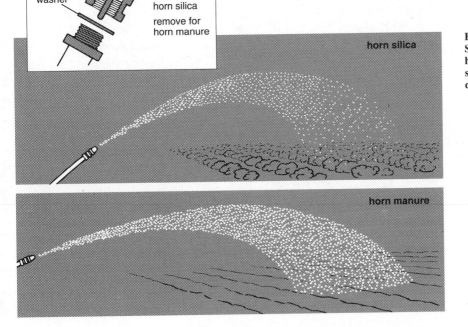

Fig. 36.
Spraying horn silica;
horn manure
sprayed in large
droplets.

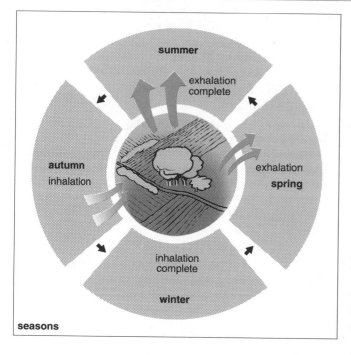

summer

exhalation
complete

autumn
inhalation

exhalation
spring

inhalation
complete

winter

seasons

Fig. 37.
**Breathing rhythm of
the earth in relation
to the four seasons**

operations, e.g. using a weed harrow after drilling or, later on, hoeing.

With reference to the cycle of the seasons, Rudolf Steiner pointed out that crystallizing powers are particularly active in the soil in the depth of winter, from mid-January to mid-February. Horns filled with cow manure are in the soil during that time. Before and after this period, and especially in November and December, minerals in the soil radiate dynamics that are important for plant growth. Applying the horn manure preparation at this time, weather permitting, has proved particularly effective. The soil should not be frozen, nor covered with snow. Talhof farm is situated in an area where the climate is harsh, so that it is not always possible to spray in November or December. When the weather does permit us to spray, we can generally count on active growth and good yields.

Under drought conditions, appli-

cation of a fine mist of horn manure to the crops in late evening or early morning will reduce or prevent damage.

Horn silica

Oxygen (O_2, the vehicle for the dynamics of life, is the most common element in the earth's crust (47%). Together with silicon (Si) it makes up almost three quarters of the outer earth's crust, which is about 16 km thick. Silica (SiO_2) is found all over the world in every type of soil, in plants, animals and humans. Rudolf Steiner pointed out that the function of silica in the soil is to mediate cosmic activities connected with light and heat.

Lime is the opposite. It relates more to the dynamics of the regions below the sun and in the earth.

Under the combined influence of these opposing principles, live humus is produced in the soil by microfauna, plants and animals to provide the basis for fruitful growth.

Horn manure supports the terrestrial or lime principle, horn silica the cosmic or silica principle.

Horn silica enhances the plant's ability to make effective use of the dynamics of light.

Assimilation starts as soon as the first green leaves appear. If horn silica is applied at this early stage, shoot and stem growth will be inhibited because it is the stage when roots are growing and spreading. The spray is very finely distributed by using a helical element in the spray head, so that it will act mainly through the foliage. This means that sufficient foliage must have developed before it is applied. The first application of horn silica is usually made when the fruiting part of the plant is just beginning to develop:

– on cereals when they begin to tiller; at that point the ear ('fruiting part') can be seen tightly enveloped in fine leaf sheaths,

– on root crops when the tops are about a hand high and the root ('fruiting part') is clearly thickening, beginning to turn yellowy red in the case of carrots,

– on pulses when the first buds appear,

– on fodder crops when an even carpet of leaves ('fruiting part') has developed and is about 10 cm high,

– on vegetables, e.g. cabbages, when the inside leaves begin to turn in,

– on fruit when it is at the bud stage, before the flowers open.

Spreading vegetative growth is encouraged if horn silica is sprayed in the early morning, the time when the earth begins to exhale. Later, when it is a question of encouraging maturation, or final development of the root in root crops, spraying is done mainly in the afternoon and evening.

The time when exhalation is complete, between 12 noon and 2 p.m., is not suitable for using the field sprays. Plant growth is not a continuous process from germination to harvest. Phases of active expan-sion alternate with periods when growth is held back, rests. Cereal crops show this very clearly:

Horn manure is applied prior to drilling. After germination the young radicles grow downwards and the plumule (shoot) upwards. Horn manure is applied again. During the next phase both root and leaf growth are not so much in a longitudinal but more in a horizontal direction. Then tillering starts and the basis for new haulms is provided. Spread is still at ground level, however. Then horn silica is sprayed for the first time. The next phase is marked by extensive growth, with the plants beginning to shoot up. This is a good time for a further application of horn silica to encourage the process. On conclusion of this phase, the ears extend, a process immediately followed by flowering, which takes only a few days with cereals. Extension of the ear prior to flow-ering and the time after flowering are also good times for spraying horn silica. It is not advisable to spray when the flowers are open, for ex-perience has shown that this results in poor seed setting.

A final spraying with horn silica may be given at the milky stage of the grain, again in the morning (as on all other occasions). At this stage haulm, leaves and ears are still green, a final phase of active vegetative growth marks the transition to the devitalization that comes with maturation. At this point, two more applications of horn silica may be made in the afternoons.

Experience has shown these to be the stages when field sprays may be used to good effect. This does not mean, however, that they should, or indeed ought to, be applied to a par-ticular crop at every one of the times mentioned.

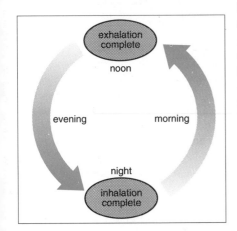

Fig. 38. Diurnal breathing rhythm.

Horn silica enhances the plant's ability to make effective use of the dynamics of light

The detailed description which has been given should enable farmers to determine the right times for spraying other crops for themselves.

In conclusion, a list is given of other factors that should be taken into account:
– the etheric geography of the site,
– soil conditions,
– weather conditions,
– time of day,
– requirements of particular species and varieties,
– number and rhythmical sequence of applications,
– positions of moon and planets.

An example of the first four factors is the following. On the dry sandy soils of Denmark, where summer days bring long exposure to light ether dynamics, the first application of horn silica should be at a later stage, e.g. when tillering is completed. If conditions are also very dry, experience has shown that good results are achieved by adding half the amount of horn manure and spraying very early in the morning, before 8 a.m., or late at night, after 6 p.m. The Talhof farm lies in a narrow valley running north to south, where there is much shade; the soil is shallow, the parent material limestone. It has been found that application of horn silica spray is most effective if done in the early hours of the morning to have plenty of dew, in good growing weather (warm and moist) and under a lightly veiled sky. If spraying in done in the afternoons, the sky should be clear and the

weather warm; spraying should have finished before the evening dew falls.

It is evident from the above that it needs sensitivity and good powers of observation to use horn silica efficiently; in this way, powerful dynamics of a rich and varied nature can be brought to bear in the farm organism.

Numerous trials have shown that three applications of horn manure and three of horn silica give optimum results with regard to both quantity and quality. For practical purposes, it is sufficient to apply each preparation at least once and ideally three times, chosing favourable times.

Finally it needs to be emphasized that little or no result can be expected if a preparation is used on its own. All of them – the compost preparations for treating manure, and the field sprays applied to the manured soil and the crops that grow in it – must be given the opportunity to develop their real potential in a farm or garden organism that is well ordered and kept in balance and harmony; they will them bring a dynamic vitality to everything that is something completely new in agriculture.

Constellations and rhythms

In the temperate regions of the earth, the breathing rhythm of sun and earth is clearly evident in the four seasons. The world of nature and human beings are more or less dependent on this.

The year of the sun is like a great breath in the 'platonic year'. It takes 25,920 years for the vernal equinox (time when the sun crosses the equator in spring) to move through the whole zodiac. A human being

10

11

12

13

On the one hand legumes improve soil 14
fertility and yields, on the other hand they
provide valuable protein-rich green fodder
and grain for the farm's animals. 11 and 12:
Fodder peas. Rapid growth suppresses
weeds and gives high fodder yields. Grain
yields can be approx. 5 t/ha. Sainfoin (12
and 13) is one of the best fodder plants.
Deep roots open up the soil, whilst bees and
bumble bees find food in abundance on this
and other members of the pea family. The
handsomely coloured flowers with their
delicate scent bring life to the fields.
Undersown clover reduces pressure damage
during the maize harvest and improves the
preceding crop value.

15

Cropping sequences including many crops and particularly legumes will ensure good cereal harvests even on poor sites if the biodynamic method is used. 15: Winter wheat grown in the shallow soil of juniper heathland made arable. Naked barley does particularly well after potatoes (16). Peas are suitable as a preceding crop for oats (17). Centre-mounted hoe (18) and weed harrows are useful for keeping crops weed-free. Hoeing also helps mineral conversion, so that yields are improved.

16

17

takes the same number of breaths (25,920) in a 24-hour day.

A calendar year and a tropical year (the time the sun takes to return to the same point in its orbit, e.g. the vernal equinox) differ by 5 hours, 48 minutes and 46 seconds, the calendar year being the shorter one. The extra day added in a leap year more or less makes up for this. It takes 33 years for the astronomical equinox to be on the same day and at almost the same hour again.

'Position in the zodiac, the sun and earth position are like a particular chord that can be heard again after 33 years.' (W. Hoerner)

Sun spot activity goes in 11 year rhythms, with three periods combining in a greater rhythm of 33 $\frac{1}{3}$ years. Many phenomena have been shown to relate to this – weather situations on the large scale, haloes and rings around sun and moon, thunderstorms, gales, glacier movements and precipitations.

Plant growth also reflects this. Thus the width of annual rings in tree trunks marks sun spot activity.

Monkey puzzle trees (*Araucaria araucana*) only replace their scale-like leaves every 33 years. The reason why certain weather phenomena recur every 100 years (Century Almanac) may well be connected with the sun spot rhythm of three times 33 years.

Not only the sun but the moon, too, has considerable influence on vital processes on earth. It has been shown to be responsible for a wide range of phenomena. It is of course more difficult to demonstrate some of these individual effects, as the moon travels faster around the zodiac than the sun does.

The most important moon rhythms are given below.

– Synodical month = return of same

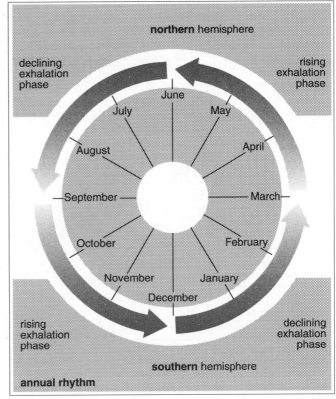

phase every 29.531 days
– Sidereal month = return to same star every 27.32166 days
– Tropical month = return to the same tropic [highest or lowest point] every 27.32158 days
– Dracontic month = return to same position in same node every 27.212 days
– Anomalistic month = rhythm of apogee and perigee [points farthest from and nearest to earth], 27.555 days

The last four cycles given above are clearly similar in length, with the synodical month only a little over two days longer.

In the past, these rhythms were taken into account by farmers in determining when to sow, manure and cultivate plants, in animal hus-

Fig. 39. Annual breathing process of the earth as a whole.

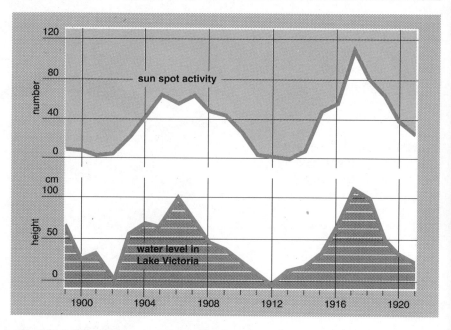

Fig. 40.
Sun spot activity
and water levels for
Lake Victoria (from
R. Mueller 1958).

bandry, for cutting down trees and many other aspects of daily life. As time went on, real knowledge of these things has largely been lost, for the effects are extremely subtle. In some parts, farmers were still quite recently doing some tasks during the waxing and some during the waning moon. In the Upper Rhine region (Alemannia), for example, farmers would always manure their fields during a waning moon.

In biodynamic agriculture, careful observations and ongoing scientific trials provide more detailed information on the way the heavenly bodies influence life. Maria Thun in particular has put much patient effort and persistence into her study of the sidereal moon rhythm and its actions; her

Fig. 41.
Relationship
between sun spot
activity and growth
of annual tree rings
(from R. Mueller
1958).

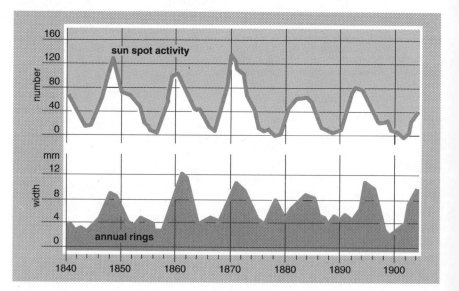

Working with the Stars. Biodynamic Sowing and Planting Calendar gives the dates that are most important for the farmer and gardener each year.

It is important to realize that in modern agriculture it is not enough to accept such given dates as if they were dogma; farmers must study the underlying principles for themselves. Many works on the subject, by Maria Thun and others, are now available. Farmers and gardeners who decide to make the movements of the heavenly bodies an aspect to be considered in their work will also need to make accurate observations on these events and take careful note of their effects in animal husbandry and crop growing.

The *synodical* month is the easiest to observe. It is usually only during the second night after new moon that one is able to see the delicate sickle-shape in a clear evening sky, indicating the beginning of the waxing phase which continues until full moon. This is a phase when growth is generally promoted, the opposite being the case during the waning phase. Other moon influences will however continually disrupt and inhibit this.

The moon's orbit is at an angle of about 5 degrees to the ecliptic (apparent orbit of the sun relative to the zodiac). Going through its orbit in 27.2 days (*draconic month*), the moon crosses the ecliptic twice at the 'nodes' (☊ , ☋). If this happens at full moon (☾ ☍ ☉ in opposition), the moon is covered by the shadow of the earth and an eclipse occurs. At new moon (☾ ☌ ☉ in conjunction), the moon's shadow falls on part of the earth and covers up the sun for that area. These eclipses of the sun may be partial, annular or ring-shaped, or total.

If drilling is done during an eclipse, one usually notes profound changes in the growth and appearance of plants and in seed quality. Similar problems arise with moon or planetary nodes when the sun is not in conjunction or opposition. It is advisable to do no drilling, cultivation or spraying on such days.

The moon's orbit around the earth is elliptical, and within 27.555 days (*anomalistic month*) the moon will be nearest to the earth at one time (perigee) and farthest from it at another (apogee). The distance between these two points is only about 50,000 km, but the effect on plants and animals is clearly evident. No work should be done on crops when the moon is in perigee, but positive effects can be expected with potatoes planted when it is in apogee.

Starting at the winter solstice, the sun, then in the Archer, rises higher and higher in the heavens each day, and the days are getting longer. The sun is then in ascent. The opposite happens in summer; from St John's tide (solstice in Twins) until Christmas, the sun's height decreases and the days grow shorter. The sun is in descent. The moon does the same thing in 27.3 days (*tropical month*), ascending from Archer (obsigend), descending from Twins to Archer (nidsigend). The full moon reaches its highest point at the beginning of winter.

The ascending phase helps the sap to rise in plants; this is therefore a good time for cutting scions (the site of the cut on the tree needs to be thoroughly smeared with grafting wax) and grafting them. The descending moon phase tends to be better for root development, with sap movement limited. The following operations are therefore best done during this phase: planting, application of compost and liquid manure,

It is advisable to avoid all work with crops on moon node days.

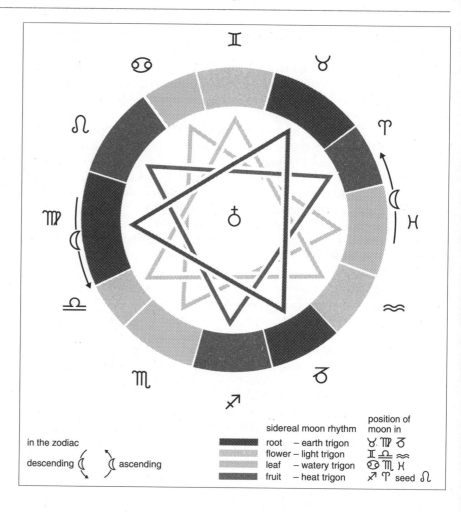

Fig. 42. Sidereal moon rhythm. The four trigons in the zodiac that act on root, leaf, flower and fruit. Based on the work of Maria Thun.

in the zodiac

descending ☽   ☾ ascending

	sidereal moon rhythm	position of moon in
�█	root – earth trigon	♉ ♍ ♑
▒	flower – light trigon	♊ ♎ ♒
░	leaf – watery trigon	♋ ♏ ♓
▓	fruit – heat trigon	♐ ♈ seed ♌

pruning of fruit trees and hedges, digging in green manure and felling trees.

The influence of the *sidereal month* (the time the moon takes to move through the zodiac) on plant growth has been investigated and described in detail by Maria Thun. With reference to the four elements of old, the plant may be seen as follows: *earth*–root, *water*–leaf, *air and light*–flowering shoot, *fire*–fruit and seed.

The constellations form groups of three known as 'trigons'; these influence specific aspects of plant growth:
1) Root system – Bull ♉ ,
Virgin ♍ and Goat ♑ .
2) Flowering shoot – Twins ♊ , Scales ♎ and Water carrier ♒ .
3) Leaf system – Crab ♋ , Scorpion ♏ and Fishes ♓ .
4) Seed and fruit region – Lion ♌ , Archer ♐ and Ram ♈ .

In the heat or fire trigon, the moon in Lion favours the development of seed and fruit and particularly benefits seed quality.

The constellations that form a particular trigon are able to bring their powers to bear on plant life when the moon passes through them; full benefit is gained in soil that is alive, well cared for and regularly supplied with all the biodynamic preparations, providing care has been taken when preparing the seed bed, drilling, planting and cultivation of crops.

The first trigon relates to carrots, potatoes, fodder beet, beetroot, salsify, celeriac, leeks, parsley and other plants that 'fruit' in the root sphere.

The second trigon relates to rape, buckwheat, sunflowers, mustard, oil radish, and all flowers.

The third trigon relates to meadows, pastures, fodder plants such as clover, lucerne, etc., all cabbage plants, spinach and lettuce.

The fourth trigon relates to cereals, pulses, maize as silage crop, tomatoes, cucumbers, etc.

The growing of summer wheat may serve as an example:

Drill in Lion, use the weed harrow nine days later in Archer and heavier harrow nine days after this, in Ram. The effect is enhanced with this triple operation.

Farmers who are prepared to work with these subtle cosmic influences are advised
– to keep careful records of all operations,
– to make as many careful observations as possible, again noting them down in writing,
– and not to forget, of course, that this is only one of many factors involved.

The following should be noted, however. If the soil is ideal for drilling summer wheat at the end of February, but the moon is close to the earth, moving through Twins and, what is more, at a nodal point, it is better to be patient and wait for a better time. If, on the other hand, the constellations are equally unfavourable in mid-April, and it has not so far been possible to get the seed

Old – established methods and experience are the backbone of regular farm management.

into the ground, drilling will have to be done nevertheless. Post drilling cultivation can then be done at more favourable times. The field sprays may also be applied in accord with the sidereal moon rhythms, though note must be taken of stages of plant growth.

Beware of getting biased or even fanatical. It seems that with long-term use of the biodynamic method certain self-regulating mechanisms also come into play in the sphere of dynamics. It should be stressed once again that one's own observations and personal experience are of vital importance; they need regular self-critical review in the light of the facts. Old-established methods and experience should continue to be the backbone of regular farm management.

Heinrich Schmid, a farmer in Korbach in Germany, and Franz Rulni have been investigating the connection between moon rhythms and the mating of cattle. Their findings suggest that apogee brings out more the male type, perigee the female. In both cases, a waxing moon will encourage swelling growth. New moon tends to promote a more slender, long-legged build, but also dry extremities and firm hooves.

At the Talhof farm, observations have now been made for over 30 years. Initially 100 herd-book cows were assessed for the above criteria. An official from a breeding station compared predictions made on the basis of service dates with the actual results. The cows had all been entered in the breeding record, i.e. had calved at least five times and rated high in performance tests; animals with poor fertility and performance had thus been excluded. In 55% of cases, prediction and result agreed, in 40% the result was markedly better, and in only 5% had the prediction been wrong.

Since then only bull calves bred on favourable dates have been used for breeding. Over a 15-year period, an average of nine out of the ten bull calves reared per annum could be presented for inspection. Only two out of 160 bulls were not fit for inspection. Among those licensed, 25% were in one of the first three places, 60% in places 4–10, and only 15% farther down the line. With cows, selection is made only after their first calving. Here, too, the above effects due to moon influences were generally noted; it is however also possible to have good, long-lived dairy cows conceived on unfavourable dates. One assumption that has not been confirmed is that more male than female calves are conceived on dates supposed to further the male constitution.

It is therefore not advisable to wait for special days for service. When it is time for a cow to be served, this should be done as soon as she is suitably in heat.

The above has been a brief outline of observations made by others; it is intended to encourage farmers to make their own. There must be many other rhythms that need to be investigated and may prove helpful to the farmer.

Pest control

If the principles described so far are applied on a farm where a good biological balance is maintained, pests will rarely present a massive prob-lem. If the soil is vitalized with ripened manures and tilled and cultivated with due care, if crop rotation includes a good variety of crops that suit the area, if the biodynamic preparations are fully and properly used and account is taken of constellations and bio-rhythms, then good conditions have been created in which both plants and animals will thrive.

In spite of all one's efforts, however, errors (working the soil when it is too wet) or extreme weather conditions may sometimes cause insects and fungi to multiply rapidly or weeds to foul the land. This does not mean, however, that one has to resort to conventional plant protectives, plough a crop in or let it perish. A wide range of biological and dynamic methods are available to help in such cases.

The first step is to do everything possible to increase the vitality of crops. Chain harrowing, rolling and hoeing to remove puddled or crusted earth, combined with rhythmical applications of the field sprays will give satisfactory results.

This has repeatedly proved to be the case at Talhof farm and elsewhere.

Mr Lichtenberg in Dortmund, Germany, has published a number of reports on good results seen in his hothouses following three applications of 500, 501 and 508 (horsetail liquor) (see page 79) made either within three hours or at the same time of day for three consecutive days. He saw remarkable results with sensitive hothouse plants treated for pests as well as fungal attack.

Horn manure is used when crops are still in the early stage of development, and horn silica at a later stage of development. The effect is enhanced by replacing some of the water used for stirring with mature nettle liquor (1:1). Aphids and Colorado beetles as well as mildew and yellow rust were prevented or, if already established, removed or reduced.

Weed control

Mechanical, thermal and tillage methods will generally keep weed growth in reasonable limits. Apart from this, Maria Thun's invest-igations of lunar and zodiacal factors have opened up interesting possi-bilities for dealing with weeds.

The germinating power of indi-vidual plant species is influenced by forces that come from different parts of the zodiac. If no seed is sown but the soil is merely tilled each time the moon enters into a new constellation, the species that germinate are tufted vetch with moon in Fishes and cleavers with moon in Ram, for example. Moon in Lion means maxi-mum stimulation, moon in Goat maximum inhibition of germination.

If a field is first tilled with the moon in Lion in spring, numerous weeds will germinate that are then killed when the seed bed is prepared. If one then does the last of the cultivation work with moon in Goat, crops may be expected to grow on well, with little interference from weeds.

Farmers working with nature will find endless opportunity to make their own observations here. Do not be put off if the expected results are not achieved immediately, for inter-ference may come in many different ways.

Rudolf Steiner gave details of how the soil may be given powers that will make it difficult for specific weeds to thrive; after four years' application they will no longer grow at all. The method, known as 'pep-pering' consists in burning seeds capable of germination at specific times and making a preparation of the ash which is then applied to fields where the weed is not wanted.

At the Talhof farm, thistles showed no reduction or inhibition of growth the year after the first application. However, 60% were attacked by rust, which only affected 10% on un-treated soil. The year after the second application the thistles did not grow well at all, reaching only a third to one half the height of untreated thistles. About half the flowers dropped off before they had fully opened. In the third year, flowers from untreated thistles had to be collected for ashing, as the stunted plants no longer produced seeds capable of germination. During the following vegetation period, only miniature thistles grew and these did not develop flower buds. The fields treated with the ash preparation remained free of this troublesome weed for a long time. After about ten years, some wind-borne seeds germinated but were easily kept under control by crop rotation and normal cultivation.

Maria Thun has done large-scale serial trials with seed ash potencies. Her findings have been published under the title *Unkraut* (not available in English). Optimum results are achieved by using the most effective potencies and applying the prep-aration in rhythmical sequence on three consecutive days.

Insect pests

Useful insects normally find the habitat they require if the landscape offers plenty of variety. This is of vital importance for the functioning of natural control cycles. In ecolog-ically well managed areas one us-

Important preconditions for effectiveness of ash preparation: Seed must be of good germinating quality; combustion must be complete (carbonization is not sufficient); apply to soil immediately.

Insect pests only increase vastly in number if the biological control system is disrupted.

ually finds a good variety of species, and individual pests will only multiply excessively and become a problem when imbalance arises due to factors such as sudden hot weather periods with insufficient rain.

It can happen that a crop of fodder beet shows serious aphid infestation within just a few days. Freshly made nettle liquor will usually help in this case. At first it will look as if the result was nil, but after a few days one often finds large numbers of helpful insects (ladybirds, their larvae, etc.) and only few aphids. The crop will soon overcome any damage it may have suffered.

Similar observations may be made with cabbage caterpillars and ichneumon wasps. Another useful method is to encourage birds. Hedges, nesting boxes and small ponds create the right habitat for all these eager helpers.

If the same insect pest becomes a problem year after year, dynamic regulation may be used the same way it is done with weeds. One burns the insects at times of specific constellations, or at other times their larvae, and distributes the ash over the affected fields. Extremely small quantities are needed, and it is also possible to use homoeopathic potencies. 1 g of ash will give 100,000 litres of the eighth decimal potency (8x) which are easily applied using a tractor-drawn sprayer. Three applications will require 300–450 litres per hectare.

On the Talhof farm, ashed Color-

ado beetles kept these pests away for several years at a time when other farms in the area had a serious problem.

Insecticides will only be required in rare and exceptional cases, e.g. to prevent total loss of a beet crop heavily infested with aphids at the 2 or 3 leaf stage. Products containing pyrethrum should be used in such cases (e.g. Spruzit, Parexan or Ledaxinsect). These act as contact poisons and are safe for bees, humans and mammals but toxic for all other insects (including the useful ones!) and fishes. The effect is enhanced by adding 0.5% of methylated spirits and heating to 40 °C. These products persist only for a short time, so that no residues will be left in crops and soil.

Their use should nevertheless be limited to absolute emergencies, for they do destroy many useful insects as well.

Fungi

Green plants are higher plants that grow in the light and convert lifeless mineral substance into living protein, starch and fats; they are the children of earth and sun.

Fungi on the other hand are entirely 'children of the earth'; they are part of the earth organism's metabolic system and do not themselves relate to light. They live in the dark, do not produce chlorophyll and are not capable of assimilation. Some push their fruiting bodies up above ground, but these are short-lived.

The actual life of fungi takes place in their mycelium in the soil. There they decompose organic matter that has dropped out of the life processes; together with other microorganisms they break them down into their original mineral constituents, making these available again for new synthesis. As the German poet, philosopher and scientist Goethe said, 'Death is a stratagem used by nature to allow it to have abundant life.'

Fungi have an important function in the compost heap and are important and useful in agriculture for as long as fungal processes remain within those limits. With the extensive use of easily soluble nitrogen fertilizers to increase yields, fungal growths are increasingly appearing on the aerial parts of plants. Chemicals to reduce stalk length add to the problem by keeping the plants closer to the ground. Dense lush growth, with light blocked out and humid warmth, creates ideal conditions for many harmful fungi to grow, so that a great deal has to be spent on plant protectives, whilst yields are likely to be reduced and quality lost.

In biodynamic agriculture the aim is once again to ensure that growing crops do not provide such conditions for fungal growth. The following are important:

– Well aerated soil permitting active fungal growth and abundant mycorrhiza* development,
– adequate humus levels,
– use of fully ripened manures.

Plus the following for areas or crops particularly prone to fungus disease:

– more frequent use of the oak bark preparation, which has special regulatory capacities in this respect,
– rhythmical applications of horn silica,
– prophylactic use of horsetail liquor or tea.

For crops that may be at risk, treat the field prior to drilling and spray again rhythmically on three consecutive days afterwards.

Horsetail gives special powers to the soil that inhibit fungal infection of the aerial parts of plants.

Acute mildew attacks on winter wheat have responded extremely well to the following spray: Mix 4 kg of Bio-S and 0.6 kg of Algifert with 50 litres of concentrated horsetail liquor, 40 litres of nettle and herb liquor and 360 litres of water per hectare. Apply to the plants as a fine spray, repeating after two or three weeks if required. In between apply horn silica on a leaf day to regenerate the foliage.

In conclusion it should again be stressed that the preparations and the cosmic dynamics described in this chapter will only prove effective if used in the right way on a farm where balance and harmony are maintained. Mineral and growth-forcing organic fertilizers will overshadow and inhibit these effects which may be subtle but are nonetheless powerful.

Allelopathy and phytoncides

Allelopathy is a term for positive and negative effects that plants have on each other that was introduced by Molisch in the 1930s. Today a number of substances secreted into the soil from roots and decaying plant matter have been identified that are capable of either preventing or encouraging germination and growth. They provide part of the explanation for incompatibility within the same species and the positive effects of crop rotation.

Positive results have been noted with certain mixed crops, but much is still unknown in this field.

Extensive researches are in progress in the Soviet Union on the subject of phytoncides. Certain plants produce hormone-like substances that have an effect on micro-organisms; their use in medicine is

* Mycorrhiza ('fungus root') means an association of fungus with the roots of higher plants – trees and also many annuals and crops. The plant benefits in being supplied with nutrients, above all phosphorus (Koepf 1980).

Dynamic methods, rhythmical applications and hormone-type activities are important factors in farming practice.

under investigation. Key examples are garlic and onion.

In a soil that is rich in humus and full of life, inhibitors of this kind are quickly digested and inactivated. Humic soils often also require greater expenditure on herbicides than unenlivened soils with low humus content.

Finally, mention should be made of suggestions made by Rudolf Steiner that come under the heading of allelopathy. Positive effects are produced by sainfoin, white dead-nettle and cornflowers grown in the margins and also among cereal crops. Field poppies have a negative effect. Horseradish grown on the edges of fields has a positive effect on root crops and tubers.

Trials with cornflowers and poppies in summer wheat have confirmed the above. With cornflowers, yields are increased compared to controls, with field poppies they are reduced.

It is to be expected that further investigations in this field of subtle effects and terrestrial and cosmic dynamics will yield many new insights.

Crop husbandry

The nature of plants

The plant world acts as a link be-tween sun and star activities on the one hand and the earth with its physi-cal matter and forces on the other.

The flowering plant grows vertical-ly upwards from the ground and to-wards the sun (heliotropism). The root is orientated towards the centre of the earth (geotropism); lateral roots and fine capillary roots estab-lish a close relationship to the miner-al and salt elements of the earth.

Roots passively take up water and dissolved nutrients as part of the transpiration process that is initiated by the sun. They are also capable of selectively taking up water and min-erals from the soil to meet require-ments. This capacity is enhanced by the presence of humus, compost rich in nutrients, well rotted farmyard ma-nure, a balanced mineral composition of the soil, and light effects that are largely mediated by the aerial parts of the plant.

With the aid of sunlight, the chlorophyll which is mainly present in green leaves enables plants to sythesize glucose and starch (carbo-hydrates) from water and atmospher-ic carbon dioxide. Oxygen is released in the process to provide the basis for all life on earth.

Green plants are therefore the pro-ductive element in the whole ecolo-

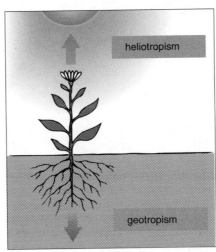

Fig. 43.
The plant between
sun and earth.

gy. The life processes of humans, an-imals and lower life forms such as fungi and bacteria depend on the plant kingdom.

Factors affecting plant growth

Plant growth is closely bound up with the environmental conditions of the biotope. Individual plant species have widely differing requirements. The growth factors
– heat,
– light and air,
– water and
– minerals
must be available in a balance suited to the needs of the species if the plants are to thrive.

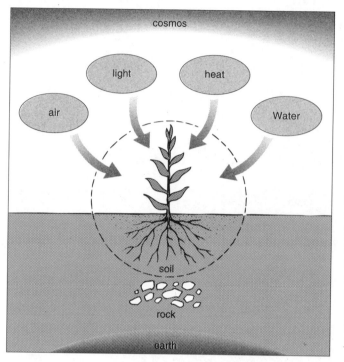

Fig. 44.
Factors influencing
plant growth.

– phototropism, i.e. turning to the light,
– short- and long-day plants,
– damage due to lack of light (susceptibility to fungal attack and pests, little or no nutrient uptake through roots, and many other effects),
– damage due to bad atmospheric conditions (sulphur).

Air is the provider of carbon dioxide for assimilation and oxygen for respiration. It must also be present in the soil, for soil organisms and roots require much air (oxygen) to enable them to function. What is more, the nitrogen in the air is fixed by free-living bacteria (*Azotobacter, Bacillus amylobacter, Clostridium,* etc.), fungi and algae (blue-green algae: *Nostoc, Calothrix* mainly in rice-growing soils), and above all bacteria living in symbiosis with plants (nitrogen-fixing bacteria and leguminous plants); it is then available to plants as organically bound nitrogen.

Water is particularly important in plant life as it makes up about 80% of a plant's body. It is involved in all vital processes:
– as a solvent in all metabolic processes,
– in biocycles,
– in biosynthesis,
– in production and maintenance of intracellular pressure,
– in temperature regulation by means of transpiration.

Water is mainly taken up by the roots in an osmotic process based on the difference between intracellular and soil solution pressure. The suction power of roots depends on the concentration of the cell sap, whilst the uptake of water also depends on suction pressure and salt concentration in soil water. Clay soils have a higher percentage of fine pores and

Moisture and heat are important if seeds are to germinate. The temperature range in which germination takes place varies enormously with individual plants. Many must have experienced the shock of low temperatures in the winter soil if they are to achieve normal growth; if this is lacking, winter cereals will not form ears, for example. Heat generally promotes life processes, but in the absence of other factors such as water it may also harm plants. More sugar may be broken down in the repiratory process during extremely warm nights than has been synthesized by assimilation during the day.

The relationship of plants to light and air is a particularly close one. Examples of this are
– photosynthesis,
– germination (seeds needing either light or darkness to germinate),
– intensification of root growth in stronger light,

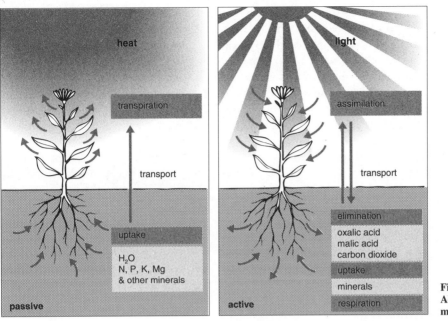

Fig. 45.
**Active and passive
mineral uptake.**

therefore a higher suction pressure than sandy soils.

The suction pressure of roots increases with the concentration of the cell sap, which the plant achieves by
– taking up minerals from the soil solution,
– supplying organic compounds and ions from its aerial parts
– controlled evaporation of water through stomata.

Other forces clearly also play a role in water uptake. The osmotic pressure gradient is limited to the cortex of the root, yet the water is still under pressure when it enters the vessels of the central vascular cylinder. Schumacher (1978) assumes that forces are involved that actively transport the water into the shoot. The energy required to produce the necessary root pressure derives from the plant's own metabolism. The energy required for transpiration, on the other hand, derives directly from solar energy with its effect on humidity and hence the water absorption

capacity of the atmosphere. Water uptake is probably chiefly by active absorption at the root tip, with passive absorption due to transpiration taking second place (Hayward & Spurr 1943). When all available water in the immediate vicinity of the root has been taken up, plants follow the water by means of root growth.

Minerals are also largely taken up by the roots. Active uptake consists in the secretion of carbon dioxide, organic acids (e.g. malic acid) and other substances (complexing agents) to dissolve the required nutrients out of solid soil elements; these are then absorbed by ion exchange. Active mineral uptake is controlled by the plant's own metabolism, which explains why there is some degree of selection in mineral absorption into root cells. The plant secretions also create a favourable environment for specific microorganisms that help to dissolve the minerals.

Passive mineral uptake consists in dissolved salts being forcibly drawn into the root by transpiration pressure (e.g. nitrogen as NO_3). In this case the plant has little or no influence on the kind of minerals taken up. Compost rich in nutrients and well-rotted farmyard manure specifically encourage the growth and branching of roots, thus increasing the active root surface area. Their use enhances plant growth more than the concentration of soluble minerals would suggest.

At the end of his *The Power of Movement in Plants*, Charles Darwin wrote (page 573): 'It is hardly an exaggeration to say that the tip of the radicle thus endowed, and having the power of directing the movements of the adjoining parts, acts like the brain of one of the lower animals; the brain being seated within the anterior end of the body, receiving impressions from the sense-organs, and directing the several movements'. Phospholipids known as phosphatides found in some concentration in animal and human nerve tissues occur mainly at the root tip in plants. Their presence, the fine division of roots by branching, with rootlets penetrating the soil much as nerves do the human organism, and the way roots grow towards water and nutrients, all suggest that these substances have a function akin to sensory perception. The faculty of selective nutrient uptake and other features are clear indications that the root system plays the same role in

Table 21. Water and nutrients taken up by plant roots (Finck 1976)

water uptake	
passive	via transpiration based on physical laws
active	involving metabolic functions
nutrient uptake	
passive phase	as far as root cortex subject to physical laws
active phase	into inner part of root by means of ion exchange and metabolic functions
selective phase	plant roots select specific minerals, taking up greater relative proportion than present in soil water (legumes – relatively higher uptake of calcium, grasses – of potassium)
'chemical weathering'	release of protons, organic acids, complexing agents, etc., active lysis from mineral and organic part of crumb

Specific enzymes (permeases) permit uptake of organic molecules, e.g. plant protection agents such as antibiotics
Release of organic substances to stimulate microbial activity in immediate vicinity of root
'The root system of a plant is in constant motion in its search for water (and nutrients).' (Larcher 1976)

the plant organism as the nervous system does in humans. Rudolf Steiner made frequent reference to this similarity.

Land use

Woodlands are the natural form of vegetation in the Central European climate. Other forms of vegetation would only occur naturally in wet moors where nutrients are reduced, in salt marshes, on sand dunes kept moving by the wind, on rocks and in mountain areas. After the last ice age, the different tree species rapidly colonized areas once the ice had gone. When humans began to settle, woodlands gradually had to give way to farm land. Grazing animals and clearance by burning kept reducing woodland areas in a process that has continued into the present age, with glassworks, salt works and mines using large quantities of wood.

Today, woodlands are essentially only found in areas where soil conditions – stony or shallow soil, sloping ground or other problems – make agricultural use impossible. They do however continue to play a vital role as suppliers of wood and water reserves, balancing the climate and improving the air (amenity work). They add feature and distinction to the landscape and provide an area for healthy recreation. In recent times, woodland has been under serious threat from pollution, a side effect of advanced industrial development.

Agricultural land use is dependent on local conditions:

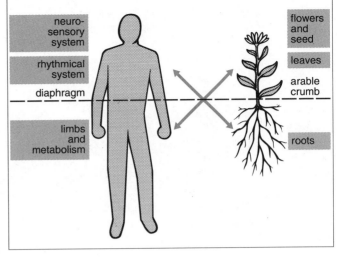

Fig. 46.
Three principal aspects of the human being and corresponding aspects of the plant.

Table 22.
Flowering, foliage and root regions of the plant and their relationship to the human being.

Flowering region:
emissions (scent, pollen), movements of flowers (opening and closing, turning to light), discharge of pollen, fruiting process, corresponds to
Human limbs and metabolism.

Leaf region:
'inhalation' of carbon dioxide (oxygen and water), 'exhalation' of oxygen and water (carbon dioxide), rhythmical sequence of leaves, corresponds to
Human rhythmical system.

Root region:
selectivity in uptake of nutrients, growth towards nutrients and water, presence of phospholipids, fine rootlets ramifying through soil, corresponds to
Human neurosensory system.

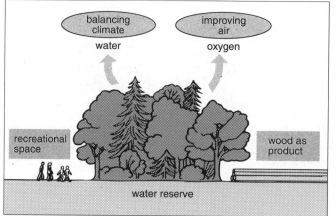

balancing climate
water

improving air
oxygen

recreational space

wood as product

water reserve

Fig. 47.
Functions and ef-
fects of healthy
woodland area.

– soil type (sand – loam – clay –
  lime – moor)
– soil qualities (shallow or deep,
  heating up easily or only slowly,
  water holding capacity, drainage)
– climatic conditions (mean annual
  temperature and temperature
  profile, amount and distribution of
  precipitation)
– moisture (ground water level,
  surface water, lack of drainage)
– terrain (level, sloping, hilly).
This also determines whether an area
is used for grassland, pasture or
arable land, horticulture, fruit or
wine growing.

Grassland

Grassland, also known as permanent
and farmed grassland, means all
areas in long-term use as meadows or
pastures.

The commonest reasons for putting
down grassland are:
– high ground water level,
– risk of periodic flooding,
– high rainfall (900 mm or more per
  annum in Central Europe),
– areas where mists are common,
  with high humidity,

– heavy soil with high moisture
  content,
– sloping ground with shallow soil,
– areas distant from farm.
   Grassland areas resistant to treading are used as pasture for dairy
cows if near the homestead and for
heifers if farther away. Rotation of
hay and grazing is the most intensive
form of management. All other
grassland areas are hayed once or
twice a year depending on the site.
   Moisture conditions in grassland
need careful management. Water logging and long-term flooding must be
prevented or dealt with, as they reduce fodder quality. The application
of well-matured farmyard manure,
careful husbandry and planned use
result in high quality fodder with a
richness of compostion that cannot
be produced on arable soil.
   There is a tendency, especially on
arable farms, to pay little attention to
such grassland as is available, thus
neglecting a valuable source of fodder.

Cultivations

All grassland, whichever way it is
used, needs the following cultivations to achieve a good dense turf
with a satisfactory mixture of plants.
   Harrowing should be reserved for
exceptional circumstances. It is well
known that damage to the turf does
more harm than good. Rolling on the
other hand is important for most
grasslands, as it firms soil broken up
by frost or other agencies. Pressure
sensitive weeds such as cow parsley
and hogweed are suppressed, coarser
stalky grasses, other members of the
carrot family, nettles, etc. inhibited,
and tillering of close-growing grasses
is encouraged. The roll must exert a
pressure of at least 1 tonne/m² to firm

the soil adequately. The time for rolling depends on moisture conditions. For good results, the soil should not be too wet nor too dry. If a heel is pushed firmly in the ground and water collects, the soil is too wet. It is too dry if the roll leaves no mark on the grassland or, even worse, dust is raised. Rolling generally encourages growth and a good yield in loose-structured grassland rich in humus. It does not normally have a positive effect on firm-structured grassland with low humus levels.

Molehills and ant hills are best levelled with a planker. Soil included with the fodder may cause digestive disorders in animals and have a negative effect on the fermentation of silage.

Regular clearing of drainage ditches is essential. The material removed from ditches makes a valuable addition when setting up farmyard manure for composting that is later used to fertilize pastures.

Potato haulms becoming available after harvesting may be used as a mulch on meadows and pastures. They protect the turf against drying out and frost damage and also have some value as fertilizer. In difficult sites and under unfavourable weather conditions such as drought and frost, a thin cover of straw or a very fine layer of fresh farmyard manure can also be helpful, especially on new sowings.

Manuring

Meadows and pastures are manured with well-rotted or almost humic compost or composted manure. Relatively small quantities applied annually are better than larger amounts used at longer intervals.

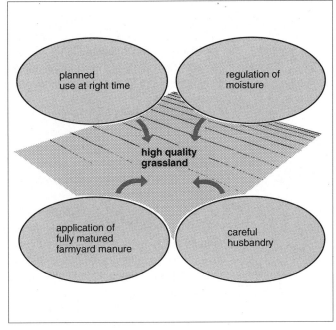

Fig. 48. **Preconditions for high quality grassland.**

Animals leave their excrement on pastures, so that 8–10 tonnes/ha a year is sufficient. Meadows used for hay and silage require 10–15 tonnes/ha annually.

The best time for compost applications is after the second or third grazing on pastures and after the first or an early second cut on meadows. The compost should be applied quickly and evenly, using a pasture harrow if necessary to rub it in. It protects the turf from drying out and stimulates root growth and rapid re-greening. Soil organisms are particularly active during the warmer part of the year and soon convert the compost into unstable and stable humus.

Grassland also responds well to an annual application of 15–20 m^3/ha of well-fermented dung liquor, either during the period of active growth when the soil is moist or towards the end of winter on top of snow cover, *provided the soil is frost-free.*

Liquid manure, whether drift or

floating slurry manure, is also best applied at these times. Relatively frequent applications of small amounts of diluted liquid manure give better results than a single application of a large amount of undiluted, concentrated liquid manure. Annual amounts are 25–55 m³/ha of grassland, depending on the amount of water added. The addition of water prevents nitrogen loss due to evaporation. Three to seven parts of water added increase nitrogen utilization to between three and five times the value with undiluted drift manure and about twice the value with floating slurry manure (Schechtner 1969) (see also the chapter on manures and manuring).

In early spring and late autumn, i.e. as close as possible to the winter season, horn manure is sprayed on frost-free grassland to provide 'vitalizing fertilizing power' (Steiner 1924). Spraying this preparation immediatly after utilization will encourage rapid greening. On pastures this is best combined with the operation to distribute the cow-pats.

When the whole area has a fairly even cover of green leaves, i.e. growth has reached 5–10 cm, horn silica is sprayed in good growing weather; this is repeated each time there is new growth. If the operation is omitted, reduced yields are to be expected. The area is not grazed cleanly.

Meadows

In the western part of Germany, about 40% of agricultural land is permanent grassland, with 56% of this meadows, most of which are cut twice a year (figures for 1975).

It is possible to increase total yield and improve the composition of plant species by changing from two cuts to more frequent cuts and making the first cut earlier.

Meadows given regular applications of compost or dung liquor during the period of active growth generally show a richer and more balanced mixture of plant species and will often allow an extra cut. Compared to this the use of fairly large amounts of not fully matured farmyard manure and mineral nitrogen leads to imbalance in composition. The best time for the first cut is when there is a good balance between quantity of yield and quality in terms of crude protein and crude fibre content and digestibility; it depends on the stage of development reached by the plants.

The time for efficient utilization is a few days longer for a meadow with a good variety of species than for one with fewer species in which cocksfoot, meadow foxtail and false oatgrass predominate. Optimum utilization is limited to a few days for the first cut; going beyond this point means a bigger yield but rapid decrease in quality, particularly digestibility, and hence deterioration of fodder utilization.

Growing conditions are different towards the end of summer and in autumn, so that delay in cutting will not seriously reduce fodder quality, though it also does not increase yield.

On meadows resistant to treading, increased numbers of weeds can be effectively controlled by grazing once a year, if necessary with a cleansing cut to follow. Utilization is earlier in this way, so that

– seeding weeds (cow parsley, hogweed, etc.) are prevented from

Small and frequent doses of well-rotted liquid manure favour a harmonious meadow flora. Heavy dressing with raw liquid manure leads to fouling with docks and weeds of the carrot family.

producing seeds capable of
germination,
– tall grasses (cocksfoot, false
oatgrass, etc.) are kept within
limits,
– light-seeking close-growing
grasses and white clover are able to
grow better and compete better and
– plants sensitive to treading
(autumn crocus, hogweed, etc.) are
damaged and may even die.

Geith found that in a meadow
grazed in three consecutive years,
useful grasses and clover species increased from 32.5% to 80%, with
weeds, poor quality grasses and bare
areas reduced from 67.5% to 20%.
The fodder quality was enhanced
(Kiel 1954). The application of compost immediately after the grazing
operation makes the result longer
lasting.

Grazing meadows even if they are
only resistant to treading for limited
periods is therefore a good method of
getting long-term improvement in
grassland crops, with improved fodder yields and quality.

Pasture and pastures mown at intervals

Generally speaking, grazing is the

more intensive form of grassland utilization. The most important point in
management is to ensure that areas
are grazed quickly and evenly, to
allow for the necessary long rest periods in between. Grazing methods
include continuous, paddock, rotational and strip (or rationed) grazing
as well as rotation of hay and grazing.

Effective use of continuous grazing
calls for detailed knowledge of potential performance on a given site
(see Table 23 for approximate figures). This is the only way of getting
the right balance between the animals' fodder requirements and grassland regrowth potential. For grazing to be reasonably even it is important to put on different types of
stock that complement each other,
e.g. dairy cows, horses and breeding
sows. There is still a risk, however,
of the better, more palatable species
being over-grazed, with the result
that they are displaced by less valuable fodder plants and the value of
the grassland crop goes down.

For paddock grazing, the total pasture area of the farm is divided into
four to eight paddocks. The animals
remain in one paddock until it has
been fully grazed, which is usually

Table 23.
Grazing methods

	paddocks	net yield	
	No.	kSE/ha	NEL/ha
continuous	1–2	400–2,000	4,000–20,000
paddock	4–8	1,400–2,800	14,000–28,000
rotational	9–18	2,000–5,000	20,000–50,000
controlled or strip*	movable fence	4,500–8,000	45,000–80,000

* daily fodder area per dairy cow c. 100 sq.metres in spring; 30–50% more in autumn.
A dairy cow producing 4,500 kg of milk on average per annum will need c. 1,300 kSE (13,398 NEL) during c. 165 grazing days.

one or two weeks. They are then taken to the next paddock. The method is particularly useful for more distant pastures grazed by heifers, as it requires less labour. On the other hand fodder loss due to treading and lying down is relatively high, and a cleansing cut will be required after each grazing period.

Rotational grazing means a further intensification of utilization. The grassland is divided into between nine and eighteen paddocks, each of which can be grazed in three or four days and is then given a rest.

Controlled or strip grazing involves division into an even larger number of sections. The animals are moved daily or after some hours. This gives long rest periods and maximum fodder yields; grazing is to maximum level and the animals are offered fodder grown to a controlled stage. The method is however the most labour intensive. The animals are feeding on young pasturage low in crude fibre, which means that their feed has to be balanced by offering hay made from more mature plants, straw (possibly including undersown clover grass), bran, kibbled oats or other material with a high crude fibre content, which is best done at milking time.

Twice-daily moves to new grazing areas are the ideal for achieving short grazing periods followed by long rests. Manure left by the animals should be evenly distributed as soon as possible after grazing, spraying the horn manure preparation at the same time. If horn silica is then applied six to twelve days before the animals are put on again, new fodder will grow quickly and the animals will find it palatable and graze cleanly.

Humified or well-rotted compost

With feeding on young pasturage, supplementary high-fibre fodder is required.

applied between grazing periods encourages the growth of valuable fodder plants.

All grassland areas resistant to treading and close to the homestead are best utilized by rotation of hay and grazing. Careful planning of utilization times – alternating early and late utilization, with reference to the growth stages of fodder plants – is the most effective form of management, since many meadow weeds are intolerant of treading and hard grazing. Conversely, plants that the animals find unpalatable are less likely to spread if cut at intervals.

Rotation of hay and grazing permits adaptation to extreme weather conditions in so far as areas designated for grazing can be left to mature for haying if they are too wet, with the sward sensitive to treading. On the other hand, an area designated for haying may be used for grazing if dry weather conditions have resulted in poor growth.

Another way of controlling and improving herbage composition on grassland is to use carefully planned rotation of hay and grazing over a number of years, rather like a good cropping sequence on arable land, combined with alternating applications of more and less rotted down farmyard manure, as shown in Table 24. Fresh dung liquor and farmyard manure will give lush growth of grasses and some herbs, e.g. caraway; well-fermented dung liquor and humified farmyard manure will favour the growth of leguminous plants and finer herbs such as common birdsfoot trefoil, slender trefoil, bush vetch, meadow vetchling, salad burnet, ribwort plantain and lady's mantle.

In 1952, I was able to see remarkable results from a change in grass-

Year 1					
Manuring			humified compost	dung liquor	
Use	graze v. early	cut	graze	cut	graze
Year 2					
Manuring			dung liquor rotted-down compost		
Use	cut rel. late	graze	cut	graze	graze
Year 3					
Manuring			dung liquor	humified compost	
Use	graze moderately early	cut	graze	cut	graze

Manuring will not be necessary in year 4.

Table 24. Management of hay and grazing rotation

land management at the Talhof farm.

Available pasture consisted of 10 hectares of very shallow weathered Upper Jurassic soil on sloping ground. The dairy herd (19 cows on average) was put on for short-day grazing (c. three hours daily) from 10 May to 1 October. During the summer, ten young animals and heifers were put on daily, usually after the cows. The cows were given sufficient home-grown fodder and meadow grass to satisfy before going on to the pasture in the mornings and again in the cowhouse in the afternoon. Pasture provided merely a good third of their total rations. The young animals also needed a small amount of additional feed.

Apart from some good grasses - mainly yellow oatgrass, smooth meadow grass, rough meadow grass and red fescue - the plant population consisted of less valuable species such as sweet vernal grass, crested dogstail, soft brome, some sedges and rushes. Remarkably, legumes and herbs were absent, except for daisies, ox-eye daisies, hoary plantain, wild carrot and a few other members of the carrot family.

One third of the pasture land was ploughed, used as arable land for two to four years and reseeded. Three years after reseeding we had the dread 'hungry years'. By then we had however built up a good store of compost made from farmyard manure, dung liquor, aquatic plants from clearing the banks of a nearby river, beech, hornbeam, oak and ash leaves from our mixed woodland area, plus a small proportion (10%) of sawdust. As far as possible – the sloping pasture land frequently cannot take vehicular traffic in wet years – all pastures were treated with 25 t/ha of compost twice a year – in early spring and then in July and August. Horn manure and horn silica

	1952	1957
grazing area	10 ha	11 ha
stock	30.6 CU	45.3 CU
grazing method	short-day	strip
	3.5 hours daily	day and night
		moved twice daily
days grazed	145	190
forages as % of total feed requirement	c.40	c. 85
feed days/CU/ha		
– with supplementary feeds	444	782
– corrected for supplementary feeds	177	665

See text for explanation

Table 25. Change to new method of grassland management at Talhof farm.

were used intensively, with five or six spraying operations during the period of active growth.

After a transition period, cows and young animals stayed in the pastures day and night. Electric fencing was used to give the dairy cows a new feeding area twice daily. Within five years, an average of 26 dairy cows and 18 young animals were getting almost their whole food requirement from 11 hectares of pasture land, with the grazing period extended to run from 25 April to 31 October. Only 10–15% of extra feed (on a dry matter basis) was required.

To our surprise and delight the herbage composition also changed. Large numbers of leguminous plants, valuable grasses and herbs made their appearance – perennial rye-grass, meadow fescue, cocksfoot, some timothy, lady's mantle, car-away, burnet saxifrage, plenty of white clover, common birdsfoot tre-foil, a perennial red clover similar to the Swiss alpine meadow type, black medick, bush vetch, meadow vetch-ling, occasional patches of lucerne or sainfoin, and on dry slopes also occa-sional kidney vetch.

When the grassland experts from the regional authority (Baden-Wuerttemberg) came on a tour of in-spection, the unanimous opinion was: 'Having seen this, we do believe you that your cows do not need home-grown high energy food, seeing the kind of pasturage you have.'

The pastures now have 10 t/ha of composted manure three times in four years, and 25 m^3 of dung liquor three times in four years. Paddocks that can take vehicular traffic are used for rotation of hay and grazing. Apart from grazing, the 100 hectares provide 20–30 tonnes of first-class hay for calf and young bull rearing.

Fifteen years after reseeding, soil analysis gave the following results: 3.8 ha ploughed and reseeded: humus 6.8%, pH 6.9, P_2O_5 38 mg/100 g, K_2O 57 mg/100 g, Mg 7 mg/100 g, total N 0.47%. 3.9 ha not ploughed, compost applied: humus 7.4%, pH 6.7, P_2O_5 12 mg/100 g, K_2O 30 mg/100 g, Mg 6 mg/100 g, total N 0.52%.

In either case, no additional organ-ic fertilizer, rock dust, calcified sea-weed or raw phosphate had been added to the compost or the dung liquor.

Well managed grassland will therefore yield fodder that offers rich variety, balanced nutrition and excellent value. At the same time the animals are able to move freely in light and air. Health and a good and long life quality are the result.

Plants and animals work together to provide stable, permanent fertility in grassland soils.

Spring and autumn grazing technique

In Germany, active growth, until then slow and hesitant, becomes rapid at an almost explosive pace in the second half of May or in June. To utilize the best harvesting time, it would then be necessary to graze or cut the whole area within just a few days.

The problem can be overcome to some extent by starting to graze very early. Cows are put to pasture by the end of April or in early May, when the plants have reached a height of 5–8 cm; they are kept on full winter rations, with grazing limited to a few hours to begin with, increasing the time day by day. During the first five days, 30 cattle units will need about one hectare of grassland. When rapid growth has started, the area required per day will decrease rapidly, despite the fact that indoor feeding is progressively reduced. The method ensures that all paddocks designated for grazing will have been grazed once before the peak harvest time arrives.

The best time for cutting crops for silage is about ten to fourteen days before the hay harvest. If grassland use is divided to good effect into silage, hay and grazing, it will be possible to harvest most of the crop at peak time without getting major peaks in labour requirements.

Plants and animals together provide stable, permanent fertility in grassland soils.

Careful grassland management also means starting grazing in a different paddock each year; otherwise early pasturing will harm the plants and result in undesirable changes in plant population as well as reduced yields (see Table 24).

In autumn care must be taken that grazing areas are not cropped too short before winter comes, as this may lead to increased frost damage. Paddocks that are to be grazed first in spring are the first not to be grazed in autumn, so that the grass can make some extra growth. The height should not exceed 10 cm, however, as extended periods under snow or flood water may result in gaps due to rot. The weeds growing in such gaps will then reduce yields. Unless the ground is too wet, it is a good idea to distribute the excrement evenly once more after the final grazing period. This operation is best not done when there is danger of night frosts in spring.

Watering

Grazing animals need free access to fresh, clean water.

Automatic drinking fountains may be put on embankments, by drainage holes and in similar places. If there are no open water places, or if the water is too polluted, pipes may be laid to automatic drinking troughs in individual paddocks. Plastic pipes are less expensive and require less

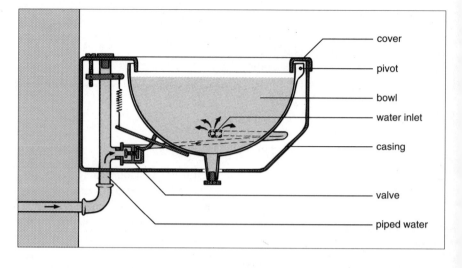

Fig. 49.
Drinking bowl for
species-adapted wa-
tering of cattle
(developed in
Weihenstephan and
by Gloeggler).

labour than metal ones.

If none of the above are available, a water cart serves the purpose. A new type of bowl has recently been developed for cattle; it meets the need for large quantities of water taken relatively fast (developed in Weihenstephan, manufactured by Gloeggler).

Black fibreglass barrels have proved useful, as algal growth is kept to a minimum. With these it is usually enough to give a thorough clean just once, at the end of the grazing period. In paddocks with electric fencing, an electric wire run round the barrel will prevent the animals from pushing or rubbing against the barrel; elsewhere robust protection will have to be fitted.

Cleansing cut

If weather conditions are good and grazing is effectively managed there is usually no need to mow paddocks after grazing. If long wet periods make it impossible for silage or hay,

Fig. 50.
Protecting water
barrel from damage
by cattle.

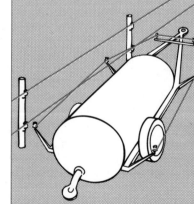

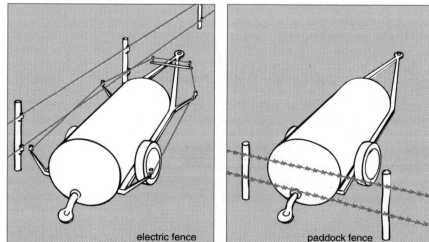

electric fence

paddock fence

the crop may go beyond maturity. In that case, grazing must be followed by a cleansing cut. Rainy periods are often followed by hot ones, so that the material, cut without a swath board, may be left on the ground to protect the sward.

Some plants will produce seed during long dry periods, which may mean an undue increase at the cost of other species. In this case, mow the paddock after grazing (with swath board), swath and collect the plants when wet with dew, before the seeds drop out. This applies particularly to caraway, which is further encouraged by farmyard manure. Cows that eat too many caraway seeds run the risk of abortion. It is therefore important to take extra care in composting and later using these residues, to make sure no seeds capable of germination get on to meadows and pastures and cause new weeds to grow.

Grassland weed control

Grassland plants are rated as weeds if they damage or seriously affect grazing stock, the turf or economic viability either singly or in massive numbers.

Management faults or omissions and site problems are the main reasons why undesirable plants appear; indicator plants may provide useful information on site conditions. Sour grasses, for example, indicate wet soil with poor drainage, kidney vetch and hoary plantain dry sites rich in lime, broom and ling a low pH, and quaking grass and ox-eye daisy soil low in nutrients.

Some of the most important harmful plants and methods of controlling

Table 26. Causes of weed problems in grassland and control methods.

Weed problem due to	Control
Management errors	
cut too late	cut meadows fouled with weeds before seed-producing weeds come into flower; graze meadows resistant to treading once a year
frequent use with inadequate rest periods	regular use, with short grazing and long rest periods
grazing not properly controlled	
injury to sward through wrong use of grassland harrow and putting heavy vehicles on wet ground	avoid injury to sward (no or only limited use of harrow, avoid putting vehicles on wet ground)
Site-related problems	
soil poor in nutrients	manure
low pH	calcified seaweed
poor drainage	drainage and keeping drainage channels clear
periodic flooding	
frost breaking of mineral soil and looseness of humus rich soil	rolling

definite weeds	'relative' weeds
poisonous:	massive populations:
marsh horsetail	carrot family
autumn crocus	hogweed,
marsh marigold	cow parsley, chervil,
creeping buttercup	ground elder, wild parsnip,
meadow buttercup	wild carrot, angelica etc.
avoided by animals:	plants difficult to utilize
creeping thistle	plants with ground rosette (dandelion,
woolly thistle	daisy)
stemless thistle	
stinging nettle	causing major losses:
ling	bistort
tussock grass	
sedges (also mat grass)	
broad-leaved dock	
curled dock	

Table 27. Grassland weeds.

them are given below (see also Table 27).

A serious view must be taken of all poisonous plant species in meadows and pastures, as they are an immediate danger to grazing stock.

Marsh horsetail is poisonous when green, and in hay and in silage. It causes a marked reduction in milk production and loss of weight. The weed is controlled by draining the land, firming the sward by frequent rolling and intensive grazing followed by an aftermath, with the plant material removed.

Autumn crocus may cause fatal poisoning whether green, included in silage or dried. It does not tolerate treading and is therefore not found on grazed land. On grassland resistant to treading it will definitely disappear after a few years of intensive grazing. On grassland used for hay only, it helps to pull out the whole bunch of leaves in May (this removes the seeds that are just beginning to form with the leaves) and by repeat-

ed mowing when the plant flowers in autumn.

The poisonous species of the buttercup family – marsh marigold or kingcup, creeping and meadow buttercup – lose their toxicity on drying. Effective control is usually achieved by draining affected areas, cutting early for hay and then grazing repeatedly.

Massive occurrence of members of the carrot family (hogweed, cow parsley, chervil, ground elder, wild parsnip, wild carrot, angelica) usually relates to high level use of fresh farmyard manure and especially dung liquor or slurries. Numbers may be reduced as follows:

- application of composted manure to which calcified seaweed or magnesian limestone and superphosphate has been added, 15 kg/ha in either case, to balance the high nitrogen and potassium levels in the soil
- mowing before weed seeds are ripe
- if possible, grazing repeatedly.

Curled and broad-leaved docks are much more difficult to deal with. A relatively sure and probably also the only measure where growth is dense is to pull the plants out of the damp soil around St John's tide, i.e. between 15 June and 30 June, in what is called the 'rootless week' in Scandinavia.

If the above measures do not help, or if these or other grassland weeds are too numerous to pull out, it will be necessary to plough, providing soil conditions permit this.

Creeping thistle and stinging nettle are controlled by keeping growth down on pastures. The plants will gradually disappear as they cannot develop sufficient foliage for assimilation. Cutting down, using a scythe on small patches, may have to be done repeatedly for some time, sometimes a number of years.

The biennial woolly thistle and stemless thistle are easily got rid off by manuring the affected areas well and cutting repeatedly.

Ploughing and reseeding of permanent grassland

Before it is decided to improve a grassland area by ploughing it up, all other methods – different ways of manuring, different use or soil improvement – should be tried. It is vital to review the water situation. On dry or consolidated soil, the application of about 60–100 tonnes of compost per hectare for two consecutive years is more likely to give good results than ploughing. Four or five applications of horn manure made during the period of active growth will markedly improve the growth of

Table 28. Example of cropping sequence after ploughing up grassland under conditions pertaining at Talhof farm.

Year 1	grassland ploughed early July cultivation for two or three weeks oats and fodder vetch cut for fodder in autumn careful winter furrow
Year 2	early potatoes soil cultivation winter rye or wheat
Year 3	harvest summer furrow intensive harrowing and grubbing plenty of composted manure winter rape or Perko
Year 4	cut for fodder in spring (April/May) prepare seed bed for reseeding grassland reseed grassland grassland seed only or nurse crop, e.g. mixture of oats, peas and vetches cut nurse crop early in dry weather

desirable fodder plants.

Ploughing is only indicated if the land is seriously fouled with perennial weeds or to cultivate uneven waste ground. Harmful weeds will only be completely removed by intermediate arable use. This does however mean considerable humus breakdown, which should be kept to a minimum and utilized to best effect by chosing the right cropping sequence. It is advisable to plough after a late first cut for hay, as reserves stored in weed roots will be low at that time. Success will depend on careful ploughing followed by thorough use of a heavy harrow and cultivator harrow. It is sometimes possible to get at least part of the roots to the surface, collect them and compost them in a separate heap. The compost should only be used once all root elements have humified completely.

Alternating thorough cultivation and fast-growing crops that give good ground cover needs repeating until there is no further risk of viable root elements causing new weed growth.

Seed mixtures for long-term grassland have to meet different criteria than the more short-lived clover and grass mixtures used for leys. The key criteria in devising a mixture are as follows:

– accurate knowledge and observation of site conditions,
– intended use (meadow, rotation of

Table 29.
Sample seed mixtures for permanent grassland
(Klapp 1951)
(amounts in kg/ha)

	cool, fairly dry site		medium and variable moisture		abundant moisture		higher altitudes	
	meadow	pasture	meadow	pasture	meadow	pasture	meadow	pasture
false oatgrass	10						5	
cocksfoot	4	2	2				2	2
meadow fescue	7	7	20	14	14	18	14	14
timothy	2	2	2	2	2	3	4	4
smooth meadow grass	4	8	3	3	2	2	3	3
perennial ryegrass		3		10				
red fescue			3		3	2	4	4
meadow foxtail			3		6			
fiorin					1	2		
common birdsfoot trefoil	3	3		4			3	3
white clover	2	2	2			1		2
Alsike clover			3		2		3	
greater birdsfoot trefoil					2	1		

Perennial ryegrass and red clover when sowing as spacer, using 2–3 kg/ha; abolutely essential to keep new growth short, otherwise threatens to take over.
Yellow oatgrass – 1–2 kg/ha a valuable addition on relatively good, dry or medium moist mineral soil.
Canary grass – use 1–2 kg/ha on flood and irrigation meadows.
Lucerne (alfalfa) – use 2–4 kg/ha on predominantly dry land suitable for lucerne (always of native origin!)

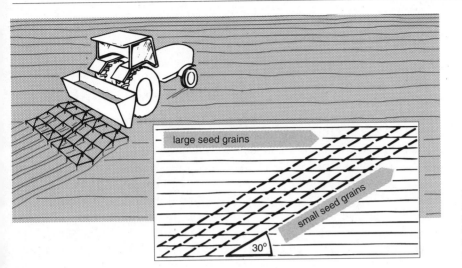

Fig. 51.
System for drilling
seed of different size
for seeding grassland
and grass/clover mix-
tures.

hay and grazing, intensive or
extensive grazing),
– growth characteristics and
competitiveness of species and
varieties.

The herbage composition of grassland areas managed in the same way
in the neighbourhood can provide
helpful information on the choice of
fodder plants for reseeding. Professor
Klapp and others have done extensive trials to establish the varieties
that are worth sowing and will 'take',
and to assess changes in herbage
composition over the years. Their
recommendations for seed mixtures
for reseeding permanent grassland
have been published.

Seed quality must be first class,
with preference given to locally
grown product where possible. If pu-
rity and germinating capacity are
low, the quantity needs to be increased accordingly, which also applies to unfavourable soil and site
conditions. A fine, compact seed bed
is important if the seed is to 'take'
well. It has proved more effective to
give the preceding crops a good application of compost, if necessary

with the addition of calcified seaweed and possibly also raw phosphate, than to apply compost when
reseeding.

Just as with rich clover mixtures on
arable land, the method is to sow the
larger seeds with the nurse crop,
putting them in more deeply. The
smaller round seeds are then drilled
travelling at an angle of 30 °C to the
previous direction, after which the
roll is used. This will rapidly give a
close sward.

Fine round seeds are more apt to
separate out from mixtures. They
should not be taken to the field in the
drill, therefore, but added in smallish
amounts at a time, giving the mixture
a good stir at intervals. In areas
where the spring seasons tend to be
dry, drill very early and at least one
centimetre deep, or drill without a
nurse crop in July or August. A nurse
crop that is not too dense protects the
tender grass and clover seedlings
from wind, hoar frost, heavy rain, direct sunlight and competition from
weeds. The nurse crop needs to be
harvested when the ground is dry and
also early enough, so that the

seedlings will have all the light and air they need. A silage cut is best, as the fodder is taken away immediately, requiring no other field operations. If the soil can take vehicle pressure at this point, leaving hardly any tracks at all, a thin veil of very fine compost and at the same time an application of horn manure spray will make a tremendous difference in encouraging the young crop to grow on.

Hedges and trees in grassland

Hedges planted along drove roads and around paddocks provide
– protection from wind, rain and bad weather and above all also strong sunlight for the stock; they also provide food for variety and health; many hedgerow plants are rich in minerals, vitamins and trace elements;
– nesting places for insect-eating birds;
– a habitat for small animals such as shrews, hedgehogs, weasels, stoats and polecats that help to control insects and mice (field mice are natives of the steppes and do not go near hedges).

The investment needed to plant and maintain hedges does give maximum benefit. No good grassland farmer will spare the effort and expense for something that benefits farm animals, landscape and environment. When an agricultural area does not include woods or coppices, life and variety are added by planting parts of pasture or low-grade arable land with groups of trees and shrubs as well as hedges. A landscape cultivated in this way offers benefits and protection to stock, makes human beings feel more at home, and also enhances the recre-

The establishment of meadows, pastures, orchards, vineyards, hedges and woodlands combined with a good variety of crops creates a cultivated landscape of genuine ecological value

ation value for visitors to the countryside.

Crops and cropping

A look at the history

Crop growing and plant breeding began when tribes started to settle. Advanced early civilizations in the Iranian uplands and Mesopotamia, along the Indus in Pakistan, the Hoangho in China, the Nile Delta and in Mexico brought intense development of farming methods and plant breeding.

Zarathustra, the great initiate of the ancient Persian civilization, instructed people in soil cultivation: 'Taking a golden dagger, he scratched the soil.' The heat of the sun and light-filled air penetrated the soil which had thus been torn open; arable soil was created, with the necessary conditions for breeding the cereal species and many other cultivated plants.

Archaeologists have found emmer (an early form of wheat) and barley in Arpachiyah (Northern Iran, Assyria), emmer, barley and vetch (*Vicia* species) in Merinda Bêni Salama, Ma'asari, Ma'adi and Fayum (Egypt), all dating back to about 4000 BC; finds of barley, flax, lentils and a crucifer species (mustard or cabbage) in Sumer and in Uruk date back to the Sumerian civilization of 3100 BC. It is evident that plant breeding and a cereal diet were an important precondition for the development of those early civilizations. The earliest traces of cereals in Europe found near Lake Mälar in Sweden date back to about 3600 BC.

Cultivated wheat, barley, millet, rice and maize appeared suddenly and always hand in hand with equally rapid progress in civilization. The many different breeds of domestic animals and useful plants (e.g. many varieties of fruit) that we have today largely go back to that early period of civilization in the fourth and fifth millenia BC.

Further new development has really only come in the last two centuries, i.e. about six thousand years later. The science of genetics and its practical application have led to the development of many new plant varieties and animal breeds. Scientific observation and the knowledge gained in physiology and biochemistry are becoming increasingly more refined and differentiated.

The introduction of modern agrochemical, farm and labour management methods has had progressively more negative results, especially in the last three decades:

– signs of rapid degeneration and increasing susceptibility to pests and diseases in plants,
– increasing loss of fertility and the appearance of new diseases in animals.

The use of new seed varieties almost every year, the increasing use of chemicals on plants, rapid rotational grazing and intensive use of prophylactic medication on animals provide only short-term solutions and do not deal with the causes.

There is increasing awareness that new ways will have to be found and followed, and this is a major challenge for the theory and practice of agriculture. First attempts made in plant breeding, for example, have shown that it will require enormous effort to find new methods that will be a real help in the foreseeable future. Existing plant species and varieties will need careful nurturing.

When a particular variety has proved successful on a farm, it is advisable to follow the methods given in the section on seed production. Optimal cropping sequences and the decision to grow only crops that suit the habitat support our efforts to develop sound farming practices.

The sidereal system

The oldest known form of crop growing is the sidereal system (from the Latin *sidus* = star, 'determined by the stars').

Wiljams (1949) states: 'The Romans took the fully developed sidereal system from the Greeks, who had adopted it from the Egyptians; they, in turn, had taken over the complete system used by the peoples of the East. Anything before this is lost in the mists of history.

'The system is to sow winter rye or mustard every one or two years after the crop has been harvested, ploughing in the rye after shooting and the mustard after flowering in late autumn.

'The Egyptians replaced mustard and rye with Egyptian clover (*Trifolium alexandrinum*), the people living in what today are the Central Asian Republics with mung bean (*Phaseolus mungo*) and those in Tadzhikistan with field pea (*Pisum sativum* ssp. *arvense*).' (Ruebensam & Rauhe 1964)

It may be assumed that the system was evolved by people with vast knowledge of the connection between stellar activities and everything that happens in the kingdoms of nature on earth.

This explains why the cultivated plants of today evolved so rapidly when farming began in 6000–4000 BC. Cultivated plants were bred from

See also the chapter on planetary movements and rhythms

Carefully planned cropping sequences are a major factor in farm productivity.

wild plants by taking account of specific stellar conjunctions and oppositions.

In biodynamic agriculture, astronomical researches are in progress to rediscover the skills and knowledge of the plant and animal breeders of ancient Persia and develop them further on the basis of modern science and the conscious mind of today.

In one particular experiment it proved possible to achieve genetic changes in cultivated plants by merely sowing and replanting them at the times of specific conjunctions and oppositions. A vast field has opened up for scientists with unbiased minds who have the courage to take this up.

Two- and three-field system

It seems that the sidereal system was lost in Roman times; the ancient Germans either lost track of it or did not have it at all.

Tacitus wrote that, unlike the Romans, German tribes were using a strict rotation of crops. A two-field system of alternating cereal crops and fallow would be used in poor conditions, a three-field system of winter cereal, spring cereal and fallow in areas with better soil and climate.

Properly managed fallowing improves humus levels and stable crumb structure and keeps weeds under control. In the 18th and 19th century red clover and other legumi-nous plants were introduced, as well as potatoes, beet, oil plants, etc., and this gave an improved three-field system, with the new crops replacing the fallow. Increased fodder production meant larger quantities of farm-yard manure, and this, together with raised nitrogen levels from the inclusion of leguminous crops, led to increased yields.

The improved three-field system also included roots and tubers:

Winter cereal (rye) – spring cereal (oats) – red clover – winter cereal (wheat) – spring cereal (barley) – root or tuber (potatoes).

Crop rotation

The improved three-field system marked the transition to crop rotation. Two-course rotation alternates non-cereals and cereals, double rotation has non-cereals twice and cereals twice. Yields are markedly better with the double system.

In polycrop rotation, cereals are grown after three non-cereals, e.g. two crops of grass and clover ley, potatoes, barley.

Cropping sequence

The productivity of farms with a relatively high proportion of arable land depends very much on a properly planned and consistently used cropping sequence. It takes a long time to work out the ideal rotation for a given site, calling for careful observation and a continuous learning process.

When a sequence has proved right for a particular site, stability and level of yield and soil improvement will increase with the second and subsequent cropping sequences.

It is often necessary to use two, and on large farms even three or more cropping sequences, as individual plots
– differ greatly in soil quality,
– the nature of the ground (stony, sloping, wet) may present problems with the use of machines,
– growing conditions are not right for certain crops, e.g. vegetables, and
– it may be necessary to have intensive cropping sequences closer to and less intensive ones further away from the homestead.

Percentage areas

The percentage of cultivated or arable land determines utilization as regards the relative area given to individual crops in a particular year. The best possible cropping sequence, i.e. the sequence in time over a number of years in a particular field, has to be evolved with this in mind.

Points to be considered when establishing relative areas are:
– fertilizer and fodder requirements
– growing soil-improving crops
– management aspects and work programme
– weeds and pests
– compatibilities

Fertilizer and fodder requirements

The two are closely connected. The home-grown fodder requirement, particularly leguminous plants, is the basis for any cropping sequence; in conjunction with livestock numbers it also determines the volume of manure and dung liquor. The combined fertilizing power of these must be such that soil fertility is maintained and if possible even enhanced under existing site conditions. Top class soils usually require only 0.4–0.8 CU/ha of farmland. If more roots, tubers or vegetables are grown (more than 25% of arable area), about 1 CU/ha will be required. The poorer the soil and the climate, the greater will be the amount of manure required and therefore also the area needed for fodder. 1–1.5 CU/ha of farmland is generally adequate for efficient management.

Once the number and type of animals needed to produce the required amount of manure has been established, it is possible to calculate the amount of fodder required. Yields from absolute grassland and fodder grown as catch crops (where conditions permit) are calculated to work out how much fodder and root plants need to be field-grown. Catch crops grown for green manuring will help to meet manure requirements.

Table 30. Gross margins for wheat, potatoes and carrots

crop	yield	work required	gross margin	
	t/ha	h/ha	DM/ha	DM/h
winter wheat	4.5	20–40	5,000–6,000	125–300
potatoes	30.0	180–220	6,000–8,000	27–44
carrots	45.0	160–250	15,000–18,000	60–113

Sales: winter wheat: 75% direct sale, 25% fodder; potatoes: 60% direct sale, 14% seed, 26% fodder; carrots: 10% direct sale, 90% juice.

Period	SC	R-H	CH	RH	LA	total
days available	16–36	21–38	41–48	27–56		
winter wheat	5	4	12	10	4	35
potatoes (medium early)	32	8	1	90	72	203
carrots	4	30–90	25–45	42	60	161–241

SC = spring cultivations; R-H = cultivation of row crops/haying; CH = cereal harvest; RH = row crop harvest; LA = late autumn cultivations

Table 31. Level and distribution of labour required (in h/ha)

Soil-improving crops

A low percentage area of absolute grassland makes it easier to include soil-improving plants in the cropping sequence since many fodder plants, and particularly legumes, are in this category. It should be remembered that crops harvested green have a better preceding crop value, as the fine rootlets are lost with increasing maturity. Root and stubble material from plants harvested at maturity also has a lower C/N ratio, which makes the rotting down of these residues more difficult. Mustard and sunflowers grown as fodder thus rank as good preceding crops except when harvested ripe. Even with legumes such as peas, field beans, vetches and clovers, crops usually have a much lower preceding crop value if grown for seed or pulses than as green fodder and catch crops, the reason being that nitrogen from the root nodules is used to produce seed protein.

Economic and labour aspects

Crops to be considered for the remaining arable area are mainly such as thrive in the given conditions, are in demand and have a market that is within reach. This is where economic considerations are paramount. Preference is given to crops where the balance between expenditure and yield ensures long-term economic viability for a sound, productive farm unit.

Gross margins range from 5,000 to 18,000 DM/ha for individual crops, with 20–250 hours labour/ha, with corresponding variation in utilization of labour hours (gross margin per working hour). It is evident, therefore, that the work programme needs to be planned. Available labour and the distribution and/or concentration of work in specific time periods will soon set a limit to the inclusion of crops that sell at a high price but also require much labour.

Seasonal variations in available days depend on the climatic conditions in different regions. The hours given in the table represent mean values and major deviations are bound to occur.

Sales potential must also be taken into account. There is a definite limit to direct consumer sales; usually a fixed group of customers feels connected with and responsible for a particular farm, its crops, animals and people. 'Agricultural communities' connected with individual farms are a recent development.

Weed and pest control by use of cropping sequences

Weed and pest control is influenced to a variable degree by the position of crops within the cropping sequence. With monocultures, the presence of a number of weed species does not necessarily have a negative but may indeed have a positive effect on growth. This only applies, however, if the weeds remain small, do not act as vectors for harmful organisms, have different requirements where soil structure, nutrient supply and root space are concerned, and do not make cultivation and harvesting more difficult.

Crops with similar requirements that are grown in quick succession encourage massive populations of individual weeds or weed combinations. Serious fouling with persistent weeds calls for special cleansing sequences. Wild oats, for example, may become difficult to control if spring cereals predominate in cropping sequences. They will be markedly reduced if not eradicated by not growing spring cereals or winter wheat for three, or even better four years. Winter rye is the most powerful competitor and most able to displace weeds; it firmly keeps down wild oat.

Several years of lucerne (alfalfa) or clover and grass mixture will usually get rid of thistles.

Couch grass needs a lot of light and therefore does not tolerate two successive crops of an oat and legume mixture within a year, as these quickly provide dense ground cover.

Cereal crops grown in quick succession encourage take-all and similar fungus diseases. Pests also tend to increase (beet eelworm and clover stem and root eelworm) with successive crops of the same family, e.g. cabbage family – cabbage, swedes and rape – or pea family – white and red clover, crimson clover, lucerne, pea, vetch or field bean.

Nematodes may persist for a long time in the soil, but a well spaced cropping sequence is the best method of prevention. Diseases and pests are frequently due to intensive growing of crops not entirely suited to the site, usually for commercial reasons. The result is reduced resistance. Another way of putting it is to say that weeds and pests make their appearance when an imbalance has to be corrected in the biological partnership between soil and crop. Other plants and organisms – in this case weeds and pests – then find better growth conditions than the weakened crops. Resistance is increased and crops are better able to withstand poor weather conditions such as extremely dry conditions alternating with wet periods if crops well suited to the site are grown in well thought-out proportions, well-rotted manure treated with the biodynamic preparations is used that will not force growth, and the biodynamic sprays are also applied.

Compatibilities

Some crops are self-compatible, others are self-*in*compatible. This latter group includes crops that will not thrive if grown again immediately or after only a short interval. Pests and weeds tend to increase, but even without this, yields will definitely be reduced. Problems of this kind are avoided by observing the required intervals.

Clover sickness is unlikely to develop if different legumes are grown in rotation.

self-compatible	self-incompatible	intervals (years)
rye	sunflowers	7–8
maize	flax	7–8
millet	red, Alsike, crimson clover	6–7
potatoes	sainfoin	6–7
(not in nematode infested areas)	sugar and fodder beet	5–6
white clover	cabbage varieties	5–6
hairy vetch	peas	5–6
fodder grasses	oats	4–5
yellow lupin	rape	4–5
soya bean	wheat	2–3
dwarf bean	barley	2–3
serradella	potatoes (in nematode infested areas)	2–3

Examples of incompatible sequences

barley - wheat	poppies - potatoes
oats - barley	red clover - serradella
sugar beet - rape	red clover - lucerne (alfalfa)
fodder beet - rape	legumes - peas
cabbage varieties - rape	field beans - clovers
flax - peas	

Wheat after barley is incompatible, but barley after wheat is compatible. All other pairs are incompatible either way.

Table 32. Examples of cropping sequence compatibilities

When a cropping sequence involves frequent use of clover species and other legumes, clover sickness may develop. Stem rot, lesser broomrape, stem and root eelworms and other problems arise. Seedlings are slow to develop and pea and bean weevils may destroy the whole crop. The plants wilt quickly in dry weather and are more susceptible to mildew and rust. Growth is stunted and winter hardiness reduced. The cropping sequence needs to be changed when such problems arise.

Catch cropping permits a more rapid succession of self-incompatible plants. 'The primary reason would seem to be that root and stubble residues from the catch crop have a higher nitrogen content and hence a lower C/N ratio than residues from the main crop and are therefore broken down more quickly by soil organisms.' (Ruebensam & Rauhe 1964). Conversion is faster in active humic arable soil than in unenlivened soil. Active soils have a better 'ability to digest' and there are fewer problems with cropping sequences.

Working with living things, we find over and over again that one cannot apply rigid principles in every situation, and this also holds true for cropping sequences. Intensive use of mineral fertilizers and synthetic plant protectives does make it possible to grow incompatible crops consecutively and continue to do so for some time, but a reaction is bound to come sooner or later:

– expenditure will become too high in relation to product, or
– yields will be less reliable, with soil structure and fertility decreasing rapidly.

With the specific measures that are part of the biodynamic method, experience has shown that some of the principles relating to cropping sequences lose significance. Legumes, for example, will grow extremely well in soil that has had biodynamic care. If calcium and phosphorus are adequate, red clover and other legumes and clovers can be grown in quick succession and will give excellent yields for many years – more than 50 years on the Talhof farm. Applications of humified farmyard manure allow peas to be grown as a vegetable twice in succession, with good results.

Principles and terminology

Before giving examples of cropping sequences, some of the principles and terminology require discussion.

Terminology

M = main crop, C = catch crop, P = preceding crop, F = following crop

Main crop: Occupies the field during main part of active growth period and provides main part of annual yield.
Example: winter and spring cereals, sugar beet.

Second crop: Main crop grown after an early cleaning crop.
Example: early potatoes followed by marrow-stem kale, in favourable sites followed by beet seedlings.

Catch crop: Grown for fodder or as green manure between two main crops to prevent leaching of minerals.
Example: winter barley (M) – Landsberg mixture (see page 216) (C) – maize for silage (M)
winter wheat (M) – spring rape, green (C) – oats

Preceding crop: Immediately precedes another crop.

Following crop: Immediately follows another crop.
Example: peas (P) – winter wheat (F).

Table 33. Complementary qualities in a cropping sequence.

	nitrogen	humus	tilth	root space
year 1: ley	+ +	+ +	+ +	+ +
year 2: wheat	– –	–	– –	–
vetch and rye (catch crop)	+ +	+ –	+ +	+
year 3: potatoes	– –	–	+ +	+
year 4: peas	+ +	+ –	+ +	–
year 5: oats	–	–	– –	+

+ + positive effect/deep-rooted   – – depleting   – negative effect/shallow-rooted
+ – neutral   + moderately deep-rooted

Every plant has slightly different requirements as regards soil, pH, water and nutrient supplies, i.e. growing conditions. On virgin soil, characteristic plant communities develop, with the species supporting, complementing or displacing and suppressing one another. Such a relationship in a given space will only prove successful in special cases such as leys, mixed spring crops and maslin, mainly if grown for fodder. On the other hand it is possible to let crops that complement or support one another follow each other in time. This is taken into account in cropping sequences, so that plants with diametrically opposed properties are grown in sequence:

– nitrogen-hungry plants and nitrogen providers,
– humus-hungry plants and humus providers,
– plants that reduce and those that help stable crumb,
– shallow-rooted and deep-rooted plants.

The examples given in Table 33 serve to demonstrate this, though it is not usually possible to take account of all four properties at once.

Preceding crop value and effect

A distinction should be made between:

Fig. 52. Preceding and following crops (Ruebensam & Rauhe 1964, based on Koennecke)

Legend

- ☐ good sequence
- X sequence possible
- A sequence possible, letters refer to aspects to be considered
- ◪ possible within limits, for exceptional cases only
- ● avoid
- B must be in ground in good time
- D suitable as nurse crop
- K serious degree of disease or pests possible
- L problems on storage
- T not in dry regions, as red clover and lucerne (alfalfa) take a lot of water
- U risk of fouling with weeds
- V poor utilization of preceding crop value; use only if no better following crop available
- Z catch crop essential or possible

Preceding crop (columns): winter wheat, winter rye, winter barley, spring barley, oats, maize – ripe, maize – silage, peas, field beans, winter vetch, spring vetch, lupins white, lupins yellow/annual, serradella, red clover, lucerne (alfalfa), rape, mustard, flax, poppies, swedes, sugar and fodder beet, early potatoes, medium early potatoes, late potatoes

following crop \ preceding crop	w.wheat	w.rye	w.barley	sp.barley	oats	maize–ripe	maize–silage	peas	field beans	w.vetch	sp.vetch	lupins white	lupins yellow	serradella	red clover	lucerne	rape	mustard	flax	poppies	swedes	sugar/fodder beet	early pot.	med.early pot.	late pot.
winter wheat	●	X	●	●		X					U						T	T	Z			B	B	Z	
winter rye	X						●		B		U			●	B		T	T	V		B		●	V	B
winter barley	X	X	●	●		●	●		B	U			●	B	B	T	T			B		●	●		B●
spring barley	K	K	●	●	●			Z	L	L	L	L	L	L	●	●	Z	Z	V	V			Z	V	
oats		Z	Z	●	●			Z	V		V	V	V	V	T	T	Z	Z	V	V			Z	V	
maize – ripe		Z	Z	Z		K	K	Z	◪	◪	◪	◪	◪	◪	◪	Z	Z	V	V			Z	V		
maize – silage	Z	Z	Z	Z	Z	K	K	Z	Z	Z	Z	V	Z	Z		Z	Z	Z	Z			Z	Z	Z	
peas	U	Z	Z	U	U			●	●	●	●	●	●	●	●	●	Z	Z	V	V			Z	V	
field beans	U	Z	Z	U	U			●	●	●	●	●	●	●	●	●	Z	Z	V	V			Z	V	
winter vetch						●	●	●	●	●	●	●	●	●			●	●						●	
spring vetch		Z	Z	Z				●	●	●	●	●	●	●	●	●	Z	Z	V	V			Z	V	
lupins, white	U	Z	Z	U	U			●	●	●	●	K	K	●	●	●	Z	Z	V	V			Z	V	
lupins, yellow/annual	U	Z	Z	U	U			●	●	●	●	K	K	●	●	●	Z	Z	V	V			Z	V	
serradella	U		Z	U	U			●	●	●				●	●	●	Z	Z	V	V			Z	V	
red clover	●	D	D	D	D	●	●	●	●	●	●	●	●	●	●	●	D		D	D	●	●	●	●	●
lucerne (alfalfa)	●	D	D	D	D			●	●	●	●	●	●	●											
rape	◪	X	X	X	◪		●	●		●	●	●	●	●	●	●	T	T	●	●	◪	●	●		● ●
mustard		Z	Z	Z				Z	V		V	V	V	V			●	●	●	●		V	●	●	Z V
flax	U	U	Z	U	U	U	U	●	L	L	L	L	L	L	◪		Z	X	●					Z	V
poppies	U	U	Z	U	U	U	U	Z	V		V	V	V	V	◪		Z	Z	V	●	●	●	●	●	●
swedes	Z	Z	Z	Z	Z			Z	Z	Z	Z	Z	Z	Z	X	X	●	●	Z	Z	●	●	Z	Z	
sugar and fodder beet	X	Z	Z	X	X	X	X	Z	V	Z	V	V	V	V	T	T	●	●	V	V	●	●	Z	V	
early potatoes	X	X	Z	X	X	X	X	Z	V		V	V	V	V			Z	Z				V	◪	◪	◪
medium early potatoes		Z	Z	Z	Z			Z	V	V	V	V	V			Z	Z	V	V	V	◪				
late potatoes		Z	Z	Z	Z			Z	V	V	V	V	V			Z	Z	V	V	V	V	◪			

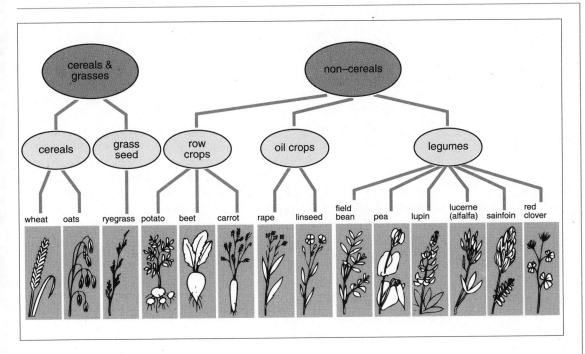

Fig. 53.
Major crops

Preceding crop value: Effect of a particular preceding crop on various crops that follow,

Preceding crop effect: Effect of different preceding crops on a particular crop that follows.

The requirements of crops and their effect on following crops determine their position in the sequence. Legumes, for instance, have a high preceding crop value even if grown as a catch crop because they fix nitrogen and are good producers of organic matter; potatoes do extremely well on this, for example. The preceding crop value of potatoes on the other hand is due to the intensive cultivation and harvesting operations that result in weed-free soil with crumby texture. It then usually needs only a culti-harrow or cultivator to prepare the seed bed for winter cereals.

As one would expect, a lean and miserable crop with many weeds will always have a poor preceding crop effect as it does not produce good crumb structure, has a low root mass, provides poor ground cover and offers the likelihood of a serious weed problem for the following crop. Koennecke's preceding crop schedule (from Ruebensam & Rauhe 1964) helps one to gain a clear picture.

Preceding crops have a good or bad influence on following crops through the condition in which they leave the soil. The schedule merely shows the immediate effect, and it is important to know and observe also the long-term effect, i.e. the extent to which a particular crop reduces humus and nitrogen levels in the soil. Potatoes grown in soil fertilized with farmyard manure, for example, are a good preceding crop for almost all other crops except poppies. In the long term, however, potatoes given an excessively great share in the sequence have a definitely negative effect on soil fertility as they require large amounts of nitrogen. It is a general principle that crops requiring intensive cultivation have a negative preceding value because they deplete the soil of organic matter. If they dominate too much in a rotation, the balance must be redressed by growing sufficient other species with long-term soil-building properties, e.g. a ley of several years.

To help readers to develop some kind of system, a brief review is given below of the properties of cereals and grasses on the one hand and non-cereals on the other.

Cereals and grasses

The group includes all cereals and grass species grown for seed. They rank lower as preceding crops because they leave a poor soil structure and seriously deplete nitrogen stores if grown for high yield. The differences between species and varieties are relatively large.

Non-cereals

These include row crops, oil crops and legumes (grown for pulses or for fodder).

Row crops are mainly potatoes, sugar beet, maize for silage and vegetables. They give high and extremely high yields but are demanding when it comes to soil quality and fertilization. Greedy for both humus and nitrogen they frequently have shallow roots and do little to help the crumb structure.

Most oil crops are members of the cabbage family, e.g. rape, mustard and oil radish. Linseed is a member of the flax family and is rarely grown as it is sensitive to competition from weeds. Sunflowers also count as oil crops. They are rarely grown in

Germany and if so only for fodder. Rape, mustard and oil radish are important catch crops because they produce a large volume of green matter in a relatively short time. If the leaf mass is not sufficient for fodder, shallow ploughing in will help to build up the soil. They are generally deep-rooted, helping the crumb structure, and are nitrogen consumers and neutral with regard to humus.

The legumes that grow in our latitudes belong to the pea family (Leguminosae). They have the advantage that their roots live in symbiosis with bacteria that fix atmospheric nitrogen, so that the soil nitrogen level is enhanced. Furthermore some species are very deep-rooted, prefer soils rich in lime and are able to make phosphorus and potassium accessible (to a depth of about a metre, sometimes a great deal more).

Pulses (field bean, pea, vetches, lentil, lupin, vetchling, soya bean) grown as green fodder leave the soil with a good crumb structure. They will use part of the stored nitrogen as they ripen. Grown for grain they have to be sown more thinly and progressively lose their foliage from below upwards, so that weeds become a late problem and crumb is reduced. Used for green manuring they are among the best preceding crops since they improve nitrogen, crumb and humus. Annual clovers – red, reversed (Persian), Egyptian, crimson and white – grown as a monocrop leave about 50 kg of nitrogen and 2 tonnes of root residues (dry matter) per hectare. Being deeprooted, they open up the soil and improve crumb structure. The organic root mass decomposes relatively quickly as the C/N ratio is lower than with perennial leys. This means an increase in yield for the crop that follows imme-

Care must be taken to see that non-cereal crops include an adequate proportion of legumes.

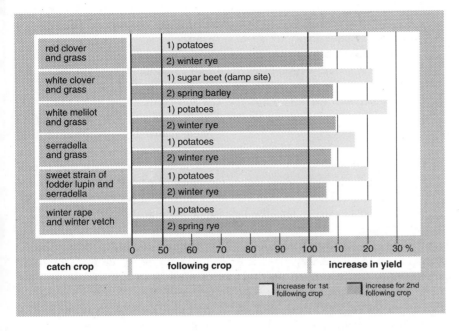

Fig. 54. Preceding crop effect of leguminous catch crops on first and second following crops (Ruebensam & Rauhe 1964). Without catch crop = 100%.

diately, but no or only short-term soil improvement. Perennial clover/-lucerne/grass mixtures are the best type of preceding crop:
– about 100–180 kg/ha of nitrogen is gained over two or three years,
– root residues make up 4–6 tonnes/ha (dry matter),
– crumb and soil structure are enhanced to an optimum degree.

The extended resting period helps the soil, and the humus level can be increased to lasting effect by mixing deep-rooted legumes (lucerne, red clover, sainfoin, white melilot, etc.) and shallow-rooted grasses with a large root mass (sheep's fescue on its own and a mixture of lucerne and false oatgrass each produce more than 10 tonnes/ha of dry root matter). Long-term leys are also important for weed control.

Within the group of grasses and cereals, the situation is approximately the same, but non-cereals show a major difference between row crops on the one hand and legumes on the

other with regard to long-term preceding crop effect. The oil crops are about half-way between. It is evident, therefore, that account must be taken not only of the relation of non-

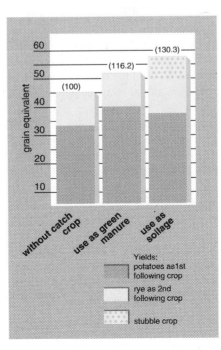

Fig. 55. Preceding crop effect of legumes as stubble crop utilized as green manure or as fodder (Ruebensam & Rauhe 1964)

cereal plants to cereals and grasses in deciding on a sequence but also of the ratio of row crops to legumes within the first group. Legumes may be grown as a catch crop to balance a high ratio of row crops where this is possible.

Catch crops

It is not always entirely feasible to maintain 'green cover' for arable land. Thus for example frost has a beneficial effect on heavy clays and loams that are ploughed and left open. An effort should however be made to come closer to the ideal of green cover whenever the opportunity arises.

Figure 54 shows the direct positive effect that legumes grown as a catch crop have on the first following crop, with the yield just on 20% higher, and on the second, with the yield about 5% higher compared to the control (100%) (Ruebensam & Rauhe 1964).

Catch crops that produce sufficient aerial parts to serve as fodder should always be used for fodder.

Greenstuff has much greater value as fodder, with manure production also taken into account. Even without the manure effect, the graph in Figure 55 (Ruebensam & Rauhe 1964) shows that the yield in grain equivalents of a lupin and serradella mixture grown as a stubble crop was 11% higher when used for fodder than for green manuring.

It makes good sense to utilize the catch crop potential of suitable sites, particularly as this also helps to balance one-sidedness in cropping sequences.

The application of composted manure to soil-building crops such as leys has a lasting effect on soil fertility.

Manuring as part of the sequence

In biodynamic agriculture the principle is that 'manuring should enliven the soil' rather than feed the crops, and this means that the manuring system is different compared to conventional methods.

As already mentioned, the use of composted manure is simpler than that of fresh or partly rotted solid and liquid dung as it permits flexible timing and there is no risk of burn when it is applied to crops. Nor does well-rotted manure suffer from exposure to sun or frost when used as a top dressing.

Soil development is encouraged by using compost in conjunction with crops that give lasting improvement in soil fertility. If Landsberg mixture (see page 216) is grown as an over-wintering catch crop preceding maize for silage, compost for the maize is actually applied in August, before the catch crop is sown. The mixture will leave the soil in ideal condition for the maize crop. An application of dung liquor after drilling the maize, or between rows when the plants are in the juvenile stage, will be all that is needed to get a good yield.

The planned use of manure helps farmers to establish a fully developed individual farm organism. The effectiveness of soil-improving crops is enhanced by the use of composted manure. With two-year leys, the manure is applied for the second year. Good results are also seen with composted manure applied to catch crops. The row crops that follow usually give good average yields in the long term, without seriously affecting the humus and nitrogen balance of the soil.

The crumb layer is best deepened

Table 34. Useful pairs for cropping sequences

field beans	– winter wheat	winter rape	– winter barley
peas	– winter cereal	(catch crop)	– winter wheat
lupins	– winter rye	winter barley	– vetch and rape
	– winter wheat		– Landsberg mixture
	– potatoes		
	– spring cereal	winter rye	– Landsberg mixture
red clover	– winter wheat		
	– spring wheat	early potatoes	– winter rape
	– oats		– winter barley
	– potatoes	med.early pot.	– winter rye
lucerne (alfalfa)	– spring wheat		– spelt*
	– oats	late potatoes	– winter wheat
	– sugar beet	potatoes	– carrots
	– potatoes		– beet
vetch and rape	– potatoes		– spring cereal
vetch and rye	– potatoes	carrots	– peas
	– maize for silage	maize for silage	– winter wheat
	– beet seedlings		– spring barley
			– spring cereal
Landsberg mixture	– maize for silage	fodder and	– winter wheat
	– beet seedlings	sugar beet	– spring cereal
	– marrowstem kale		

Table 35. Suitability of different cereal sequences.

	preceding crop		following crop	suitability
winter rye	winter wheat		winter rye	1
oats	spring barley	spring wheat		2
winter barley				3
oats			winter wheat	1
winter rye				2
spring barley	winter wheat	spring wheat		4
winter barley				5
winter rye			winter barley	1
spring wheat	oats			2
winter wheat				3
winter barley	spring barley			5
oats	winter rye		spring wheat	2
spring barley	winter barley	spring wheat		3
winter wheat				4
winter rye	winter wheat	spring wheat	spring barley	2
spring barley				3
winter barley	oats			5
winter rye	winter barley	winter wheat	oats	1
spring wheat				4
spring barley	oats			5

1 = excellent; 2 = excellent or good; 3 = moderately good; 4 = not good; 5 = unsuitable.

*Spelt is self-compatible and comes between winter rye and winter wheat for its qualities in cropping sequences.

Six examples of cropping sequences to demonstrate the wide range of possibilities.

Table 36. Example 1.

non-cereal 33% cereal & grass 67%	six fields NCCNCC	16.7%/field
1) potatoes CC	sugar beet	peas*
2) rye CC serradella	wheat rape/mustard	wheat rape/mustard
3) spring barley CC red clover sown	spring barley red clover sown	spring barley red clover sown
4) red clover* CC	red clover*	red clover*
5) oats CC	oats	oats
6) winter rye CC lupins**	winter wheat wh. clover/black medick **	winter rye serradella*

legumes			33%
main crop	16.7%	16.7%	16.7%
CC	33%	16.7%	
row crops	16.7%	16.7%	–
cruicifer family	–	–	–
CC	–	16.7%	16.7%

Table 36. Example 2.

non-cereal 37.5% cereal & grass 62.5%	eight fields NCCNCCNC	12.5%/field
1) potatoes CC	fodder beet	sugar beet
2) winter rye CC serradella	winter wheat peas/vetches	spring wheat
3) spring barley CC red clover sown	oats mustard*	winter rye red clover sown
4) red clover CC	peas	red clover
5) oats CC	winter wheat* wh. clover/black medick	oats
6) winter rye CC Landsberg mixture**	spring barley red clover sown	winter rye Landsberg mixture**
7) maize for silage white clover undersown	red clover	maize for silage CC white clover undersown
8) spring barley CC lupins or ** white clover	winter rye lupins**	winter wheat peas/vetches**

legumes			
main crop	12.5%	25%	12.5%
CC	50%	37.5%	37.5%
row crops	25%	12.5%	25%
cruicifer family	–	–	–
CC	–	12.5%	–

*half quantity of composted manure, c. 18 tonnes/ha
**full quantity of composted manure, c. 35 tonnes/ha

N = non-cereal crop; C = cereal or grass for seed; CC = catch crop

Table 36.
Example 3.

| non-cereal 40% | five fields | 20%/field |
| cereal & grass 60% | NCCNC | |

1) potatoes	sugar beet	field beans
CC		
2) winter rye	winter wheat	winter wheat*
CC	rape/mustard	peas/vetches
3) winter barley*	oats	spring barley
CC red clover sown	vetch and rye**	red clover sown
4) red clover	maize for silage	red clover
CC	white clover	
5) oats/winter rye	spring barley	oats
CC peas/vetches	peas/vetches**	rape/mustard*
lupins**		

legumes			
main crop	20%	–	40%
CC	20%	60%	20%
row crops	20%	40%	–
cruxifer family	–	–	–
CC	–	20%	20%

Table 36.
Example 4.

| non-cereal 50% | six fields | 16.7%/field |
| cereal & grass 50% | NCNC etc. NNCCNC | |

1) potatoes*	potatoes	ley
CC		
2) winter rye	carrots/fodder beet*	ley*
CC Landsberg mixture**		
3) maize for silage/beet	winter wheat*	winter wheat
seedlings		
CC peas/vetches	peas/vetches	
4) oats	spring barley	oats
CC rape-mustard	red clover sown	rape/mustard*
5) peas	red clover	field beans
CC		
6) winter rye	winter wheat	winter wheat*
CC serradella*	peas/vetches**	ley sown

legumes				
main crop	16.7%	16.7%		50%
CC	33.3%	33.3%		16.7%
row crops	33.3%	33.3%		-
cruxifer family	-	-		-
CC	16.7%	-		16.7%

*half quantity of composted manure, c. 18 tonnes/ha
**full quantity of composted manure, c. 35 tonnes/ha

N = non-cereal crop; C = cereal or grass for seed; CC = catch crop

Table 36. Example 5.

non-cereal 62.5%	eight fields	12.5%/field
cereal & grass 37.5%	NNCNNCNC	

1) ley CC	potatoes	ley
2) ley* CC	carrots/beet*	ley
3) winter wheat CC peas/vetches**	oats rape/mustard	winter rye
4) potatoes CC white clover**	peas	winter rape*
5) field beans CC lucerne (alfalfa) sown	winter wheat*	potatoes
6) winter wheat CC rape/mustard*	lucerne (alfalfa) rape/mustard	winter rye
7) peas CC	lucerne (alfalfa)	peas
8) winter barley* CC ley sown	spring wheat vetches/peas**	winter rye ley sown

legumes			
main crop	50%	37.5%	37.5%
CC	12.5%	12.5%	12.5%
row crops	12.5%	25%	12.5%
crucifer family	–	–	12.5%
CC	12.5%	12.5%	12.5%

Table 36. Example 6.

non-cereal 67%	six fields	16.7%/field
cereal & grass 33%	NNNCNC	

1) lucerne (alfalfa) CC	ley	red clover**
2) lucerne (alfalfa) CC	ley**	potatoes
3) lucerne (alfalfa)* CC	potatoes	carrots/beet*
4) spring wheat CC rape/mustard*	winter rye rape/mustard	winter wheat
5) peas CC	winter rape*	peas
6) winter wheat* CC lucerne (alfalfa) sown	winter rye ley sown	winter barley* red clover sown

legumes			
main crop	67%	33%	33%
CC	–	–	–
row crops	–	16.7%	33%
crucifer family	–	16.7%	–
CC	16.7%	–	16.7%

*half quantity of composted manure, c. 18 tonnes/ha
**full quantity of composted manure, c. 35 tonnes/ha

N = non-cereal crop; C = cereal or grass for seed; CC = catch crop

by ploughing in composted manure when a ley of several years is ploughed in summer. The beam should be set high and narrow for thorough mixing and aeration. Care must be taken to incorporate not more than one, or at most two, centimetres of subsoil in the topsoil at intervals of six to eight years. Root residues and compost will ensure lasting results with this operation.

Examples of cropping sequences

The principles discussed so far must be taken into account in designing the best possible cropping sequence. A good first step is to set out crops that in the given site make good pairs in a sequence. See Table 34.

When cereals follow one another, catch crops should be grown in between if at all possible. It appears that so far no accurate experimental data are available on cropping sequences in organic farming. Practical experience shows enormous variation at local and farm level. In many cases accurate data are not available on yields and weather conditions. Table 35 provides a rough indication for the suitability of different sequences (Deutsch 1972).

Seeds and sowing techniques

Next to a good seed bed and the application of manure, the inherent quality and external features of the seed are important factors in achieving good yields. In the past, numbers of local ('land race') varieties well adapted to local conditions were suc-

cessfully grown for long periods. They suited the geographical and soil conditions and also met the special food requirements of the local population.

Years of work in modern plant breeding have produced highly selected strains that give high yields in conjunction with intensive applications of mineral fertilizers. They are however more susceptible to fungus attack, pests and extreme weather conditions than the older varieties, necessitating extensive use of plant protectives. Degenerative changes occur when such seed is grown on through successive generations. Marked reductions in yield mean that new seed has to be used after two years; this is the case with cereals, particularly rye, which is a cross-pollinating crop. In Germany, approximately 50 % of cereal seed is bought in as certified seed. The advice is actually to buy 100 % new seed every year. Certified seed is produced from approved basic seed obtained directly from the breeder; it is not intended for further seed production and must meet a number of legal and other requirements and derive from listed varieties.

The aim and purpose of biodynamic farming methods – to develop a farm that is as far as possible an independent entity – means a totally different attitude with regard to seed provision.

Choice of variety

The first step is to find the right variety. Careful note taken of trials run in different localities by the agricultural advisory centres points us in the right direction. The problem is that large amounts of readily soluble mineral fertilizers are used in these trials, so

Carefully nurtured, a variety of proven value will become a site-adapted ecotype resistant to degenerative changes and performing well.

5% or more above mean yield	Mean yield (up to 5% above and below)	5% or more below mean yield
1 Vuka	9 *Carsten 6*	20 *Stir. Farino*
2 Disponent	10 M. Huntsmen	21 *Breustedt Werla*
3 Saturn	11 Kormoran	22 *Derenburger Silber*
4 Okapi	12 Diplomat	23 *Baulaender Spelz*
5 *Merlin*	13 *Heine 110*	24 *Hauter 2*
6 Caribo	14 *Peragis*	25 *Hess. Landsorte*
7 *Carsten 2*	15 Ural	
8 *Heine 4*	16 *Pfeuffer Schernauer*	
	17 *Rimp. Bastard*	
	18 *Sv. Kronen*	
	19 *Carsten 5*	

Names given in italics are old varieties.

Table 37. Comparative yields of 9 highly selected modern varieties of winter wheat, 15 old local varieties and 1 spelt. Site: northern Hesse, biodynamic farm. Mean figures for 3 years' grain yields (ranking order). Manuring: c. 15 kg org. N/ha and year (dung liquor) (Padel 1983)

that the results may be misleading.

A variety has to be grown for a number of years before useful information on its inherent qualities is obtained. Long-term fertility depends very much on resistance to poor growing conditions and adaptability to variable growing conditions These two qualities indicate the inherent vitality of the variety.

Inspection walks are a regular feature in the work of regional biodynamic farming groups. The observations made on these walks often permit reliable predictions to be made as to the usefulness of individual varieties. The final decision will depend on trials done on one's own farm for a minimum of three years. Once a particular variety has proved suitable, every effort should be made to keep it sound and productive for many years on one's own farm. Trials done in Kassel/Witzenhausen have shown that both old and highly selected varieties may prove suitable.

High yield capacity depends on the plants' assimilation and mineral uptake capacities (leaf and root development). Modern varieties frequently have the two uppermost leaves especially broad, long and robust. Light utilization is improved by having the leaf more horizontal to the stem.

The effectiveness of horn silica is partly due to improved assimilation; horn manure and biodynamic seed baths encourage root development. Observations made at Talhof farm have shown that following the application of horn silica the leaves are at a good angle to the light, exposing as much of their surface area as possible as they follow the movement of the sun.

Trials with new varieties that had shown particularly well-developed upper leaves in variety tests gave good results at the Talhof farm. 'Adler' (Eagle) is a spring wheat variety that has given good yields and quality and stayed in good health on the farm for 16 years. The period of extreme dryness in 1976 caused premature ripening of this crop. After much thought, the miserable, shrivelled grain, which however had good germinating power, was used for seed and produced healthy crops with good yields. 'Nackta' is a naked barley grown successfully for 15 years. A spring wheat variety that a breeder had originally supplied for trials has now been grown for nine years.

Growing quality seed

Some indoor and outdoor gardeners are said to have 'green fingers', for their plants always do well. In the days when fields were still sown by hand, some farmers always had particularly strong and healthy crops. Neighbours would seek them out and ask them to sow their fields for them.

Farmers who wish to produce their own seed and keep it healthy and vital for long periods need to develop special skills. These include the faculty of careful observation and the ability to judge the quality of crops and individual plants. We need to familiarize ourselves with the growth rhythms and special needs of crops and their companion herbs and grasses. It means that farmers have to develop an inner relationship to the plant world, and the same of course also holds true for the breeding and keeping of animals.

Sowing times

It is immaterial to a plant whether it is grown for food or fodder or for seed. For the fruit, however, the distinction has to be made, for it certainly matters if it is to have more nutritive or reproductive power.

Cultivated plants differ from wild species mainly in that they provide more nutrients, though this is at the cost of their ability to reproduce themselves.

Trials suggested by Rudolf Steiner and done at the Pilgramsheim estate in Silesia have shown that cereals sown close to the winter months produce seed with high reproductive power. Sowing closer to the summer season tends to enhance the nutritive value.

This relationship to the seasons can be utilized by sowing winter crops later and spring crops earlier to obtain healthy seed with high growth and yield performance. Timely and thorough preparation of fields to be sown close to the winter season will go even further in assuring good results. Nutritive quality is enhanced

1st sequence	2nd sequence
1st year: rye	1st year: rye
2nd year: ley	2nd year: red clover
3rd year: ley	3rd year: potatoes
4th year: potatoes	1st year: rye
5th year: wheat	
6th year: oats	
7th year: peas	
1st year: rye	

Table 38. Selection of field for seed production as part of cropping sequence, using rye as an example.

The first cropping sequence includes five crops (and a two-year ley) sown in six years. It is the better one for growing rye seed. In the 2nd sequence the interval between growing rye is only two years.

seed is taken from here

Fig. 56. Part of the field suitable for collecting seed.

by tilling the soil and sowing food and fodder crops closer to the summer months, i.e. earlier for winter crops and later for spring crops.

Experience will show which are the best sowing times for different crops on a particular site. The shift towards winter or summer should not differ from these times by more than three months, or yields may be reduced.

When plants have grown for seed close to winter for two years, the next sowing must be at the 'normal' time, or even a little closer to summer, to avoid one-sided development. As a precaution, save some seed for the following autumn to avoid losing a variety that has proved successful on the farm; this can be used if the new harvest has poor germinating power and does not produce useful seed.

Choice of growing site

Crops grown for seed are best included in the existing cropping sequence. If several sequences are used on the farm, chose the field where the interval for the same crop is the longest.

Parts of fields where the soil is in

extremely rich or poor condition are not suitable, nor are headlands and marginal strips. This leaves a sufficiently wide strip down the middle of a field for growing for seed, with the rest of the field used to grow the same crop for food or fodder in the usual way. Marker posts and good seed bed preparation allow drilling close to the winter season even if there is light snow cover, taking account of relevant astronomical data (see chapter on planetary movements). The soil should not be frozen, however. For spring crops, prepare the chosen site in autumn.

Areas selected for seed growing are either not fertilized at all or given just a small amount of well rotted or humified manure (12–16 tonnes/ha); they should not be given rich manures that would force growth.

In-field selection

Having chosen the sowing time and the field, another operation to ensure healthy and vital seed is in-field selection. 'Positive mass selection' consists in selecting strong healthy specimens spaced at regular intervals, i.e. with no gaps between them nor as solitary plants. Ears and panicles should be filled with well developed grain, including base and tip. Preselection is done during the active growth period, taking special account of leaf and culm development and using stakes to mark selected specimens. Final selection based on the above criteria is made shortly before the whole field is harvested. The selected ears and panicles are cut off below the uppermost node in the case of rye, wheat and oats, and at the second highest node in the case of barley. This material provides the basic seed; it must be dried with care and stored in a separate place. It is then grown for seed in a selected field during the next season and provides the basis for subsequent food or fodder crops.

It does need perseverance to acquire the knowledge and skills needed for in-field selection and not every farmer is prepared to put this kind of effort into maintaining and enhancing seed quality. A simpler method that is reasonably effective is 'negative mass selection': carefully remove all abnormal and atypical specimens and all plants of different species from the field selected for seed growing and use a combine harvester to harvest the seed crop separately from the food crop.

An additional measure is to sort the machine-cleaned seed by hand every three or four years during the winter, discarding all abnormal, damaged

and discoloured seed as well as seed from other species.

This is a labour that has to be done. It is good to remember that such intense involvement with plant nature will develop completely new relationships, capabilities and powers.

Within the regional group, individual farm communities may each take responsibility for a particular crop in which they have a special interest and which suits their particular site. Any form of plant breeding that goes beyond this exceeds the limits of practical farming and calls for special capacities and equipment.

Seed baths

In conventional farming, seed is usually treated with more or less toxic dressings to protect it from pests and fungus attack. The mercury com-

Table 39.
Seed baths
(Kuenzel & Lippert)

horn manure	Stir for 1 hour immediately before use. Use for spinach.
valerian preparation	Stir for 15 minutes before use, a tablespoonful to 10 litres of warm water. Use for wheat, fodder beet, sugar beet, leeks, onions, tomatoes, celeriac, potatoes
birch pit concentrate	1 part + 4 parts rain water + 5 parts whole milk; stir vigorously for 5 minutes, leave to stand for 20–24 hours, stir another 5 minutes before use. Use for fodder and sugar beet, carrots, potatoes (made up without milk).
yarrow preparation	Stir 1 portion (c. 1–2 ml) in 3 litres of hand-warm rain water vigorously for about 5 minutes, leave to stand for 20–24 hours (an occasional stir helps); stir briefly before use. Use for rye, grass seed.
wild camomile preparation	As for yarrow. Use for legumes, radishes, rape, mustard, tulips, cabbage varieties.
nettle preparation	As for yarrow. Use for barley.
oak bark preparation	As for yarrow. Use for oats, lettuce, potatoes, dahlias.

Seed grown on the farm for many years must be kept clean. Foreign elements of any kind, weed seeds as well as seed from other cultivars, are deleterious.

pounds that were formerly used are now banned in Germany.

Martha Kuenzel and Franz Lippert have done trials for many years and developed a seed treatment that strengthens the vitality and resistance of plants. This involves seed baths using selected biodynamic preparations for different plants. Plant growth is enhanced as a result, germination tends to be faster, no doubt partly due to moisture uptake. Legumes have been found to produce greater numbers of nodules. These result from the activities of nitrogen-fixing bacteria living in symbiosis with leguminous plants. Growth is improved and compared to untreated controls these plants prove healthier and give better yields. They are able to cope better with poor weather conditions and develop a stronger and more extensive root system.

Seed and plant material is treated with the appropriate extracts the day before sowing. Table 39 gives details of seed baths for different seeds.

Cereal and legume seeds will need two to three litres per 100 kg. Using a hand-brush, or a knapsack sprayer for larger amounts, spray the mound of seeds, turning it three times with a shovel in the process. Cover with sacks and leave for two hours. The small amount of moisture will distribute itself evenly through the heap in this time. Spread it out to dry, so that there will be no problems with the drilling machine, and turn once more if necessary.

Put smaller amounts into fabric bags and suspend in the liquid for 15–20 minutes; dry in a shady place before sowing. Seeds of row crops require two hours' soaking.

Seed potatoes are also sprayed, turning the heap at the same time, but this is done three times in two weeks. Birch pit concentrate will improve the quantitative yield, whilst valerian gives better resistance to degenerative diseases and late blight (*Phytophthora infestans*).

Carrot seed is best dried in a spin dryer after treatment and sown immediately. All bathed seed and plant material must be sown or planted within two days, which means that the operation cannot be done in advance to utilize slack times.

Seed bath treatment gives farmers opportunity to give the powers of their heart to the seed, letting a stream of forces enter into plant development.

External qualities of seed

Size, weight, shape

All effort will be in vain if the seed does not meet certain external quality standards. The size and shape of seed grains should be typical for the species and variety. Overlarge grains frequently come from jagged ears that are not full or from single plants grown in a part of the field where conditions were too favourable, e.g. due to overlap of manure and dung liquor applications. The grain size should always be barely above average. Grains that are full and round are given preference; they are fully ripe and of the right weight.

Clean seed

Care must be taken to see that seed grown on the farm for many years is clean. Foreign elements of any kind, weed seeds as well as seed from other crops, are deleterious. Just a few grains of rye can seriously contaminate wheat seed.

Utter cleanliness will therefore be essential at every stage:
– Sacks must be thoroughly clean.
– Broadcasting machines and seed drills must be free from grain residues, with tubes, disks and every nook and cranny scrupulously clean.
– Where fields are immediately adjacent, with no margin between, close the shutter for the outermost drill tube on the appropriate side.
– Combines and other machines used for harvesting have to be carefully cleaned. Special care must be taken when threshing is done on the edge of a field, to avoid inclusion of other seed.
– All conveyor equipment such as pneumatic grain conveyors, augers and elevators, and the seed cleaner, must be kept clean.
– Great care is also needed in the seed store.

With bought-in seed, especially fodder plant seed, great care must be taken to see that no seeds of undesirable persistent weeds are present, for it is in this way that farms, and particularly farms growing a high percentage of fodder crops, are fouled with curled and broad-leaved dock (*Rumex crispus* and *R. obtusifolius*). Prevention consists in using farm-produced seed of clover species again, with all weeds carefully removed from crops intended for seed production.

Germinating power

Reduced germinating power may be due to a vast number of reasons and it is advisable to do a germination test on farm-produced seed. Spread a sample of 100 grains between two sheets of wet blotting paper on a plate. The method may be used with cereals, fodder vetch, rape, cabbage and clover species. Large seeds such as maize, field bean, beet and pea are pushed into moist sand, keeping the top of the seed level with the surface.

Points to be considered when doing germination tests:
– Keep moist but not wet (lack of oxygen) at all times.
– Light conditions do not matter with agricultural seeds such as cereals, pulses, beets, cabbage and its allies, rape, etc., as they are neutral to light. Only grasses need light for germination, so that the sample should not be left in the dark. Horticultural species often need darkness to germinate (onion, cucumber, tomato, etc.).
– Room temperature is normally adequate. Alternating temperatures accelerate germination.

Germination tests for cereals may have to be done at low temperatures (8–12 °C) if seeds have not ripened by autumn.

After ten days, or for grasses 14–21 days, depending on species, count all seeds that have germinated properly, discarding any that show abnormalities such as glassiness, twisted sprouts, fractures or mouldiness and seeds that have merely swelled up.

The number of properly germinated seeds is equal to the percentage germinating power.

Table 40. ▷
Quality criteria for seed.

Crop	thousand seed weight g	germinating power (approved seed) %	viability years	weight per hectolitre kg	minimum germinating temperature °C	sowing depth cm
wheat		94	3–4	65–84	2–4	2–4
large grain	50					
small grain	40–50					
barley		94	2–3	60–65	2–4	2–4
large grain	50[1])					
small grain	40–45[1])					
rye		94	1–2	60–80	2–4	2–4
large grain	35					
small grain	30–35					
oats		94	2–3	35–56	2–4	2–4
sorted	35–45			(50[2])		
unsorted	25–35					
maize		85[3])–90	2–3		8 (10)	4–8
large grain	<400	85				
small grain	100–250	85				
millet	2.2–5.4[4])	85	3–4	60–70	6–10	1.5–2
sorghum	8–14[4])	85	3–4		10–12	2–2.5
rape			3–4		2–3	2–3
winter	4.0–6.5	94				
spring	2.5–4.5	90			2–3	1–2.5
turnip rape			3–4		1–3	2–3
winter	2.0–4	94				
spring	2.0–3.5	90			1–3	1–2.5
flax for fibre	3.4–5.3	90	2		2–4	1–2
flax for oil	5.4–14	80[5])	2		2–4	1–2
flax for oil & fibre	6.0–8.0	80[5])	2		2–4	1–2
white lupin	340–520	80[5])	poor		4–5	3–4
blue lupin	150–200	94	poor		4–5	3–4
yellow lupin	110–200		poor		4–5	3–4
field bean			3–4		3–4 (9)	5–8
large seeded	600					
medium seeded	500–600					
small seeded	350–500	88				
dwarf bean	250–600	94	2–3		8–10[6])	5–6
vetchling	250–400		3–4		3–4	3–4
green pea	150–450		3–4		1–2[7])	6–8[7])
field pea	100–200	88	3–4		1–2	2–5
soya bean	80–200				8–10	4–7
common vetch	20–140	88 (83)[8])	3–4		1–2	2–3
lentil	25–70	92			5–8	2–3
hairy vetch	25–40		3–4		3–4	1.5–2.5
red clover	1.5–2.5	85[5])	1–2	c. 75	0–5	1–2
white clover	0.65–0.86	85[5])	2	76–80	0–5	1–2
Alsike clover	0.6–0.7	85[5])	1	75	0–5	1–2
Egyptian clover	2.6–3.2		1		2–6	1–2
lucerne (alfalfa)	2.0–2.5	85	3	c. 77	1–6	1–2

Crop	thousand seed weight g	germinating power (approved seed) %	viability years	weight per hectolitre kg	minimum germinating temperature °C	sowing depth cm
white melilot	1.8–2.0	80⁵⁾	1		1–6	1–2.5
melilot	1.7–2.0				1–6	1–2.5
crimson clover	3–4	85	1	76–80	3–8	2–3
black medick	1.2–2.0	85⁵⁾	1	76	1–6	1–2
birdsfoot trefoil	1.2	75⁵⁾	4–5	70–78	1–6	1–2
greater birdsfoot trefoil	0.5	75⁵⁾	–	78	2–6	2–3
serradella	4	75	1–2		3–8	4–5
sainfoin					1–6	4–5
whole pod	20–25	80	3–6	33		
seed	12–15		1–2			
kidney vetch	2.4	75	1		0–5	2–3
awnless brome grass	4.0		3–4			
false oatgrass	3.2	80	2–3			
perennial ryegrass	2.0	90⁹⁾	2–3			
Italian ryegrass	2.1		1 (2)			
hybrid ryegrass	2.3		2			
annual ryegrass	2.5		1			
meadow fescue	2.1	86	2–3			
creeping fescue	1.1	86	3			
cocksfoot	1.0	85	2–3			1–2
meadow foxtail	0.7–0.8	70	3			
reed grass	0.5–0.9	75	2–3			
yellow oatgrass	0.2–0.4	70	3			
timothy	0.4–0.5	90	2–3			
smooth meadow grass	0.4	80	3–4			
swamp meadow grass	0.2	(75–80)¹⁰⁾	3–4			
fiorin	0.05–0.08	85	3			
dogstail	0.5	80	2–3			

¹) Spring barley - down to less than 25 g acceptable; winter barley, down to 30–35 g.
²) Seed quality
³) Germinating power sometimes only 80%, due to high water content (20–35% or more) at harvest. Careful drying increases germinating power to 95% or more.
⁴) For absolutely dry seed.
⁵) Low because of hard seed coat – see Table 41.
⁶) *Phaseolus* species
⁷) *Pisum* species
⁸) spring vetch (winter vetch)
⁹) ryegrasses
¹⁰) *Poa* species

lupin	high (highest for yellow lupin)
red clover	6–10%
white clover	10–25%
Alsike clover	5–20%
melilot	10–15%
black medick	generally low, but may be up to 25%
birdsfoot trefoil	20–40%
greater birdsfoot trefoil	10%

Table 41. **Germinating power reduced by hard seed coat: percentage of hard seed** (Huebner 1955)

Water content

Water content is a major factor in the keeping quality of seeds. Cereals containing 16–20 % of water must not be stored in sacks; above 20 % the grains swell up. Permissible levels have been given by Huebner (1955):

cereals and pulses 15.0 %
rape and related species 12.0 %
clover 12.5 %
grass 14.5 %
vetches 14.0 %

Table 40 gives a comprehensive overview over the most important quality criteria, minimum germination temperatures and depth of sowing for a number of agricultural crops.

Sowing techniques

Density

Crops have to have a certain density in a particular site if optimum yields are to be achieved. With cereals, for instance, these depend on the number of eared culms per square metre. It is well worth the effort to assess different varieties for the number of eared culms per germinated seed. It is a good idea to make a wooden or light-metal frame that is a metre square and place this on the crop. The num-ber of plants, or of eared culms per square metre is then quickly counted. By keeping a record of the various counts for a number of years it is possible to determine the ideal num-ber of plants per square metre or hectare for a given site. The amount of seed required is then easy to work out from

– the desired number of
   plants/m^2
– thousand seed weight
– germinating power
– losses (%) (also determined on
   site) and
– tillering (%).

Hoeing of cereals will mean 15 % losses on average.

Depth

The sowing depth depends on grain size, soil condition, climate and weather.

Large seeds need more moisture to swell and germinate and are more likely to find this in deeper soil lay-ers, which is why they are sown more deeply. They also have greater powers of penetration, so that they are able to come up to the surface from below. The depth should be such, however, that sufficient oxygen is still available for germination. Seeds should be sown less deeply in

$$\text{Seed required (kg/ha)} = \frac{\text{No. of plants/m}^2 \times \text{thousand seed weight (g)}}{\text{Germinating power} - \text{losses} + \text{tillering} \ (- \text{loss through hoeing})}$$

$$\text{Seed required for winter wheat:} \quad \frac{400 \times 49}{95 - 10 + 15} = 196 \text{ kg/ha}$$

seed in kg/ha	140	200	230
seed in g/m²	14	20	23
no. of seeds/m² (mean thousand seed weight = 45 g)	311	444	511
seeds capable of germination/m² theoretical = 95%	295	422	485
plants/m² (theoretical emergence in field = 90%; normal range 85–95%)	266	380	437
crop density = ears/m²	306	437	503
(theoretical 15%; normal range 10–20%)	293–319	418–456	480–524
crop density = ears/m²	260	372	428
with 15% loss due to hoeing	249–271	355–388	408–445

wet and heavy soils with poor aeration than in well-aerated loose, light soils.

In areas where the climate is wet, or in wet weather conditions, it will also be necessary to sow less deeply than under dry conditions. It is generally best to sow as shallowly as conditions permit, as this will mean faster germination and an earlier start to assimilation. Plants that come up quickly are able to compete better against weeds.

Distance between rows

This will depend on the space required by the cultivar and on necessary cultivation operations (hoeing, harrowing, weed harrowing). Plants grow best if each is given approximately the same space. So far, however, no sowing technique has been evolved to achieve this. Closer rows mean a greater distance between plants in the row. Reducing the space between rows does get one closer to

Table 42.
Crop density calculated for winter wheat
(Goetz & Konrad 1978)

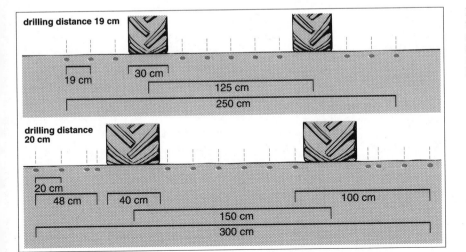

Fig. 57. Distance between rows for cereals allowing for different widths of tram lines to permit hoeing

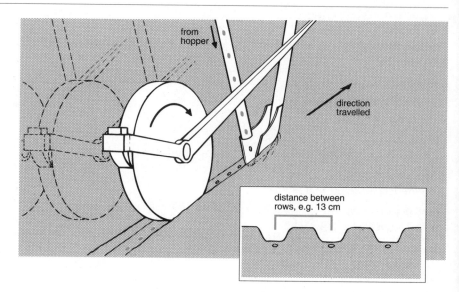

from hopper

direction travelled

distance between
rows, e.g. 13 cm

**Fig. 58.
Effect of roller**

the ideal of sowing at equal spaces. Plants will then cover the ground more quickly and suppress weeds.

With cereals, a distance of 12–20 cm between rows has proved effective, leaving tram lines to suit the vehicles to be used. If the tractor leaves very wide wheel marks, two rows may be sown close together next to the tram lines.

Crops grown on good growing soil or in well-manured fields will do well if sown in rows that are further apart. There will be fewer ears but the yield per hectare may well be increased as the ears are fuller and individual grains heavier.

Seed bed preparation and sowing

A well-settled soil with a top layer of fine crumbly tilth is the goal of seed bed preparation. The top layer needs to be coarser for larger and coarser seed grains and have a finer crumb for small seed.

Growth is assisted by sowing in a

north–south direction, as this gives better warmth and light conditions. This is the method of choice where the situation permits. On sloping ground follow the contour lines to prevent or at least reduce soil erosion.

Modern drills are designed to deposit seed at regular intervals and at the required depth. Implements may be fitted with rollers to ensure contact with soil moisture for the seed. Coverers serve to loosen and spread a fine layer of earth over the seed, thus reducing evaporation. Compared to rolling the whole surface, this method reduces water loss to a much greater extent and is particularly valuable when drilling beet, maize and fine seeds such as carrot, rape, cabbage and its allies and onion. It may also prove useful when drilling wheat. Young wheat plants are somewhat better protected from frost in the slightly deeper grooves, with snow remaining in the grooves even in strong winds and protecting them.

The soil should have a moderate degree of moisture when drilling operations are carried out. This will also enhance the effect of horn manure applied to encourage seedling and root development. Appropriate sowing dates should be adhered to whenever possible.

Post drilling cultivations

The responsibilities of ecologically conscious farmers extend beyond the growing of crops to all the plants that are part of the local ecosystem.

On the one hand it is necessary to create conditions in which sufficient produce can be grown that meets high standards regarding taste, nutritive value and keeping qualities. On the other hand wild plants, too, are life forms that have their definite place and value in the ecosystem even if they cannot be said to have immediate economic value. Yarrow, wild chamomile (scented may-weed), nettle, dandelion, valerian and oak, for instance, are needed to produce the compost preparations. Others benefit field crops merely by their presence, typical examples being sainfoin and cornflower in cereal crops.

Post drilling cultivations are designed to create and maintain the best possible conditions for healthy growth. Other important factors are crop density, a well-planned cropping sequence and good manuring practice. If a field is well prepared and in good tilth when drilling takes place, cultivation operations will keep it in that state until the crop itself provides the ground cover needed to protect the soil from the inclemencies of the weather. The com-

bined effects of fibrous roots, soil organisms and ground cover produce a stable crumb that provides the best growing conditions. Cultivations also include weed control.

The agricultural system, site conditions and climate give rise to a specific accompanying flora. When flax was no longer grown, for example, the plant community that went with its cultivation (flax darnel, *Lolium remotum*; Linetalia or flax-associated flora) (Knapp 1971) disappeared. Increased cultivation of maize is favouring a special flora consisting of millet species, lesser bindweed and couch grass that is difficult to control. Farmers and the work they do clearly have a major effect on the natural environment.

Natural associations have been seriously weakened if not destroyed, which is evident from the fact that beekeeping is no longer possible in some agricultural areas in Central Europe. The rich variety of herbs and flowering plants has been banished from the fields, leaving only rape. And what good is it to partridges to be listed as an endangered species when they can no longer find the food and the cover they need? This impoverishment of the environment reflects the inner life of modern society, where economic values are so much to the fore that humanity fails to maintain the very basis of existence both in the physical world and in regard to the spirit.

Available methods

Farms run on biological principles will usually have balanced cropping sequences with a good proportion of fodder crops. Undesirable herbs and grasses in arable and grassland pro-

Schedule 8 of the Wildlife and Countryside Act of 1981 (UK) lists 62 fully protected plant species.

Table 43.
Indicator plants

vide an indication of site conditions. Knowledge of such 'indicator plants' is therefore considered important in ecological farming practice as they enable farmers to draw conclusions as to local soil conditions if they ap-

Condition of soil	important for	
	grassland	arable land
poor drainage of top and subsoil		
common horsetail (Equisetum arvense)		×
corn mint (Mentha arvensis)		×
coltsfoot (Tussilago farfara)	×	×
marsh woundwort (Stachys palustris)	×	
common reed (Phragmites australis)	×	×
poor structure and low concentration of lime		
pennycress (Thlaspi arvense)		×
common sorrel (Rumex acetosa)	×	×
curled dock (Rumex crispus)	×	×
broad-leaved dock (Rumex obtusifolius)	×	×
heartsease, wild pansy (Viola tricolor)		×
hare's foot clover (Trifolium arvense)	×	
corn spurrey (Spergula arvensis)		×
smooth finger-grass (Digitaria ischaemum)		×
meadow buttercup (Ranunculus acris)	×	
wild camomile or scented mayweed (Chamomilla recutita)		×
lack of stable crumb structure		
creeping thistle (Cirsium arvense)		×
knotgrass species (Polygonum sp.)	×	×
scentless mayweed (Matricaria perforata)		×
comfrey (Symphytum officinale)	×	
wind bent grass (Apera spica-venti)		×
good crumb structure for row crops with good supply of nitrates		
black nightshade (Solanum nigrum)		×
annual mercury (Mercurialis annua)		×
petty spurge (Euphorbia peplus)		×
annual nettle (Urtica urens)		×
common chickweed (Stellaria media)		×
stable crumb structure and neutral reaction		
lesser bindweed (Convolvulus arvensis)		×
scarlet pimpernel (Anagallis arvensis)		×
annual mercury (Mercurialis annua)	×	×
forking larkspur (Consolida regalis)		×
common toadflax (Linaria vulgaris)		×
white campion (Silene latifolia)		×
dandelion (Taraxacum officinalis)	×	
yellow vetchling (Lathyrus aphaca)		×
meadow clary (Salvia pratensis)	×	
summer pheasant's eye (Adonis aestivalis)		×
chicory (Cichorium intybus)	×	

pear in large numbers. Table 43 gives details based on the work of Boas, Ellenberg and others (Appel 1979).

Another way is to classify such plants according to specific aspects. For instance, the appearance of weeds such as chickweed, deadnettle, wild camomile (scented mayweed), wind bent grass, slender foxtail or cornflower relates to weather conditions. Weeds common in fields used for spring crops are corn marigold, hemp nettles, charlock, wild radish, knotgrass and scarlet pimpernel. Orache, fat hen, gallant soldier, black nightshade and small nettle are typical associates of row crops. Other important categories are weeds reproduced by seed or root and those that need frost, light or darkness to germinate.

The presence of indicator plants cannot always be directly related to specific cultivation operations. Wild camomile or scented mayweed (*Chamomilla recutita* or *Matricaria chamomilla*) for example is considered indicative of lime deficiency. Excessive spread of this plant may however also be due to other causes and these need to be treated as well as applying lime. Wild camomile germinates in the light and tends to spread in areas of low crumb stability where the soil is inclined to puddle and encrust. Consolidation of the soil at middle level may also be responsible. Mulching and biological measures will overcome structural weaknesses of this kind.

A loose crumb structure may be maintained by loosening the soil, shallow digging in of compost and continuous use of weed harrow and roller, which prevents wild camomile from germinating.

Massive occurrences of coltsfoot, horsetail and corn mint indicate poor

Manure and compost containing a high proportion of weeds should go on grassland rather than arable land.

drainage in both crumb and subsoil. The condition may be improved by draining fields and grasslands. Useful methods are to put in effective drains, remove water by means of open drainage ditches and to create a herringbone ridge and furrow system for surface drainage, possibly combined with the creation of small ponds. As the water is drawn off, air penetrates the soil, supplying vital oxygen. The result will be a large increase in the microbe population and improved soil structure.

The next step is systematic fertilization with well-rotted farmyard manure and fermented dung liquor or slurries. The organic matter vitalizes the soil, which encourages the activity of soil organisms. Weed seeds are also more likely to be attacked by the increased fungus and bacterial population and this, possibly coupled with the production of inhibitory compounds, reduces their germinating power and vitality. Manures should be kept as free from weed seeds as possible, which is done by keeping heaps well covered and controlling humification by maintaining temperature and moisture levels. This may sometimes necessitate turning the heap. If there is still any doubt as to safety and quality, stick to the well-established rule: manures containing a high proportion of weed material should go on to permanent grassland, not on to arable land.

Cropping sequences

Even the best planned cropping sequence will do little for crops that are thin or show gaps. This applies not only to winter wheat in spring, but also to red clover in summer. Couch grass and thistles will spread rapidly under those conditions. Defective crops should not be left to themselves, hoping that they will grow stronger and suppress the weeds. Inaction results in reduced yields and an increasing volume of weed seeds, with the rhizomes of perennial weeds growing on unimpeded. Undersown clover will help to some extent by providing ground cover. The advantages of planned cropping sequences have already been considered. Individual species differ in competitiveness, and one factor to be considered in designing cropping sequences is the balanced combination of 'weed promoters' and good 'weed suppressors' (Rauhe). Spring barley belongs to the first category; little straw and a short period of active growth mean that the soil is given little shade and hardly ever has complete cover. This offers plenty of opportunity for undesirable weeds to develop. The opposite is the case with winter rye, which does not even allow creeping thistles to come up.

Gaps in red clover due to the depredations of mice, clover crown and stem rot or winter kill help the spread of thistles and couch grass. One way of dealing with this is to use the more vigorous tetraploid red clover which is less susceptible to clover rot and gives better ground cover. Fields badly fouled with thistles were completely cleared by growing tetraploid red clover, and the wheat that followed was completely thistle free. Frequent cutting of long-term leys seriously upsets the growth rhythms of perennial weeds. Such leys should be planned for at least two years of use; three years of lucerne and grass are even more certain to give results.

If such a time interval is not available and growing conditions are good, one summer crop of reversed or Persian clover will give almost the same result. To begin with, the clover can hardly be seen among the annual weeds, but after the first cut it will spread and suppress the germination of undesirable plants. Thistles do not tolerate four or five successive cuts. If necessary, turning the soil to some depth will suppress them further. The effect of under-sowing winter crops with white clover and black medick tends to be unreliable. Dense cereal crops (more than 4.5 tonnes/ha) seriously inhibit their growth, with the result that there are bare areas in autumn where more weeds will grow. Recent developments have brought some improvement. A return to the use of mechanical hoes and hence an increase in the distance between rows to 17–20 cm helps the clover and black medick to establish better. Seeds from weeds such as wild oats cannot reach the soil and are caught up in the dense 'clover pelt' where they perish. It is remarkable how quickly bothersome weeds can be controlled in this way.

Fodder mixtures of rape or mustard, field beans, vetches and peas as a catch crop will also contribute much to weed control if drilled in good time by the end of August or early September and if the weather is favourable. The weed seeds will germinate at the same time but be unable to compete with the vigorous growth of mustard and/or rape. The mixture also helps to suppress perennial weeds.

Densely grown crops quickly followed by catch crops are excellent for weed suppression.

If sufficient nitrogen is available, dense stubble-sown crops of phacelia (*Phacelia tanacetifolia*) will rapidly form a dense carpet, inhibiting and killing off all other plants. Cattle do however take some time to get used to them. If the plant comes into flower it provides welcome 'autumn pasture' for bees. Phacelia belongs to the rare nemophila family (Hydrophyllaceae) and therefore adds to the variety of species grown on the farm. It inhibits nematodes and helps to improve soil health and structure.

An excellent way of combating weeds is to sow a rapidly growing summer fodder mixture of field beans, peas, vetches, sunflowers, maize, vetchling and oats. Cultivate twice yearly and use for soilage or silage.

Row crops are often effectively preceded by a weed-suppressing and structure-improving catch crop (Landsberg mixture – fodder vetch, crimson clover and Italian ryegrass; Italian ryegrass and crimson clover; vetch and rye; turnip rape).

In southern Germany, and especially in damp areas, slender foxtail or black grass (*Alopecurus myosuroides*) is a troublesome weed grass, difficult to control chemically and causing serious reductions in yield if it gains the upper hand. The seeds ripen and drop during the summer weeks and germinate mainly at the end of September, i.e. at the same time as winter cereals. Winter barley is the first to be affected, but dense and vigorous growth permits it to stand up to the competition. Winter wheat, on the other hand, needs a long time to emerge in autumn and will only tiller by the end of winter,

Table 44. Percentage of seed released by weeds before winter wheat and spring barley are harvested with a combine (Koch & Hurle 1978)

weed	% of total seeds released
wind bent grass (*Apera spica-venti*)	95–100
slender foxtail (*Alopecurus myosuroides*)	65–75
wild oats (*Avena fatua*)	65–95
ivy-leaved speedwell (*Veronica hederifolia*)	100
common field speedwell (*Veronica persica*)*	60–95
common chickweed (*Stellaria media*)	60–90
pennycress (*Thlaspi arvense*)*	40–70
shepherd's purse (*Capsella bursa-pastoris*)	40–70
charlock (*Sinapis arvensis*)	55
hairy tare (*Vicia hirsuta*)	55
smooth tare (*Vicia tetrasperma*)	55
cleavers (*Galium aparine*)	20–40
black bindweed (*Fallopia convolvulus*)	20
redshank (*Polygonum persicaria*)*	occasional
pale persicaria (*Polygonum lapathifolium*)*	at most
wild camomile or scentless mayweed (*Chamomilla recutita*)	low

* Low-growing species; retained seed not picked up by combine.

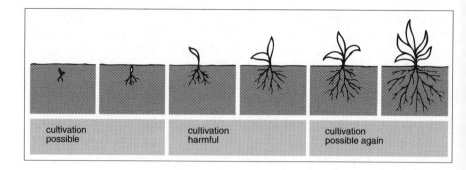

cultivation   cultivation   cultivation
possible   harmful   possible again

Fig. 59. Growth
stages of cereals
when harrow and
weed harrow may be
used (Koch & Hurle
1978)

and in bad weather conditions not until early spring. Slender foxtail (black grass) can make good use of such an opportunity, so that a field of winter wheat may look very much like a meadow in spring. Hoeing will only have limited effect and the best method is to drill the wheat late between the end of October and about 10 November – having first used tillage implements to combat the weed. 'Modern' combine harvesters unfortunately no longer allow one to collect the weed seeds at harvest time.

Mechanical measures

Modern technology (combine harvesting) has made harvesting dates much later. The result is that weeds reach full maturity and scatter their seeds. Table 44 lists the major species involved.

Combine harvesters also blow the chaff all over the stubble field, so that post harvest tillage has become most important. Stubble ploughs and grubbers cause weed seeds to germinate and help the following catch crop to grow apace, suppressing undesirables. Sufficient rain and adequate applications of dung liquor will strengthen the crop and enhance the effect.

During dry autumns, troublesome perennial weeds (e.g. couch grass) can be effectively controlled by repeated tillage operations alternating deep loosening with harrowing, so that the rhizomes dry up. No catch crop will be grown in this case. Root sections that remain in the soil use up their reserves and finally perish from exhaustion in late autumn if deeply buried. It is evident, then, that a plough can be effectively used in weed control by combining it with deep loosening and surface tillage. This applies particularly to spear thistles with their active growth in spring and seed production in summer, so that they are exhausted by early autumn. Their stolons thrive mainly on ploughpan which needs to be broken up and if possible resolved completely. Complete success will however depend on the farmer's personal engagement and observation. A spade test done year after year in critical sites is highly commended.

A good autumn furrow will not only bring thistle and couch grass stolons to the surface but also those of coltsfoot and other weeds. This interrupts vegetative reproduction, the parts desiccate and decay on the surface or are attacked by frost. A spring furrow will not give the same result; instead, it brings seeds to the surface that germinate quickly and establish a new weed population.

The combination of deep and superficial tillage in alternation, and the sowing of a catch crop will also deal with curled dock. Renius (1979) advises drilling a ley and after the second cut ploughing as deep as possible, using a coulter, so that the dock is buried deeply. A vigorous, well-manured catch crop will prevent new shoots from coming up. The method may be used after winter barley that can be cleared early. Skimming at the end of July or in August (to cut off the roots below the collar) is followed by three to five deep grubbing or loosening operations at weekly intervals, after which winter rape or Landsberg mixture is sown.

In spring, the float or harrow is always used before putting in cereals or roots. This will cause the first generation of associated weeds to germinate, with the seedlings destroyed in the drilling process. The harrow should be used again three or four days after drilling, followed by further operations, preferably using a weed harrow, before the first tips appear and then again at the four leaf stage. A weed harrow is more flexible and adapts better to uneven ground; it has greater effective width. The speed is about 12 km/h, compared to 6 km/h with a harrow. Both bury weed seedlings.

Mechanical hoes are used on a routine basis on row crops or vegetables – e.g. potatoes, beet, maize and carrots. They are now also being used again on cereals, the advantage being that times are less critical. Mechanical hoes can be used until the plants close up or shoot development starts; it is contraindicated only if wheel tracks are clearly causing damage in rainy weather or when there is a risk of frost.

The following points are to be considered when working with mechanical hoes:
– Both annual and perennial weeds are attacked.
– The method can be used for a relatively long part of the period of active growth. Early winter crops in good sites will tolerate a first hoeing operation in late autumn, which is then easily repeated in spring.
– In autumn, the share should not go below 0.5–1 cm, whereas 3–4 cm is advisable in spring.
– Spring hoeing will stimulate further weeds into germination, so that winter crops may be contaminated with typical summer crop weeds and grasses unless further hoeing operations are done.

Fig. 60. Effect of harrowing on total weed populations at different growth stages (Koch & Hurle 1978).

growth stage	no. of weeds prior to cultivation		percentage of weeds after harrowing		
	absolute	relative	unharmed	torn out	buried
cotyledons	2834	100	44	5	52
small rosette	5772	100	64	7	29
large rosette	5627	100	82	5	13
mean		100	64	6	31

These should be shallow to avoid damage to superficial roots.
– There is also an earthing-up effect. This does not really matter with cereals but can be a disadvantage for a following ley, as uneven ground makes mowing more difficult.
– If the share is 10–12 cm wide, the distance between cereal rows should be about 18–20 cm.
– With an effective width of 2.5 metres the time required to hoe one hectare is about 3 hours for the first pass. About 2 hours should be reckoned for subsequent passes.
– Hoeing also has a positive effect on soil structure, it stimulates mineralization and reduces evaporation.

These benefits of mechanical hoeing should not blind us to the questions that remain open, nor indeed to its disadvantages:

– There are no problems with row crops, and if weather conditions are good both winter and spring wheat and spring barley come to no harm.
– Extreme caution is needed with oats and rye because of their shallow roots. In both cases the decision will depend on the state of the crop, the soil and the weather. There should be no more cold nights to follow, as sensitivity to frost will be heightened. Winter barley should not be hoed at all.
– Hoeing sometimes causes cereals, especially oats, to ripen unevenly, which is due to increased tillering.
– In sites where the climate is poor and very harsh, wide distances between rows are bad for soil structure. Crops will be late closing up or never do so.
– In stony fields, stones will often damage seedlings or cover them

Fig. 61. Effective use of mechanical hoe with cereal crops.

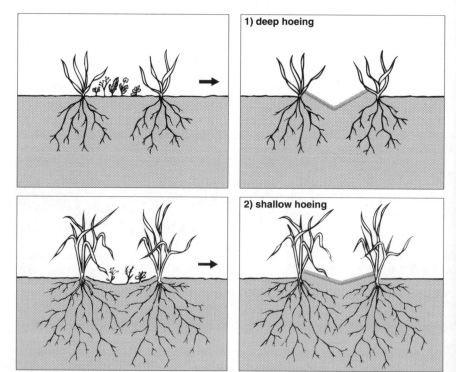

up, so that yields are reduced.

Hoeing operations applied to cereals thus call for personal experience and careful observation.

The method should be more widely used in cereal cultivation, combining it with the use of weed harrow and harrow. Crops respond by growing at a better pace and weeds are kept down.

Thermal control

Biological farmers use steam and propane gas for thermal weed control. Steam sterilization is a completely nontoxic way of treating soil, compost heaps and greenhouses. Small appliances are handy for the purpose, or contractors may be employed using large units, mostly in horticulture.

Flame weeding with propane gas is coming to be more and more widely used on farms, especially on field-grown vegetables. In biodynamic agriculture, the first trials were made in 1967. In suitable weather conditions and with some basic knowledge, the implements can be used to good effect. The method is nontoxic as the combustion products of the gas are carbon dioxide and water. The weeds are not actually burnt. The rapid rise in temperature causes the fluid in the cells to expand and burst the cell walls. Death is also due to the fact that plant proteins coagulate at 50–60 °C.

At first the only visible effect is that the plants turn a darker green. Pressure marks left by one's fingers demonstrate that damage has occurred.

A flame weeding operation done at the right time will destroy numerous seed-bearing and grass weeds. Weeds with vigorous root systems such as thistles and dock do resprout, however, so that the operation may have to be repeated a number of times.

Flame weeding causes minimal if any damage to soil organisms, for at a speed of 1–7 km/h the high temperatures do not penetrate the soil to any depth.

M. Hoffmann (1980) distinguishes four methods:

1) Total: Burns all plant growth over the treated surface area. To be regarded as a preventive measure only.
2) Selective: Used to remove undesirable weeds in crops that are relatively heat-resistant (woody stems). Good results have been noted and the method is increasingly used with maize crops, in tree nurseries, orchards, soft fruit plantations and vine yards.
3) Pre-emergence: Treatment of vegetable rows before the plants emerge (use of pressure wheel). Hand roguing may follow later.
4) Spot: Deals with weeds that form colonies and persistent weeds. The method also give good results in gardens, farmyards, around shrubs and along roadsides.

Different types of appliances may be used:
– Knapsack flame weeder for very small areas; may also be used in fields that cannot take vehicular traffic in very wet springs.
– Hand-operated two-wheeler flame weeder; useful in vegetable fields and when larger vehicles cannot be used after rain.
– Large add-on units for use with tractors; a number of designs are on the market.

Pre-emergence flame weeding effectively controls early weed growth in vegetable crops that are slow to germinate, such as carrots.

A practical example from a farm

It is usually only older farmers who are still familiar with mechanical weed control. Below, Guenther Graf Finkenstein describes the methods used on his farm.

Winter cereals

To permit the use of hoeing machines – this appears necessary on all heavy soils – we drill with spacings of 17–20 cm.

For good results the duck's foot should be at least 10 cm wide. The difference between row spacings and width of shares should be not less than 7 cm to allow the implement to be guided. Depending on the effective width of the seed drill, it is a good idea to block outlets matching the wheel distance of the tractor used for post drilling cultivation; this reduces damage from cultivation operations. 40 cm per wheel is usually sufficient. Losses due to this are within reasonable limits for a 6 metre drill. With narrow drills, one way of keeping losses down would be to position the gaps as for the light break method, and another would be to use narrower wheels.

Drilling needs to be done with reasonable care. The first post drilling cultivation using a weed harrow on winter barley and rye may be done just before or at first emergence, but we have no experience of this. We hardly ever grow winter barley and with rye there appears to be little need, especially when there is so much other work do be done in autumn. It is highly likely, however, that the method will be successful in controlling some difficult weeds. The soil must be firm enough so that the

harrow does not tear out the germinating grain that is lying just below the surface.

The first spring cultivation depends on the condition of both soil and crop.

If frost has lifted the soil, a Cambridge roll is used when the soil is dry enough. The plants must be of a size where not too many will be buried as clods are pressed flat. After rolling it is usually necessary to wait a day, as the crop has been flattened. It must be upright again before the weed harrow is used, otherwise the risk of plants being buried is too high.

If the soil has puddled after a wet mild winter, rolling would cause serious damage; what the soil needs in this case is to be torn open.

Like any other operation used on weeds in the germinating or cotyledon stage, early use of the weed harrow is much more effective than anything that is done later. A second pass may be made at any time prior to hoeing.

Once the plants are big enough to cope with the slight ridging effect, a mechanical hoe with 10–12 cm wide shares is used, as already mentioned. When a rye crop is badly fouled with black grass or foxtail (rye is more sensitive to this than wheat) we use 12 cm shares and work at a slow pace. We use tool carriers and centre-mounted frames, with the harrow connected to the rear hydraulic element. This has proved particularly effective in wet years, with weeds growing between rows either cut into and ripped out or chopped off and dragged away. This reduces the risk of weeds taking root again after the next rain.

A question that keeps coming up is whether mechanical hoes can be used

Rye crops with a serious weed problem need shallow hoeing.

on rye. According to reliable reports from W. Renius, accurate trials run after the First World War showed no increase or loss in yields. Appreciably fouled rye therefore needs shallow hoeing, particularly if the weed in question is foxtail.

During the first years after conversion our winter wheat was so badly fouled with foxtail that one could no longer see the rows in some parts. One pass with the hoeing machine followed by a pass with the weed harrow gave the crop sufficient air. The mature crop was reasonably weed free, despite the fact that duck's foot harrows will only cut about 50% of the weeds. Wheat offers powerful competition to foxtail growing in the rows. An essential precondition is sufficient crop vigour and proper management. Initially we had been rather doubtful about the method, but thanks to these encouraging results the appearance of foxtail in cereal and other crops no longer constitutes a major problem.

The good thing about mechanical weed control is that specific intervention in the weed population allows us to retain a desirable variety of plants at a level where they do not compete with crops. Russian researches into phytoncides suggest that certain arable weeds have direct or indirect positive effects on crops.

Spring cereals

Except in extreme cases, weed control can be entirely mechanical with spring cereals. It does need good drilling technique under dry conditions and the kind of good crumb structure you get with an autumn furrow or on soils that can be ploughed in spring.

We normally drill at a depth of not less than 2 cm; otherwise the crop is not sufficiently anchored and may be ripped out during the first pass with a weed harrow. Rolling after drilling prevents the harrow from going too deep, especially in the first and second passes. If the soil is still rather fresh (moist) after drilling, we wait a few days before harrowing. Rolling should however be done before the cereal has produced the first fine rootlets. From then until the white leaf shoots pierce the surface, vehicles should only go on the field if tramlines can be followed exactly. At this stage of plant development, any new tracks or hoof marks from draught animals will cause gaps.

If rain firms the soil after drilling, rolling will not be necessary. It is still possible to roll when the crop is just emerging, but the timing is critical, so that one needs to be ready for instant action at this time. The weed harrow on its own may also be used between light showers or if necessary on a Saturday afternoon or a Sunday at approximately 5 ha/hour.

The first harrowing pass should be made at first emergence at the latest. Once the cotyledon has opened out, no cultivation can be done until the 3 or 4 leaf stage, as the tender seedlings will die if covered by small clods of earth or by stones.

Weeds not destroyed at the time of first emergence of cereals will be in the small rosette stage when the cereal crop has developed 3 or 4 leaves and can then only be controlled to a limited extent. In cases of serious fouling this may result in failure. It is therefore vital to get the work done at the right time, another reason being that this will reduce the time during which weed control is impossible to its minimum. Potential weather problems are reduced by

Timing is vital with mechanical cultivation operations.

blind harrowing a few days earlier, when the white leaf spears in the soil have not yet come to the point of emergence. Blind harrowing will in any case be required as an additional measure if the weed problem is severe.

Early passes with the weed harrow can be done rapidly and should be shallow. From the 3 or 4 leaf stage onwards passes must be made slowly to avoid covering the seedlings with small clods of earth or stones. One has to get down from the tractor, take a look and adjust the speed as required.

If the right times for blind harrowing and first emergence work have been missed, duck's foot shares need to be brought into play as soon as possible. This has to be done at low speed to avoid burying the crop in the ridges. After this, the method is the same as for winter cereals.

We take account of the positions of the stars whenever possible, basing ourselves on Maria Thun's calendar. For work that has to be done within a certain time, e.g. for using the weed harrow at first emergence, we merely aim to avoid unfavourable times. In planning the week's work, we try to coordinate other necessary cultivations according to their favourable times. If the weather, the labour situation or other reasons make this impossible, we limit ourselves to avoiding unfavourable periods.

**Fig. 62.
Origin of the seven cereals.**

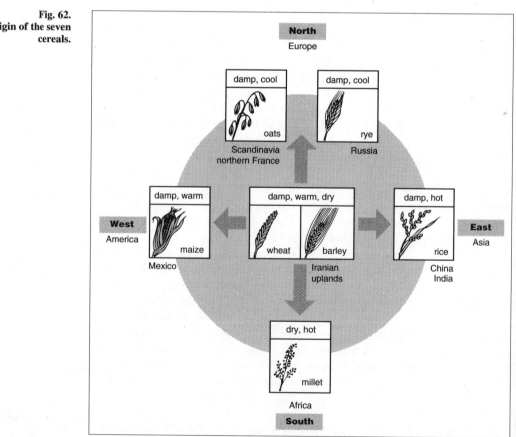

Arable crops

Cereals

As mentioned in the historical review, most cultivated plants originate from a few limited areas on the globe, mainly the uplands of subtropical regions which are known as sites for the gene pools or centres of variation. As may be seen from Figure 62, the seven cereals – wheat and barley; rice or millet; oats, rye and maize – come from the different continents (except for Australia). The centre of post-Atlantean civilization, the Iranian uplands, was the original home of wheat and barley, which are probably the oldest grain crops, and of many other crops such as lentil and pea, flax, mustard, vetches and numerous fruit and vegetable species.

In Central Europe, wheat is the principal bread grain today, with rye coming second; malting barley is specifically grown for beer brewing, and the other cereals serve as feed-stuffs in animal husbandry and intensive livestock farming. Almost half the world population lives on rice, whereas millet is much less eaten now than formerly.

Almost two thirds of the arable land in the western part of Germany is used for cereal growing, with cereals advisedly making up between 30 and 60% of the cropping sequence. Depending on local conditions, a good balance can be achieved between legumes and oil crops on the one hand and cereals and row crops on the other, providing for harmonious alternation of phases during which humus builds up and is depleted, a good crumb structure is established and reduced and nitrogen is fixed and utilized.

Cereal growing is important from

In Central Europe, wheat is the principal bread grain, with rye coming second.

the point of view of labour intensity. The work is easily mechanized, and on a highly specialized farm it takes about ten hours of labour per hectare to do everything that is required.

Cereals belong to the family of grasses (Gramineae), with winter and spring varieties. Many different varieties offer a wide range of characteristics, so that it is easy to choose one that meets local needs regarding drilling time, weather, soil and fertilizer requirements, intended purpose (e.g. wheat for bread or pasta production) and harvesting time.

All cereals require a firm seed bed but winter crops especially so, for plants need to be firmly rooted to survive both intermittent and black frosts. Winter barley and rye need to be drilled at low depths and in good time, as tillering should occur in autumn. Proud growth due to unusually mild weather conditions can be corrected by letting sheep graze under careful control. If this is not done and there is extended snow cover during winter, the crop may suffer damage from snow mould.

In a mild climate, cereals may be hoed in autumn, with the slight ridging effect providing added protection. If drilling is done later, so that hoeing will not be possible, drag rings fitted to the seed share on light soils or pressure wheels and coverers on heavier soils produce the same effect, with the seedlings growing in a slight furrow, protected from wind and black frost by the walls.

Winter damage may also be pre-

vented by the following methods:
- Use a harrow or roll to break up snow crusts and prevent lush growth from asphyxiating in frost-free ground.
- Roll frost-lifted soil in early spring so that rootlets that have become exposed are again brought into contact with moist earth.
- Use harrow and roll when active growth is in progress to break up puddled and crusted soil.

If conditions permit, a thin layer of fully humified compost applied to the field will give added protection and cause the soil to warm up more quickly in spring. Further cultivation with weed harrow, harrow and hoeing machine is as described above.

The ear or panicle begins to develop early, at the time when the plant tillers, and this is the time for a first application of horn silica. Tillering may start in autumn with winter barley and rye and frequently also with spelt and winter wheat if drilled early. An autumn application of horn silica has therefore been found to be of definite benefit under favourable weather conditions in mild climates. Results have been less good in harsher climates.

The addition of a drill fertilizer to winter and spring cereal seed has proved effective. The following may be used:

1) Drill Oscorna (a mixture of horn, bone, blood, meat and feather meal, with large particles removed by sieving).
2) 60% Drill Oscorna, 20% basalt rock dust, 10% calcified seaweed.
3) 25% Drill Oscorna, 10% basalt rock dust, 10% calcified seaweed, 55% fine humified compost (maximum moisture level 20%).

Nos 2 and 3 really need a two-hopper drill to work efficiently. Add

Q_0 = swelling number, a unit used to express gluten quality. For winter wheat, an Q_0 of more than 16 and a moist gluten level of more than 22% are desirable.

10% or at most 20% of the chosen mixture per 100 kg of seed and mix thoroughly. The mixture may separate, and it is therefore advisable to put in only small quantities at a time and check that there is an even flow of the right number of seeds. Drill fertilization will usually
- accelerate and improve root development,
- encourage tillering in thinly sown crops,
- promote ear and grain development and
- frequently result in earlier maturity and harvest.

On sites where conditions are otherwise not exactly ideal (e.g. unfavourable annual weather conditions) wheat will have a higher gluten content and quality.

Wheat

Wheat (*Triticum aestivum*) is the most exacting cereal crop; being less able to release and utilize minerals it needs soil with a good supply of nutrients and lime. Wheat does best after preceding crops like rape, legumes (peas, field beans, clover and clover/grass ley) and row crops that can be cleared early.

The seed bed needs to be firm and not too fine on the surface. Wheat is the cereal that tolerates late drilling best of all.

Although the most resistant of all cereals to mechanical cultivation with weed harrow, harrow and hoe, it tends to react rather sensitively to massive competition from weeds. In the west of Germany, winter wheat has the greatest number of varieties (c. 50), with winter barley coming second. It is not as adaptable as rye (c. 10 varieties), but it is always possible to find the right variety for the intended purpose and the given situation. Most spring wheat varieties have good blending properties and may be added to less good winter wheat to improve baking quality and achieve a mean moist gluten content of c. 30% at a Q_0 of 16–22. Coarse meal from grain of this quality will produce well-flavoured wholemeal bread.

Spring wheat needs to be drilled as early as possible from the end of January, depending on local conditions. Unlike winter wheat it does not tolerate being 'rubbed into' the soil. Regarding preceding crops its needs are the same as those of winter wheat. Clover and grass/clover leys are best, especially as they allow a late cut for soilage in autumn. In areas where there is a risk of winter kill, it is advisable to grow spring wheat on part of the wheat area; it will give better yields than winter wheat that has suffered damage. Fields occupied by winter cereals also tend to have more of a weed problem. Spelt (*Triticum spelta*) is probably an ancestor of our ordinary wheat (*Triticum aestivum*) and is only grown to a limited extent. There has been a slight increase in demand for dried unripe spelt and special baked goods. The glumes remain attached after threshing, so that spelt needs an additional tanning process to remove them. The glumes are left on for seed. The grain is flinty and the flour a pale yellow.

Spelt is less exacting where soil and climate are concerned, except that it needs slightly more lime than wheat does. Its preceding crop value lies between that of wheat, which is less, and rye.

Rye

Rye (*Secale cereale*) is the most frost resistant of the cereals; it is classed as a secondary crop plant, which means that it was initially a wild plant found in wheat and barley fields and only gradually developed into a plant of economic value. It benefited from its ability to inhibit the growth of other plants – both weeds and crop plants – and suppress them, probably by excreting growth inhibitors (allelopathy) in the root region. Rye has three seedling roots and rapidly develops a root system that spreads horizontally at first and later also downwards. Contrary to common belief, the nutrient requirement for an equal yield is higher than for wheat. On the other hand the root mass and root performance are greater, so that adequate yields may be achieved even in relatively poor soils and climates, including podsolized heath and woodland soils and lean shallow slate-based soils.

Rye needs a fine, firm seed bed to ensure shallow, even drilling and prevent winter kill due to frost lifting. The soil needs to be dry for drilling. Careful use of weed harrow and harrow is well tolerated in spring (caution is needed if there is a threat of frost). Hoeing is indicated only if there is a serious weed problem.

In spring, growth will be rapid once the soil has warmed up, so that rye also makes a good fodder catch crop, either on its own or mixed with winter vetches. It is resistant to black frost, being able to survive temperatures down to –30 °C. It is less resistant to intermittent frost, water logging and high snow levels, as there is a risk of rot and extensive snow mould (a fungus). Rye is relatively sensitive to cold at the flowering stage. Late frost may be responsible for uneven ears, so that it is usually safer to grow spring rye on sites

'Schmidt' rye was bred by Martin Schmidt in Hessel in Germany, using his own specially developed method (ear plot selection).

where there is a risk. Spring rye is not much grown. It may do better than winter rye on very light sandy soils or in areas where waterlogging is common in winter; otherwise it is only grown, if at all, to make up for winter kill. Drilling should be as early as possible.

'Schmidt' rye has been used to some extent in biodynamic trials. Rye is particularly difficult to breed as it is a cross-pollinating crop, self-sterile and sensitive to inbreeding. To maintain a variety and its yield for any length of time, care must be taken to keep a good distance between different varieties of rye; the distance should be 600 metres, and 1000 metres in the main wind direction. Otherwise alien pollination may result in hybridization.

Ergot is best prevented by mowing baulks early, so that the fungus does not spread to the rye from grasses that flower earlier.

Barley

Barley (*Hordeum vulgare*) is one of the oldest cultivated plants if not *the* oldest; it has played a major role as a food in the past, mainly in form of gruel and flatbread. 'Barley grits' was the staple breakfast and supper dish in some parts of northern Germany until quite recently. Today barley is grown mainly for brewing and fodder, almost a quarter of the arable land in western Germany being used for the purpose.

Winter barley is generally used for fodder. In recent years, two-rowed winter varieties have been increasingly grown for malting. It requires timely drilling in firm soil having a good lime status. Winter rape is the best preceding crop, with vegetable peas, early potatoes and early-clear-ing grain peas to follow. Barley is an exacting crop where weed control is concerned, but does tolerate careful harrowing and hoeing. Its early harvesting date makes it a good nurse crop, providing grain fodder in early July.

Demand for human consumption is limited, and spring barley is best for the purpose, especially glumeless varieties. Barley grown as a cereal for special diets should have similar qualities to malting barley: glumed barley should have 8–12% of fine glumes, 75–85% yield of malt, a germinating power of not less than 95%, good smell and colour, high thousand grain weight and low protein content (less than 12%). These characteristics are enhanced by early drilling in a fine crumb. Row crops, above all potatoes, have proved to be the best preceding crop; they leave the soil weed-free and well-structured, full of life but not liable to force growth. Any kind of fertilization tending to force growth must be avoided as it causes increased protein levels that are liable to cause severe flatus. The seed rate needs to be fairly high, otherwise increased tillering will result in uneven growth and maturity. Whilst barley makes a good nurse crop for clover, quality may be lost and harvesting made difficult if the clover growth is too vigorous. The clover therefore needs to be drilled at a later date, e.g. after tillering.

Cattle like eating barley straw with dried undercrop hay.

Oats

Oats (*Avena sativa*) developed relatively late as a crop but then spread rapidly in the damp and cool parts of Central Europe, where they were the staple food for a long time. The pro-

The earliest finds of barley as a cultivated plant in the Nile Delta go back to predynastic times, those in northern Syria and Assyria to 4000–4500 BC.

tein content is one of the highest among cereals and the fat content the highest. Oats have a high nutritional value because of their high iron and calcium levels. Oat gruel and porridge are important for children and invalids. Young stock also do well on oats. In temperate regions oats are fed to horses, taking the place of the barley that is fed in hotter regions (e.g. Arabia).

Oats have the most effective root system, with good yields even from a second or third successive crop. Owing to a high capacity for dissolving minerals and its deep-rooting qualities, oats also do well on ploughed up long-term grassland.

Oats are considered the best preceding crop among the four cereals. They act as a cleaning crop in close cropping sequences, suppressing take-all.

Oats are an unexacting crop; high yields can be achieved on good sites and best yields of all cereals even in unfavourable conditions. They do however require plenty of moisture. Dry conditions after stem elongation may seriously affect the yield. Winter oats are grown only on sites that are consistently dry in spring.

Naked oats demand better soil quality and are particularly sensitive to prolonged dry periods. They will then give low yields, compared to the 4 t/ha that are not uncommon for this crop even on poor sites if weather conditions have been favourable. Naked oats are in demand for human consumption and also make an excellent feed for young stock, but it is advisable to grow them only in areas where the climate suits. Experience has shown that they tend to revert to glumed oats, so that new seed has to be bought in every two or three years. Storage of the harvested grain

If seed is not treated, various fungus diseases may cause serious damage.

requires great care as it tends to pack down tightly and easily grows mouldy, decreases in germinating power and acquires a musty smell and taste.

Oat straw harvested dry and in good condition provides excellent fodder for young stock and supplementary feed for cows because of its relatively high phosphorus, potassium and magnesium content. Early maturing oat varieties make a good nurse crop for oversown crops, with the longer straw preventing the undercrop from growing through, a risk that exists with spring barley. In dry areas or years, competition for soil water from the undercrop may reduce yields.

Cereal cyst nematode will attack spring wheat and barley and a number of grasses as well as oats and may cause serious losses in cropping sequences with a high proportion of cereals. The only way out is to cut down on oats in favour of winter crops and to intensify the use of catch crops.

Smut and seed treatments

The exclusion of chemical seed treatments may result in epidemic spread of a number of fungus diseases, the most important of these being covered smut or bunt (*Tilletia caries*), which may cause up to 50% losses. Transmitted via the grain, the fungus inhibits reproduction.

The warm water treatment, originally introduced to combat loose smut (*Ustilago nuda*) in wheat and barley, effectively killed the fungus for many years but failed to do so on many farms in 1984. This suggests that resistant strains have developed. The Biodynamic Research Institute in Darmstadt, Germany, is currently conducting trials with physical and biological methods to combat covered smut. The fungus is transmitted by spores adhering to the grain and safe ways have to be found to remove, inactivate or kill these.

A grain washing plant will remove up to 95% of the spores, depending on intensity. A simple practical method is to wash the seed in a concrete mixer. Subsequent treatment with cattle dung liquor, calcified seaweed and wood ash or fungicidal plant extracts (e.g. mustard or allium oil) will enhance the protective effect. Seed low in vitality is known to have low resistance to fungus attack, and it is advisable to do everything possible to improve seed quality and hence also natural resistance. This is all the more important in view of the fact that infection with covered smut when seedlings are more than 2 cm in length will merely result in latent disease. Seed baths with extracts of medicinal plants (see page 147) and the use of horsetail tea or liquor as recommended by Rudolf Steiner (see pages 78 and 79) are helpful in this respect.

The warm water treatment continues to be indispensable in dealing with loose smut. The method consists in immersing the seed in water at a temperature of 47 °C for two hours, using a thermostat, and then drying it in a cabinet at a temperature not exceeding 33 °C to a moisture level of not less than 15%, or better 16%. This will prevent damage to the ger-

minating power, especially if drilling does not follow immediately.

Row crops

Hoeing was the earliest form of cultivation used when people first began to settle. Using digging sticks and primitive hoes, virgin soil was made sufficiently fertile to grow cultivated plants – mainly palms, bananas, melons, pumpkins, cucumbers and two kinds of tubers: taro and yams. Fields had to be abandoned after a few years and new ones cultivated,* as yields would be getting low. Even today millions of people base their existence on this type of agriculture, most of them in the jungle regions of Africa, Asia and South America.

Sheep and goats were the first domestic animals, probably soon followed by pigs.

These developments generally went hand in hand with a matriarchal society, where women did most of the hoeing in the fields. The development of patriarchal societies brought the domestication and breeding of horses and cattle. Ploughing then became possible, and cereals came to be bred and improved as the great early civilizations evolved.

The row crops, or 'hoed crops' as they are called in German, grown in our latitudes today are potatoes, beet, beetroot, carrot, cabbage, maize for silage and the majority of field vegetables. All give high yields per area, and intensive cultivation means a reduction in weed populations and enhanced mineralization of the nitrogen stores collected by a high volume of leguminous crops. Farmyard manure improves yields even further. Manuring and labour requirements are relatively high. These plants consume much humus; 15–35% of them

*'Cultivate' derives from the Latin *colere*, *cultus* = inhabit, protect, honour with worship (Oxford English Dictionary).

in a cropping sequence will on average deplete dry organic matter by 2–4 t/ha. Labour is required during different periods than for cereals and, providing the proportion is not excessive, row crops help to maintain a balanced work programme.

In biodynamic agriculture in Germany, the most important row crops are:
– potatoes grown for food
– beetroot and carrots for juice and for food
– cabbage for making sauerkraut
– mangels and swedes for fodder and
– field vegetables for immediate sale or winter storage.

Maize for silage is only grown to a limited extent, e.g. to bridge gaps in fodder supply in August and September in a dry year.

Potatoes

The potato (*Solanum tuberosum*) comes from South America, where it has been grown in the High Andes since 3000 BC if not before. The first tubers reached Spain in about AD 1560, but it was not until the 18th century that this crop with its high area yield became the staple food of Europe. Good harvests initially helped with the hunger years that occurred at regular intervals. More and more potatoes were grown, but then late blight (*Phytophthora infestans*) caused potato famine all over Europe. Crop failures due to this were the reason for massive emigration from Ireland to America from 1845 onwards, with a vast reduction in the Irish population.

Before potatoes were introduced, cereals and pulses were the staple diet in Central Europe. It is known that special eating habits have a marked effect on inner development in humans ('you are what your eat'). A diet with a high proportion of meat tends to encourage aggressive tendencies but also heroism and courage. A vegetarian diet usually results in more gentle behaviour but may also lead to fanatical propaganda for specific life styles. Potatoes as a stem element growing in the root region address mainly the nerves and senses, especially the midbrain. An almost exclusive diet of potatoes prepares the ground for materialistic ideas and actions.*

The potato is a member of the nightshade family (Solanaceae) and its reactions to light are peculiar. On exposure to sunlight the green parts of the plant produce the toxic alkaloid solanin. The nontoxic 'fruits', which are tubers and have not arisen through a flowering process, ripen in the dark earth to provide food for humanity. If precipitations of unusual force or cracks in the soil caused by dryness expose these to the light, they too will turn green and become toxic.

Unlike plants that have more of the nature of light in them, above all the cereals, potatoes produce lush vegetative growth, usually a very dark green, of the kind normally only seen in plants that grow in the shade.

They respond quite definitely to intense use of the biodynamic field sprays, especially horn silica, the light mediator.

Soil and climatic requirements. Potatoes are highly adaptable as regards both soil and climate.

Extremely heavy, wet and cold soil conditions are least suitable, whilst loosely structured soils rich in humus that allow air, water and warmth to move as required will encourage growth, health and good yields. High

* Rudolf Steiner, lecture given in Dornach, Switzerland, on 22 September 1923.

pH values (sandy soils above 6.0, good loams above 6.5–6.9) mean increased risk of common potato scab (*Streptomyces scabies*), and liming will increase the tendency.

The haulm is sensitive to low temperatures – it may suffer frost damage even at –1.5 °C – so that frost exposed sites are not really suitable. If late frosts kill the young shoots at a very early stage of development, new shoots will usually grow from dormant eyes and yields may still be good if weather conditions are favourable. It is however not advisable to use plants that have been subject to late frost for seed, for such weakened plant material is more susceptible to degenerative changes. This is also why cultivations carry more of a risk in such sites. Early frosts in autumn on the other hand do not have such negative consequences. Tubers may still make good growth in the milder weather that follows, even if the leaf mass has been much reduced.

Potatoes do well in areas where average daily temperatures are in the region of the 20 °C isotherm. The water requirement only increases at the flowering stage, when the plants need a good, reliable, but not excessive supply.

Preceding crops. Suitable preceding crops are those that leave a well-structured, friable soil with a good root space, above all legumes, and on sandy soils mainly lupins and serradella. When stubble-sown after field crops that clear early, e.g. winter rape, winter barley and winter rye, lupins will show vigorous growth by autumn; they may be used for fodder or, better, allowed to remain over winter, exposed to frost killing and then ploughed in in early

Degeneration is evident from reduced yields, increased susceptibility to pests and diseases and loss of germinative power.

spring. This will give ideal conditions for a good potato harvest. Green manuring also helps to reduce the risk of scab.

More or less the same holds true for Landsberg mixture (see page 216) in areas where a spring furrow is possible. Ploughed-in permanent grassland may also be considered, unless there is a problem with white grub or wireworm. On heavy arable soils, leys of several years make the best preceding crop. As with permanent grassland, ploughing needs to be done in good time in late summer; otherwise harvest residues and root residues hinder cultivation and nitrogen mineralization in spring.

Potatoes are largely self-compatible; the only possible problem with successively grown crops would be black scab or eelworm.

Soil preparation and manuring. Cultivations should aim to give the soil a loose structure. This ensures good growth and clean work with special planting and harvesting implements. Medium and light soils will take a spring furrow, others need to be ploughed in autumn.

For sound, well-flavoured potatoes with good keeping qualities, it is recommended to use 20–30 t/ha of well rotted manure on the preceding catch crop. Experience at Talhof and other farms has shown that a further application of humified composted manure prior to planting helps plant development and reduces susceptibility to late blight and Colorado beetle. The addition of pigs bristles guaranteed free of residues to the composted manure has a positive effect especially on heavy soils, whilst direct application favours fungus and Colorado beetle attack. If the quantity is too large, crop quality is reduced. The same applies to applications of dung or dung liquor liable to force growth, which also affect the flavour.

Seed and planting. Apart from mellow soil, a good preceding crop and appropriate manuring, seed quality is the major factor in growth and yield. Seed potatoes should
– come from well-matured crops,
– be the right shape for the variety,
– weigh between 35 and 60 g, depending on variety,
– have been stored under suitable conditions, either in well made clamps or indoors at temperatures between +2 °C and + 6 °C (a relative humidity of 65–80% will improve keeping quality),
– not have been treated with sprout inhibitor,
– not have sprouted during winter storage and
– be ready to sprout when planted.

Degeneration is more marked with potato than with any other agricultural crop. The term is used to define reduced yields due to increasing deterioration and increased virus susceptibility in home-grown seed. Stunted plants, gaps where seed has failed to sprout, diseases of the stem base and susceptibility to blight increase year by year and rapidly lead to crop failure.

To prevent this, conventional farmers use fresh certified seed annually in endangered areas or every two years on better sites.

The causes of degeneration are in the first place the many modern farming methods that are mainly designed to increase yield. On the other hand potatoes do adapt to a wide range of climatic and soil conditions and this is helped by choice of the right variety. Unsuitable environ-

Healthy planting material can be obtained by growing potatoes from true seed.

mental conditions will however weaken their vitality and constitution in the long run. It is also possible that breeding for resistance to black scab has increased susceptibility to viruses. This susceptibility originates from a single scab-resistant variety with which all other varieties were crossed in the 1930s.

The real cause is probably consistent omission of the sexual phase, i.e. growing the potatoes by vegetative propagation for generations.

The potato is an annual. The true seed produces remarkably delicate small plants with a single shoot and relatively vigorous root growth, developing tubers the size of hazelnuts. It needs two years of vegetative propagation to produce potato haulms and tubers of normal size. With vegetative propagation, on the other hand, the reserves of the parent tuber give rise to vigorous young plants with multiple shoots and a limited root system.

Healthy planting material can be obtained by growing potatoes from true seed.

Asked what could be done to improve the regenerative powers of potatoes, Rudolf Steiner told Ernst Stegemann to use a special chitting technique. The method is as follows. Mark plants in the field that show healthy, vigorous growth and harvest these separately (plant selection). Discard any tubers that are bad or show rot and store the rest in a separate clamp or place. Three or four weeks before the ideal planting date, the eyes are cut. Use only fully de-

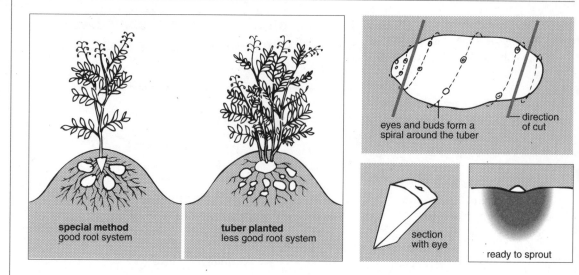

eyes and buds form a
spiral around the tuber

direction
of cut

section
with eye

ready to sprout

special method
good root system

tuber planted
less good root system

Fig. 63.
Special chitting
method to improve
potato seed.

veloped single eyes that are well apart from others and have not yet started to sprout. Cut off the heel and rose ends of the potato. Leave only the minimum of tissue around the eye, but enough to prevent it from drying out completely. Care must be taken not to damage the bud as this would increase susceptibility to blackleg (*Erwinia carotovora*) and stem canker (*Rhizoctonia solani*). Wedge-shaped sections with the bud at the wider end are the best.

Mix with wood ash and fine siliceous sand and spread out flat in a well-lit place that is frost-free but not too warm. The buds need to come to the point where they are ready to sprout, producing 2–3 mm long sprouts in the light. If planting has to be delayed, an application of horn silica made in the morning will inhibit further sprouting.

The seed baths are given as follows: the first one about fourteen days, the second one about seven days and the third two days before the planned planting date. Valerian and oak bark have proved more effective with chitted potatoes than birch pit concentrate. Keeping the

potato material moist for the week preceding planting will specifically stimulate root growth.

Make the rows with the planting machine and place the eye pieces by hand so that they lie flat, with the bud on top. Potatoes chitted by this method tend to produce large single tubers; reducing the distance in the row to 15 cm counteracts the tendency, so that you get evenly medium-sized potatoes. The distance between rows is the usual 62.5 cm, or 75 cm with larger tractors. With chitted material, development is slightly delayed compared to whole potatoes. In the right weather conditions the plants soon develop a vigorous root system, but herbaceous growth from the single compact shoot lags behind right into July. The active growth that follows generally produces vigorous, well-developed foliage so that the whole field looks a lighter green. Unless attacked by frost, the haulms persist longer in autumn. Ripeness is assessed by checking the firmness of the skin of the tubers.

During the period of active growth, two or three passes are made to remove all degenerated plants, putting these in a separate compost heap for use on permanent grassland only. Tubers from well-developed plants are selected to provide planting material for the next year. The rest are used to grow potatoes for food. Potatoes selected from 1/100 ha and chitted by the above method provide material for planting c. 1/10 ha. The yield from this provides the seed for 1 ha of table potatoes.

With more plants/ha and the rose and heel ends cut off, the method does not give a saving in seed material, and it is also very labour intensive. Potatoes grown from seed produced by this method will sometimes have a more earthy taste.

The method is designed to provide healthy seed that is not subject to degeneration. It should not be used for any other purpose.

Seed not set aside for special chitting is also taken from store about four weeks before planting and spread in a well-lit place that is frost-free but not too warm (c. 12–14 °C). Under these conditions the tubers shrivel and dormancy ends more quickly. The metabolic processes that precede sprouting – increasing conversion of sugar, cleavage of starch, degradation of inhibitors and rising concentration of growth hormones – are stimulated in the bud region, and compact sprouts develop in the light. The tubers are getting ready to sprout. As a result of this treatment, a satisfactory number of buds will sprout, something not even achieved with relatively low soil temperatures.

Seed baths, used as above, support these processes and also stimulate root growth.

The optimum number of plants/ha is considered to be 50,000. With rows 62.5 cm apart, this means a distance of 30–32 cm in the row. The distance needs to be shorter with smaller tubers grown for seed and longer if larger potatoes are to be grown for food. Depending on the weight per tuber, this gives a seed requirement of 1.75–3 t/ha.

Soil preparation should be such that weed control is on the whole complete 4–6 weeks before planting.

Planting depth is 5–10 cm, and should be as consistent as possible to avoid losses on clearing. A thin but complete cover of earth protects from frost and helps the soil to warm up. In heavy soils and with late planting, the tubers should be planted less deeply.

Cultivations. Post planting cultivations aim to maintain a loose, friable soil and build ridges that are as even as possible. Weed control needs to continue until the plants cover the ground in each row and are able to keep the soil friable and weeds at bay on their own.

Prior to emergence, alternating or combined use of ridging tool and weed harrow has proved effective; mechanical hoeing follows later. Cultivations need to get progressively more shallow as the crop develops, to avoid inhibition of growth through damage to the fine roots. A weed harrow (chain harrow) is sufficiently flexible to adapt to the ridges; working shallowly, it gives intense crumb formation and weed control over the whole surface. It may still be used when the plants are hand-high, but there is a risk of virus transmission to injured plants. The problem is largely avoided by fitting a ridge weed harrow unit to the ridging body (ridging weed harrow).

When plant growth is in the more advanced stage, vehicular traffic should be kept to a minimum. Lateral

The special chitting method is designed to produce healthy seed; it is labour intensive and may affect the flavour. The method is therefore not suitable for growing table potatoes.

pressure from tractor wheels compacts the soil in the ridges and this inhibits growth in the tubers. Haulms are more resistant to fungus and insect attack if c. 30 kg/ha of calcified seaweed is dusted on to the leaves. Fungus attacks may be treated with 3–5% sodium silicate (waterglass) or with Bio-S (see pages 79–80).

If Colorado beetles are found, ladybirds may be utilized for biological control. A high ladybird population is achieved by providing habitats for them – woodland, hedges and baulks. Then aphids have to be present to attract the ladybirds to the potato field where they will mate and lay their eggs. The larvae will feed on the eggs of the Colorado beetles that arrive at a later date, greatly reducing the extent of the damage.

In an emergency, with a large Colorado beetle population and too few ladybirds present, Spruzit (liquid or dust) may be used. It is only really effective against the young larvae. (In the UK, Colorado beetle is a notifiable pest.)

Dynamic measures. Potatoes react quite noticeably to dynamic measures. Thus one-sided trends develop if all soil preparation, planting, cultivation and spraying (to stimulate root and tuber development) are done at a root trigon, as determined by the relative positions of moon and zodiac (see Fig. 42). Experiments of this kind done at Talhof farm have shown the following:
1) Stem and leaf development tended to be weak and stunted, so that in spite of a well-developed root system and a good number of tubers per plant, poor assimilation meant that the yield was not satisfactory.
2) Perennial weeds such as bindweed,

couch, thistles and lucerne initially produced only limited aerial growth but extensive root systems. Late summer then brought vigorous growth, little impeded by the limited shade produced by the potato haulms. The result was late weed development in the field.

We therefore do not limit operations to root days
– but also work at leaf trigons during the main period of foliage growth (horn silica sprayed in the morning, hoeing and ridging) and
– at seed and fruit trigons to support the ripening process (horn silica in the afternoon).

Fig. 64 shows a work scheme to illustrate the method.

The scheme merely serves as a general guide. As always, soil condition, plant development and weather conditions are important aspects that must be given prime consideration with every operation.

On sites where there is little risk of degeneration and fungus attack, birch pit concentrate may be used for the seed bath. It will usually give increased yields but also increases susceptibility. The valerian preparation is better on heavy soils, the oak bark preparation if there is a high risk of degeneration and fungus attack. Seed baths should as far as possible be applied at root trigons. In humid climates that encourage prolific growth a single application of horn manure will suffice. Potatoes respond well to frequent applications of horn silica.

In sudden and extreme weather changes, e.g. from hot and dry to damp and warm, horn silica applied on three consecutive days gives good results. This certainly was the Talhof experience in 1983, a dry year. Our

Using a horse for cultivation work avoids compacting the soil and consequent losses in yield.

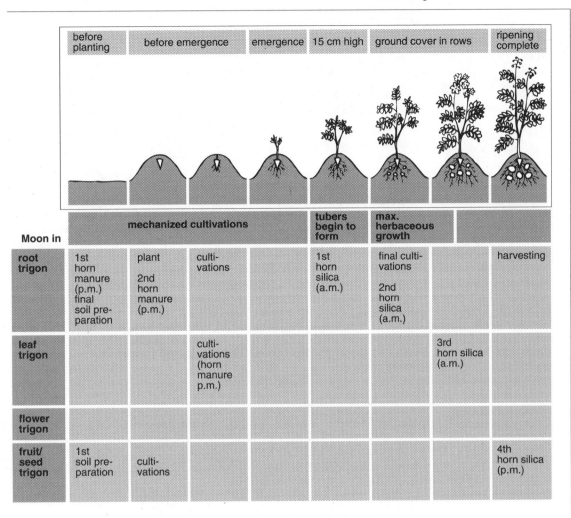

Moon in	mechanized cultivations				tubers begin to form	max. herbaceous growth		
root trigon	1st horn manure (p.m.) final soil preparation	plant 2nd horn manure (p.m.)	culti-vations		1st horn silica (a.m.)	final culti-vations 2nd horn silica (a.m.)		harvesting
leaf trigon			culti-vations (horn manure p.m.)				3rd horn silica (a.m.)	
flower trigon								
fruit/ seed trigon	1st soil pre-paration	culti-vations						4th horn silica (p.m.)

Fig. 64. Sample cultivation schedule for potatoes.

potato crops were completely fungus-free. Colorado beetles did not attack, though on other farms in the area insecticides had to be used repeatedly to get them under control. The biodynamic field sprays should not be regarded as direct control measures; they have an indirect effect by strengthening crops and making them unattractive to pests and diseases.

Horsetail tea is sprayed in autumn and spring on fields intended for potatoes to prevent fungus attacks. Spraying on three consecutive days has proved particularly effective.

If there is a risk of late or early frost, we spray valerian the night before temperatures are expected to go down. Experience has shown that this will prevent damage at temperatures down to –3 °C, or at most –4 °C.

Harvest. Potatoes should only be harvested when the tubers are fully ripe. With most varieties, the moment of ripeness coincides with the withering of the leaves. Blight may cause the haulm to wither and die in just a few days. In that case the tubers need to be harvested as soon as possible; otherwise the infection reaches the tubers and even healthy looking speci-

Potatoes sprayed with horn silica to increase resistance in relation to changes in weather conditions.

In damp warm weather or risk of this, potatoes are sprayed on three consecutive days (always at 7 a.m. sun time). In 1983 this was done three times at Talhof farm.

risk periods		changes in weather conditions:	
	rain mm	max./min. temperature °C	rel. humidity %
1) 7 July	5.9	12.5/27.0	86
8 July	7.1	16.0/27.5	92
9 July	0.0	13.5/30.0	89
2) 20 July	1.8	15.0/26.5	81
21 July	0.0	6.5/23.5	68
22 July	0.0	4.0/29.5	68
3) 9 Aug.	0.0	8.0/27.8	86
10 Aug.	8.8	8.0/28.0	91
11 Aug.	0.2	10.0/25.0	93

Neither leaf nor tuber blight developed. Colorado beetle did not attack.

Table 45. Example of horn silica applications

mens may soon rot when stored.

As already mentioned, plants grown from specially chitted seed stay green longer. In this case the tubers are tested for ripeness. They separate easily from the shoot, the skin is firm, and when a medium-sized potato is cut in half the cut surface is dry.

Potatoes harvested at a root trigon normally keep better, store better and show better dormancy. This has been shown in experiments carried out by Maria Thun. However, if the other criteria – physiological maturity, dry soil and weather conditions – are met, it is not advisable to wait for a favourable moon position at this late season.

After the harvest, potatoes are left to rest and dry for one or two weeks before they are sorted and put into winter storage.

Sugar beet

Sugar beet (*Beta vulgaris* ssp. *vulgaris* var. *altissima*) is not normally grown as a biodynamic crop as it makes tremendous demands as regards soil, climate and manuring. Separate sugar production would also mean making very large deliveries to sugar factories. Because of the physiology of nutrition, there also is no demand for refined sugar from biodynamic sources. The sugar beet required for the manufacture of Demeter Syrup is grown by the method used for fodder beet.

Fodder beet, mangels and swedes

Fodder beet and mangels (*Beta vulgaris* var. *alba*) and swedes (*Brassica napus* var. *napobrassica*) are considered an excellent, palatable succulent feed as part of the winter rations. Being eminently digestible and high energy-yielding, they may be used as a protein balancer in dairying. It has been established that milk protein levels may be enhanced by feeding fodder beet.

Labour requirements are relatively high if no herbicides are used, adding to the peak requirement created by the first cut for fodder. If the fodder beet area is relatively large, therefore, the necessary cultivations may compete with silage cutting and haying. It is wiser not to grow beets if beet cultivation will not leave enough time for the fodder harvest; top quality roughage has absolute priority with cattle. However, even small amounts of beet may be of benefit in so far as they improve the digestibility of the whole ration. Fodder sugar beet makes an excellent addition to the ration for horses and sows.

A wide range of varieties is available so that fodder beet can be grown in almost any soil and climate. Varieties with a larger proportion of root in the soil are more suitable for light, relatively dry soils as they will do better during dry periods. Swedes do particularly well in cooler climates with high humidity, as do fodder beet or mangels, which have a higher proportion of root above the soil; these also do better in heavy soils.

Suitable *preceding crops* are above all long leys and potatoes, as the need for weed control operations is reduced.

Leys need to be ploughed up in good time, producing a deep summer furrow; root residues will then not interfere with hoeing operations and it is possible to have two or three weed clearing operations. If it should be necessary to plough again in autumn, the furrow needs to be shallow to prevent bringing up new weed seed.

Phacelia (California bluebell) may be useful as ground cover and green manure. It is helpful to manure with humified composted manure or well fermented liquid manure before shallow ploughing-in when the plants are about 10–20 cm high.

Fodder beet responds particularly well to one or two applications of dung liquor. The best method is to use a liquid manure drill and make application between rows on slightly damp soil when the plants are at the right stage of development.

When preparing the seed bed in spring it is important
- not to loosen settled top soil, but work it shallowly,
- to take special care to protect the soil water, whatever the operation ,
- to allow as many weeds as possible to germinate and remove them before drilling.

Floats, culti-harrows and seed bed combinations may be used for the purpose.

Spaced drilling (using pelleted or monogerm seed) with the drills designed for that purpose greatly reduces the labour required for subsequent cultivations. Row spacings of 50 cm and within-row spacings of 15–20 cm have proved effective in producing the optimum yield of 80,000–10,000 roots per hectare. Within-row spacing should be reduced where there is a risk of pygmy beetle or wireworm attack.

Depending on soil and weather conditions, the first pre-emergence cultivation is done blind, using a weed harrow, harrow, mechanical hoe or flame weeder. The wheel marks left by the drill provide the necessary orientation. It may sometimes be necessary to use the roll to reestablish soil closure during a dry spell or break up puddled or crusted

Beet and swede cultivation without the use of herbicides competes with silage and hay making; only limited field space is therefore given to these crops.

top crumb.

Subsequent cultivations serve to provide good growing conditions for the crop until ground cover in the rows is complete, and tilth will then be created and maintained in the leaf shade provided by the crop itself. If crops can be kept weed-free until then, late weed growth will normally be prevented right up to harvest time. It is important to see that the upper crumb layer between rows is always kept loose by timely hoeing using angled and duck's foot shares, initially with leaf protectors fitted. This makes it difficult for weed seeds to germinate, whilst the roots of the beet crop are given good growing conditions. In sufficiently humid weather conditions where the soil has plenty of life in it, the soil is covered with a dense felt of fine white rootlets. High yields are achieved in this way and the soil is left in good condition for following cereal crops.

Swedes, and fodder beet, too, are good crops to plant providing there is the prospect of rain when planting is done, or the field can be watered with sprinklers. The method permits full utilization of the good preceding crop effect of a dense winter catch crop of fodder plants (e.g. Landsberg mixture), which leaves the ground weed-free. Soil structure and nitrogen enrichment provide excellent conditions for the seedlings.

The camomile preparation is used as a seed bath for swedes, and birch pit concentrate made up with diluted whole milk for fodder beet. As with potatoes, rhythmical applications of horn silica made early in the morning on three consecutive days strengthen the crop to withstand extreme weather conditions. Pests are usually kept under control by spraying with 24–36 hour old nettle liquor.

Pelleted seed without added fungicides and insecticides is now being developed for single seed sowing.

Beetroot

Like the carrot, beetroot (*Beta vulgaris* ssp. *vulgaris* var. *conditiva*) is important as a food and for health. Raw salads made with beetroot, apples, celeriac and parsnip or beetroot juice increase human resistance to disease. Beetroot juice is much in demand, so that this is an important field vegetable.

Beetroot and fodder beet both belong to the goosefoot family (Chenopodiaceae). The requirements for soil preparation about the same. In a cropping sequence beetroot will still do well if grown as a second crop; potatoes are the best preceding crop. As with other beets, the 'fruit', i.e. the part that is harvested, develops through thickening of the hypocotyl (the part between stem and root), and may store excessive amounts of nitrate (NO_3). Only well rotted composted farmyard manure should be applied directly to ensure good flavour and storage qualities; the method of choice will always be to manure the preceding crop.

For juice production on an industrial scale, beetroot is grown as a main crop, with 4–6 kg/ha drilled in rows spaced at 50 cm, with within-row spacing at 6–10 cm. Drilling is done relatively late, when the soil has warmed up, so that germination and growth will proceed apace. This reduces the period when the young plants are susceptible to damping off (due to a fungus) and pests such as pygmy beetle.

Large roots are required for industrial processing, smaller ones for sale as a vegetable. Smaller beetroot is grown as a second crop after winter catch crops, leeks or lettuce, the within-row spacing being 4–6 cm. In favourable sites beetroot may still be planted after early potatoes, winter rape or vegetable peas. It is important not to remove the root tips as this may delay growth and result in fanginess.

The leaves and the cake left after juicing make a valuable supplementary cattle feed.

Carrots

The carrot (*Daucus carota* ssp. *sativus*) belongs to the family known as the Umbelliferae. Its tradition as a major vegetable crop in Europe and Asia goes back over more than 4,000 years, and it has tremendous importance as a food for young children as well as fodder for young animals.

The intensely coloured root is rich in carotene, indicating that in this plant the 'flowering' and 'fruiting' processes have moved down into the root region, whereas in most plants they take place under the influence of light and heat in the flowering region. All plants produce carotene (vitamin A) under the influence of light in their green parts, but the vitamin is soon broken down again when the plant dries in the sun. In the human and animal organism, carotene is converted to vitamin A if there is sufficient exposure to light. The vitamin is important for good eyesight and for the function of the skin and all mucous membranes. Deficiency may result in night blindness; in animals it may cause fertility problems and increased susceptibility to infections of the respiratory and gastrointestinal tracts such as influenza and diarrhoea.

Carrots grow best in deep, medium and humic soils with an adequate supply of lime.

As to climatic conditions, extended dry periods in spring can be a problem; prolonged droughts in July and

Carrots do best in deep humic soils with an adequate supply of lime.

August, when the tap root is developing to its full extent, may cause deformation. Subsequent rain or the use of sprinklers will sometimes cause the carrots to split. The crop is relatively frost resistant, taking no harm in quite low temperatures in autumn. Mild and warm weather periods in late summer and autumn allow the roots to ripen fully, giving high top quality yields.

Carrots are best preceded by crops that leave the soil loose, with a good crumb and largely weed-free. Potatoes are good, as are cereals that can be cleared early, so that further weed control operations are possible after harvest. On heavy clay, carrots can be grown after a long ley, providing this is ploughed in sufficiently early.

Direct manuring has an adverse effect on the quality of the crop, which assimilates nutrients easily. The only exception is fully humified composted horse manure; up to 20 t/ha will give high yields, sound plants and top quality. Apart from this, manuring should be limited to the preceding crop.

Cultivations aim to prepare a firm seed bed, with garden-fine tilth at the surface, free from subsoil and underground consolidation. Although seedlings are well able to withstand late frosts, it is advisable to drill late – in the second half of April but no later than mid-May, as the roots may not ripen completely with a later drilling date. Final preparation after use of a seed bed combination or the like consists in a pass with the roll; this will make hoeing easier at later stages. Field crops for food are drilled in rows spaced at 35–50 cm, using about 2 kg seed/ha; with carrots for industrial processing, rows spaced at 50 cm and a maximum of 1.5 kg/ha have been found ideal. Damage due to pressure from tractor wheels is best avoided by spacing rows further apart where the wheel tracks are. Fanginess is increased in areas where spring cultivations have consolidated the soil.

Precision seed drilling with pressure wheels will permit blind cultivations and make crop cultivation easier.

The seed frequently takes three or four weeks to germinate. Seed baths with birch pit concentrate shorten this period by about a week. It then takes several weeks until inter-row ground cover is complete, with the seedlings highly sensitive to competition from weeds. Pre-emergence weed control is essential, flame weeding being highly effective. Implements may be suitably combined to effect blind harrowing and flame weeding in one pass immediately before emergence. Crusts should not develop, as they tend to break up on hoeing and move sideways, damaging seedlings even if protectors have been fitted.

Further cultivations start as soon as the seedlings appear. Machine hoeing comes first, working as close to the rows as possible, with protectors fitted. It is followed by hand weeding. Quick and efficient work will usually win the battle against wild plants. As the crop grows, rows are ridged slightly by putting the duck's foot shares at an angle. Less of the root then shows above ground and carrot flies have less opportunity to deposit

Fig. 65. Cultivations required at different stages of plant growth for carrots.

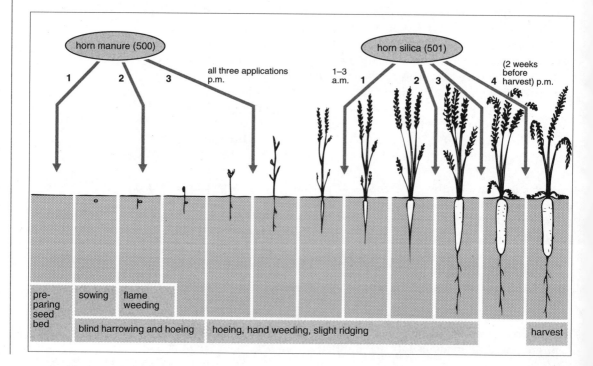

their eggs. Singling has its dangers for this very reason. Ridging also prevents the tops of roots from greening.

The first application of horn silica is made when the foliage is about hand high and the root begins to thicken. Before that, horn manure is applied two or three times. Two or three more applications of horn silica before the rows close up will enhance the sweet and delicate flavour of the roots. Further applications made in the mornings may cause hardening and bitterness. In early autumn, when the roots develop their main bulk, horn silica is sprayed in the afternoons about six weeks and then again three weeks before the proposed harvesting date. This helps the roots to ripen fully in a balanced way, improving nutritional value, flavour and keeping quality.

White and red cabbage

Cabbages, like swede and rape, belong to the large, widespread and vigorous crucifer family (Cruciferae). White and red cabbage (*Brassica oleracea* var. *capitata* f. *alba* and f. *rubra*) are the most likely to be grown as field crops. Lactic fermented cabbage, sauerkraut, is particularly important in human nutrition. It is digestible and promotes health and vitality.

Cabbages are generally considered to be rather indigestible, putting a strain on the metabolism. This is not the case, however, with cabbages grown as part of a rich and varied cropping sequence, using balanced manuring techniques that will not force growth and regular applications of biodynamic field sprays. Again and again we have found that customers who had found cabbage quite

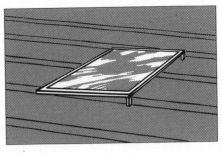

Fig. 66. A piece of glass put over the rows after sowing accelerates germination.
Method of finding the right time for pre-emergence flame weeding.

indigestible before keep coming back for Demeter quality cabbages and sauerkraut, having found them perfectly digestible and highly palatable.

White cabbage requires about he same kind of soil and climatic conditions as swedes, except that more moisture is needed. Red cabbage is more exacting with regard to soil quality and prefers a milder climate.

All crops are suitable as preceding crops except for members of the crucifer family, which are subject to the same pests and have similar requirements.

Vegetable seed of biodynamic origin is frequently superior to conventionally produced seed. Crops will be healthier and more resistant, and this applies particularly to cabbage seed.

Seedlings for main crops are best grown in the field intended for the crop itself. Spacing the rows 50 cm apart permits machine hoeing and produces strong, resistant plants. A well developed main stem acts as a water reservoir. Planting is done in a well prepared, weed-free field; once the plants have come upright, a mechanical hoe may be used, creating slight ridges. One or two more passes in which the ridging is increased will make hand hoeing largely unnecessary.

Cabbages grown for storage are best given individual spacing of 33 by 75 cm. This reduces leaf damage and allows cultivations to be done also at a relatively late stage. Yields will be no less than with narrower spacings.

Much can be learned from the way pests have been dealt with at Dottenfeld Farm (Dottenfelder Hof):

No action needs to be taken with aphids if there is a good *Trichogramma* wasp population and the crop is in good condition. Care should be taken, however, to overcome the inhibition of growth that has given rise to the attack, e.g. by using sprinklers to overcome dryness. Occasional stunted plants will retain sufficient aphids to provide food for the parasites and prevent a further massive attack.

1976 was a dry year when approximately every plant in a 1.5 ha field had two sets of cabbage white eggs. The resulting caterpillar population was horrendous, eating away the leaves from the margins. When the caterpillars were about 2 cm long, every single one died – they had been attacked by the wasp. The harvest was good, yielding top quality cabbages.

Massive attacks from cabbage fly, cabbage flea and cabbage stem weevil on young plants need treatment with Spruzit (see page 104); older plants are not threatened by them. Pests often prefer nearby crucifers such as charlock and pennycress and will only move on to the vegetable crop following their removal.

Timely applications of freshly made nettle tonic will increase crop resistance and inhibit the development of the pests.

Clubroot, a fungus disease (*Plasmodiophora brassicae*), may cause serious losses. The only way of combating this is to keep crucifers well apart in cropping sequences and make sure the soil has sufficient lime (pH not less than 7). The fungus attacks all crucifers and may persist for years on the arable weeds belonging to the family.

Legumes

All pulses belong to the pea family (Leguminosae), the 12,000 species of which grow in all parts of the globe. 20–30 species are grown as agricultural crops in Europe.

Pulses have always been important providers of protein for both humans and animals. Vetches and lentils are known to have been in existence as early as 4,000 BC. In the Old Testament we have the story of Isaac's son Esau selling his rights as the first born to Jacob for a dish of lentils. Diocles (a 4th century BC Greek physician) and Hippocrates wrote that the hyacinth bean or lablab black bean (*Dolichos lablab*) was widely eaten in Italy. This bean still provides the basic protein for people and animals today in many parts of India, South America and Africa. It contains sufficient lysine (an essential amino acid) to prevent protein deficiency diseases. Other types of beans and lentils and peas also serve as foods.

Legumes have the important ability to fix atmospheric nitrogen through nodule-producing bacteria that live in symbiosis with them (*Rhizobium*). They are known as 'nitrogen accumulators'. They are also well able to dissolve soil minerals, thus leaving a topsoil rich in available nutrients for the following crop. The pea family are therefore classified as nitrogen assimilators and enrichers as well as nutrient processors, compared to most other plants which consume and

Cabbage seed for field-grown crops is sown at row spacings of 50 cm to permit mechanical hoeing and produce strong, resistant planting material.

reduce both nitrogen and mineral stores.

The most important grain legumes are the following large-seeded species:

  peas (*Pisum*)
  vetches (*Vicia*)
  vetchling (*Lathyrus*)
  lupin (*Lupinus*)
  beans (*Phaseolus*)
  lentils (*Lens*)
  soya beans (*Glycine*)

They are grown for grain to produce pulses for human consumption and animal fodder and as green fodder or green manure, sometimes as main, but generally as catch crops.

Small-seeded legumes are major field fodder plants, together with grasses and members of the crucifer family, with some of them also extremely valuable in leys:

  lucerne/alfalfa (*Medicago*)
  clovers (*Trifolium*)
  birdsfoot trefoil (*Lotus*)
  serradella (*Ornithopus*)
  sainfoin (*Onobrychis*)
  melilot (*Melilotus*)

Peas

Both garden peas (*Pisum sativum*) and field peas (*Pisum arvense*) are grown, the first mainly as a vegetable but also for large-grain fodder grain, the second mainly as green fodder and green manure and to produce fodder grain. Many different varieties are available so that the right kind can be found for almost any site. Peas grow best in mild sites rich in humus and in warm places with medium soil. Clays and loamy sand with good lime and humus levels are still just possible for peas; heavy clay, lean sandy and low-lime boggy soil are not suitable. Field peas in-

Legumes are able to enrich the soil with nitrogen from the atmosphere fixed by nodule-producing bacteria on their roots.

clude some less demanding varieties, such as the grey pea, which will also give reasonable results in less desirable sites, providing there is sufficient lime.

Field peas are also less demanding concerning climate. Peas generally like dry, warm sites best and need adequate moisture when flowering in May or June. Very high temperatures and drought prevent the seed from setting; more than half the flowers may wither and drop off. The plants cope well with occasional late frosts; prolonged cold spells in spring with frequent night frosts will however seriously delay and inhibit growth. It is better to drill later in such areas, though generally speaking drilling should be done quite early.

A camomile seed bath is highly effective. It accelerates germination and the development of root nodules. Repeated field trials have shown that plants from untreated seed are slower to develop and have fewer nodules.

The more demanding varieties produce less foliage and therefore need better weed control. They give better yields when following on row crops, potatoes or root crops than on cereals. Crops preceded by weed-free cereal crops and a crucifer family summer catch crop may however give equally good yields.

Crucifers and peas help one another. Some added mustard (*Sinapis alba*, 0.7 kg/100 kg peas) provides excellent support for peas. The mustard seed is only mixed in each time the hopper is refilled during drilling, otherwise it will separate. All one has to do is sprinkle it over the peas; it will mix in on its own.

A good seed bed is important, with the first weed generation removed before drilling the peas. Depending on vigour and local conditions, rows are spaced 20–30 cm apart. Depth of drilling depends on the size of the seed – about 3 cm for small seed and up to 8 cm for larger ones. It is possible to put the peas in deeper if there is a risk of pigeons or crows eating them, and this also makes subsequent cultivations easier. Depending on growing conditions, 700–900 times the thousand grain weight (TGW) is drilled

$$(e.g. \frac{300 \text{ g TGW} \times 800}{1,000} = 240 \text{ kg/ha}).$$

Too little seed will mean gaps in the field.

Peas are relatively slow to develop and need special attention (competition from weeds). It is generally helpful to use a light harrow until the peas are 10 cm high and a mechanical hoe after this. Once the peas begin to develop tendrils further cultivation operations would cause damage.

On difficult sites it has proved useful to add peas to cereals rather than grow them on their own. Add about 20 or 30 kg/ha of peas to the normal amount of oat, wheat or rye seed. The main crop will give the usual yield, and an appreciable number of peas are an extra gain. In unfavourable sites the method will at least produce sufficient pea seed for green manuring and fodder. A helical grader will separate the peas from wheat and rye.

Peas and field beans grown for grain provide good farm-grown protein to add to the winter rations for dairy cows.

The valerian preparation will markedly improve flowering capacity and therefore yields. It is sprayed the first time when the plants are 10–20 cm high and a second time just before flowering.

The varieties now available ripen evenly and are therefore all suitable for combine harvesting. Sufficient peas are generally dropped to produce a good green fodder or at least green manure crop to follow. Even a heavy dew will cause the seeds to swell up; it is therefore advisable to bring in the straw quickly and work the stubble with a disk harrow or other suitable implement.

In a favourable climate peas may be followed by winter rape, winter barley or winter wheat. A successful pea crop will leave them a clean, fertile soil with good crumb structure.

Field beans

Field beans (*Vicia faba*) need more water but are not as dependent on warmth as peas. Sites with high atmospheric humidity and deep, well structured soils are ideal. This crop has poor tolerance for heat during the flowering period. Black bean aphid is liable to attack as well, reducing yields even further. Two applications of valerian will help with flowering.

Well-rotted composted farmyard manure applied in early autumn after the preceding crop (generally cereals) will enhance the development and preceding crop value of the beans. Early maturity and timely clearance – not always possible – provide good conditions for winter wheat as a following crop.

Drilling is done as early as possible at a depth of 6–10 cm, depending on size. Rows spaced at 25–35 cm permit mechanical hoeing, with the crop responding well to this. Post drilling cultivation until the plants are 15–20 cm high is done with harrow and weed harrow, moving at a speed to suit the stage of development and soil conditions. As already mentioned, there is a risk of late weed development, as the lower leaves die off during the relatively long time the seeds need to mature. About 10% of fodder peas added to the seed provide the necessary ground cover and prevent weed growth.

Vetches

Common vetch (*Vicia sativa*) is mainly grown for green fodder. The grain can be used for feed but the grain yield is too low to make this really worth while. The crop is less demanding than field bean and pea but sensitive to dry periods, which may result in a poor crop. On the other hand it does do well even on tough clayey soils.

Growing for grain is best done together with late maturing oats, beans and oats, or spring wheat. 120 kg/ha of vetches and 60 kg/ha each of beans and oats have proved a useful mixture. Varieties should be chosen that mature all more or less at the same time. Seed required for growing fodder can be added (10–20 kg/ha) to oats of spring wheat. Vetches tend to ripen unevenly and it is therefore helpful to windrow as soon as the lower pods begin to turn brown. Leave to dry for a day and turn carefully before picking up with the combine the next day. The grain usually needs additional drying (risk of mould attack).

Hairy vetch (*Vicia villosa*) and Hungarian vetch (*Vicia pannonica*) are grown mainly as winter catch crops.

Lentils

The lentil (*Lens culinaris*) is generally considered the finest of the pulses. Large-seeded varieties grow best in light to medium soils or in shallow soil on limestone parent material. Lentils do not tolerate the wet well and do better in warm, dry weather, especially from flowering to maturity. They are highly sensitive to competition from weeds, which is why they are often grown after potatoes – sometimes mixed with early maturing spring barley. 100 kg seed/ha is combined with 60 kg/ha of spring barley; with lentils only one needs 150 kg/ha. Spacing between rows is 18–20 cm, depth 3–5 cm. Weed control is necessary before and immediately after drilling. Lentils do not tolerate harrowing or weed harrowing once they have emerged. Before the young plants begin to entwine, a pass is made with the mechanical hoe. Lentils can be windrowed like vetches; they are turned and only picked up with the combine when fully ripe.

The camomile preparation has proved most effective as a seed bath, as with all legumes. Lentils and vetches are treated with valerian by the method given above for peas.

Healthy lentil straw harvested when dry is approximately equal to medium quality hay in its value as animal fodder.

Lupins

Distinction is made between bitter and sweet (low in bitter compounds) lupins. Bitter lupins can only be used for green manuring. They do not make suitable fodder because all parts contain the bitter compound lupinidine. The most important species are yellow lupin (*Lupinus luteus*), blue lupin (*L. angustifolius*)

Small-seeded field bean varieties may also be used in green fodder mixtures.

and white lupin (*L. albus*). Sweet lupins provide highly palatable green fodder and protein-rich feed grain. All varieties have long tap roots and are therefore used as a pioneer crop for light soils (white lupins also perform this function in heavy soils). Soil fertility is given a long-lasting boost, and lupins make the ideal preceding crop for cereals, row crops and above all potatoes. They do require a fairly warm climate, otherwise development tends to be delayed in the early stages. Lupins tolerate late frosts with temperatures down to –3 or –4 °C.

During germination and at the juvenile stage lupins need adequate moisture; they are drought-proof once the tap root has fully developed. Dry weather is desirable for the flowering period. Blue lupins need some atmospheric humidity even then, otherwise some of the flowers will drop. Sites more than 300 metres above sea level are not suitable for seed production.

Yellow lupins prefer light sandy soils and are highly sensitive to lime. The pH should not be less than 4.3, however.

Blue lupins are slightly more exacting, with seed production requiring soil of the same quality as that needed for oats; sensitivity to lime, on the other hand, is slightly less.

White lupins definitely need better quality soil such as clay or loess. They are more tolerant of lime than other lupins but also will not grow in weathered limestone soil. In the central European climate white lupin seeds ripen very late, if at all, compared to end of July to early August for blue and middle to end of August for yellow lupins.

With initial development slow, the field must be free of perennial weeds. Annual weeds can be controlled with harrow and weed harrow after drilling.

The amount of seed required is 150–180 kg/ha for yellow varieties, 160–200 kg/ha for blue, and 200–250 kg/ha for white lupins. The depth should be not more than 4 or 5 cm as the cotyledons are brought above ground and therefore do not tolerate being covered too deeply. Germinating power tends to be on the poor side (hard seed coat), so that a germination test is essential. Rows spaced at 20–30 cm have proved effective.

Mechanical hoeing starts as soon as rows of seedlings are visible, using protectors and repeating the operation as required until the lupins cover the soil. Later on the dense crop will suppress weeds completely.

Lupins are self-pollinating, though yellow varieties also tend towards cross pollination. Care must thus be taken when growing for seed that no other variety is growing nearby, especially no bitter lupins (not even for green manuring). The first time lupins are grown the seed needs to be inoculated with bacterial cultures (*Bacterium rhizobium lupini*). Damage by game tends to be high in fields close to woods where the game population is high. It may prove necessary to put up fencing. The pods of modern varieties are burst-resistant so that a combine may be used for harvesting. Further drying will be necessary.

Miscellaneous crops

Winter rape

In conventional farming, winter rape (*Brassica napus* var. *napus*) is considered a good cleaning crop in crop-

Adequately wilted, lupins mixed with oats and peas provide valuable silage material.

ping sequences with a high proportion of cereals. It leaves an excellent crumb structure and is one of the best preceding crops for wheat.

Rape oil of biodynamic origin has only a very small market, which is why rape is limited to a few particularly suitable sites and to large farms. The information given below comes from a large farm in the Cologne/Aix-la-Chapelle bay.

Rape is very demanding with regard to cultivation, climate and manuring. It needs to achieve considerable growth very early in the year, before biological activity starts in the soil. Rape is therefore considered a difficult crop. Suitable preceding crops are legumes, one or two year leys, or peas grown for grain. Rape grown after cereals requires plenty of composted manure to which commercially available organic fertilizers such as pigs bristles has been added. This is not advisable, however, as the use of such compost is apt to result in massive pest attacks, with serious damage caused by rape flea, aphids and blossom rape beetles.

The seed bed needs to be prepared at least four weeks before drilling to allow the ley turves to rot down sufficiently. An early second cut and an application of composted manure (15–20 t/ha) are followed by shallow rotavation and later by grubbing. Repeated applications of Maria Thun's cowpat preparation enhance the conversion activity in the soil.

On parabrown earths of soil number 90 drilling may be done immediately after ploughing, with packer, and fine seed bed preparation, the seed having been dusted with wood ash to prevent rape flea damage.

Development tends to be rapid, so that three applications of horn silica can be made in autumn, always in the

Rape is an exacting crop as regards cultivation, climate and manuring.

early dew.

If there are many weeds whilst the rape is in the early growth stages, these are easily removed by mechanical hoeing in rows spaced 30 or 40 cm apart. Later the crop will suppress all weeds including thistles, since it is cut while still at the flowering stage, using a windrow combine. A seed furrow for the following stubble-sown catch crop enhances the effect.

Blossom rape beetle (*Meligethes aeneus*) may attack in spring. The local climate is mild, with winter rape coming into flower early, so that there is little damage. Flowering will be more rapid if there are sufficient beehives placed on the baulk; the beetles generally disappear soon, and increased yields may be expected. After a one-year ley as preceding crop, yields of erucic acid free varieties are in the region of 2.4 t/ha, after a two-year ley about 2.8 t/ha.

Summer rape generally yields about 0.5 t/ha less. Flowering is later so that blossom rape beetle is often a problem. Summer rape is not to be recommended therefore, or at least only for fodder.

Flax

Linseed is important in the rearing of young stock, as a feed for horses and a medicine. Flax (*Linum usitatissimum*) is therefore a useful crop for home consumption.

Linseed is grown from special varieties that require less moisture than flax grown for fibre. They like a fairly warm climate and grow in almost any kind of soil except on poorly drained or extremely lean sites. Deep loams are best in dry regions.

Varieties grown for fibre need a good water supply and a weed-free field; otherwise cultivations have to be frequent. Flax harvesters do not function well if the crop includes many weeds.

Both types of flax will grow after any preceding crop, but row crops are best for flax grown for fibre because they leave the field clean. For good quality fibre the flax needs to be densely grown, and after legumes there is a definite risk of the crop becoming lodged. Legumes are therefore better before flax grown for linseed.

The seed bed must be of garden quality and firm. Drilling is done at a depth of 2 or 3 cm in the first half of April. An old saying is that flax needs to be drilled on the 100th day of the year (10 April) and can be pulled on the 200th (20 July). Rows are spaced at 12 cm, up to a maximum of 18 cm; 18–25 cm for linseed. Flax grown for fibre needs 120–150 kg seed/ha (ideally 2,000 plants to the square metre), linseed 70–100 kg/ha (1,000 plants to the square metre).

The only suitable manure is humified composted manure, preferably made with horse manure. It is spread at the end of the winter and worked in shallowly when preparing the seed bed. This will accelerate development in the early stages and avoid the risk of the crop becoming lodged or being seriously attacked by flea beetles.

Linseed from crops given heavy applications of mineral nitrogen may produce traces of prussic acid when made into a decoction to feed young stock; only biodynamically or organically grown linseed should therefore be used.

Cultivation is limited to one or two passes with the mechanical hoe for linseed. Fibre varieties need hand hoeing in addition, and later on tall weeds liable to be a nuisance have to be pulled by hand. Hoeing operations must be finished by the time the plants reach a height of 20 cm.

Linseed is combine harvested when dead ripe. The straw may be used to produce coarse linen goods like sacking or oakum. Fibre varieties have to be pulled, either by hand or, in larger fields, by machine. The stems should be a yellowy green at this time, the lower leaves dead and the upper ones yellowed. Seed maturity is immaterial in this case.

Special care is needed with seed baths, as linseed will easily go mucilaginous if wetted. Fibre-producing varieties are treated with yarrow, linseed-producing ones with valerian. In this particular case cold rather than warm water is used (2 litres/100 kg) and the bath is applied in split doses. Spray the seed first with one third of the required amount, ten minutes later with the second and fifteen minutes later with the third third, gently turning the seed with a shovel between treatments. It is definitely worth the effort to achieve more rapid development and healthier and more resistant plants.

Horn manure is applied when drilling and before or during one pass with the mechanical hoe; horn silica is sprayed when the plants are 25 cm high, when buds are fully developed and after flowering.

Valerian is sprayed just before buds begin to form, as with all flowering plants.

Linseed yields are 1.5–2 t/ha. The harvest from about 0.1 ha is sufficient for about 15 calves.

Grazing is the healthy, species-spe- 20
cific form of animal husbandry.
Dandelion provides a palatable
feed for cows in spring (19). All the
cows in the pasture take an interest in the new-born calf (20). Red
clover is resistant to treading and
grazing and provides such a good
feed that the cows take no notice of
the photographer (21). When rearing young bulls, daily exercise is
important for the proper development and position of the limbs.
Appetite and the senses are stimulated.

22

23

24

25

Tethered housing needs to be complemented with daily open-air exercise. 23: Solid-floor yard and roofed lying space with litter. Cows are happy to be there after milking, feeding and on return from pasture. The hen run is a good place for tethering the breeding bull (25 and 27). The healthy chickens in their free runs are happy to keep him company. In winter, loose housing with litter and a yard (26) are suitable for young stock. Hens with chicks need a run where they are protected from wild predators (24).

26

27

Mustard

White mustard (*Sinapis alba*) is one of the oldest cultivated plants and very much a long-day plant. It therefore needs timely drilling to grow for grain, between the end of March and mid-April, though late frosts may cause damage. Later drilling means that the plants come into flower too soon, before they are fully developed, resulting in extremely low grain yields. It is best to wait with stubble-sowing for green fodder until mid-August or later to ensure a long period of vegetative growth when green matter is produced.

Seed rate is 10–12 kg/ha with rows 20–25 cm apart; denser crops will yield less seed.

Manuring, cultivations and seed bath are as for rape.

Mustard grains from plants grown as a support for peas are easily separated out and provide seed for green manure and fodder crops.

Buckwheat

Buckwheat (*Fagopyrum esculentum*) is attractive to bees and deserves brief mention as there is some demand for the grain.

Grain crops will only do well on light or loamy soils. Buckwheat is fast-growing and frost-sensitive, so that drilling at a seed rate of 60 kg/ha is done in mid-May, and in mild, warm climates also after early-clearing cereals up to the end of July. Rows are spaced at 15–20 cm, drilling depth is 3–2 cm.

Cultivation is not necessary as the crop soon covers the ground, suppressing all other plants. Manures apt to force growth should not be used if growing for grain as they encourage vegetative growth at the cost of seed production.

The crop is harvested when the majority of seeds show a certain hardness and the colour of ripeness. This is chestnut brown for the smooth-seeded species (*F. esculentum*) and a uniform grey and brown or greyish black for the rough-seeded species (*F. tataricum*). Harvesting is as for phacelia.

Buckwheat is not grown for fodder because of its fagopyrin content and low volume of greenstuff. Fagopyrin causes fagopyrism in animals, making them sensitive to light.

Stinging nettle

Generally considered a weed today, the stinging nettle (*Urtica dioica*) was widely used in human and veterinary medicine in the past. Nowadays, fresh plants, nettle juice, the dried herb and alcoholic extracts are used
– in medicated feed
– for rearing young stock, especially poultry
– as an additive to dung liquor and in compost production
– as plant liquor to overcome setbacks in crops and for pest control
– to produce the biodynamic compost preparation
– in natural medicine and
– as a health food or vegetable.

Stinging nettle is perennial and its flowers are generally unisexual and on separate plants. Yellow roots, much branched in young plants, less so but thicker in older specimens, give rise to erect pale green or reddish violet square stems. The leaves are in opposite pairs always at a right angle to the preceding pair; they are dark green, hairy, heart-shaped and pointed with toothed margins. In May–October, flowers grow in pseudo-spikes from the upper leaf axils of

Buckwheat is one of the best bee plants.

side shoots.

It would be difficult to find sites and conditions where the stinging nettle does not manage to grow. It also seems to have a particular affinity for human habitations, always growing in the immediate or almost immediate vicinity. Transitional sites are preferred, e.g. the edges of woods, hedgerows, fences, among old buildings and unused machinery, on the banks of streams and ditches, in rubbish dumps and soils rich in nitrogen. These are the places where the plant really thrives.

Boggy and loamy soils rich in nutrients and with adequate moisture are suitable for nettles. Dry sites do not suit.

Nettle seed does not germinate easily and needs below zero temperatures to do so. It is therefore easier to use root sections or mature stolons for vegetative propagation. For relatively large crops, rhizomes may be collected from friable soil in early spring or in autumn using a rotary cultivator or harrow or a cultivator moving at a slow speed. Each is divided into three or four cuttings. Stolons may be up to 60 cm in length and should be cut in sections of not less than 15 cm.

Planting is done by machine or hand, using dibber or trowel, in weed-free friable soil fertilized with manure, partly rotted-down woody material or compost. Space rows to half the width of the tramlines (62.5 or 75 cm), with an inter-row spacing of 50–60 cm, giving c. 25,000 plants per hectare.

Cultivation operations must be done early as stolons will soon sprout. No further cultivation should be done in subsequent years as it may damage the runners that are spreading just below the surface and cause

growth to be delayed.

Long-term crops are fertilized with untreated raw liquid manure, as this meets the special need of nettles, which like to change chaotic soil conditions liable to lead to forced growth into a balanced good crumb state. It is not advisable to use fresh farmyard manure containing a high percentage of straw, as unrotted straw will get mixed up with the harvested nettle material and cannot be separated out.

Nettles are highly sensitive to compacted soil and to the pressure from tractor wheels when cultivations and manuring are done on soft, wet ground.

Utilization begins in early spring. Fresh shoots may be eaten as a vegetable and used to make tea and juice for 'spring cures'. Nettles are ready for cutting for medicinal use when the leaves are fully developed. The flowering plant is dried for medicated feed and used to make the biodynamic preparation.

Large areas are harvested with available mowers. A double knife bar set none too low is best for rapid aftermath and a good quality cut. Rotary windrowers have proved useful for careful windrowing of the plants which have been allowed to wilt only slightly and are 120–180 cm long, and for loading them on to trailers. Warm or hot air drying is the only method of preserving relatively large quantities without losses. The field must be level and stone-free to avoid contamination of the product and making it unsaleable.

Depending on site and weather conditions, two or three cuts may be made a year. The nettles lose their vigour after four to six years. Dandelion and white clover, too, may spread. The crop is no longer mar-

See also pages 84 and 85.

ketable but still provides good supplementary feed for the farm animals.

The average annual yield is 5,000
kg/ha of dried nettles for sale.

Fodder crops

As stated in the chapter on grassland
management, efficiently cultivated
and manured meadows and pastures
provide the ideal basis for supplying
farm animals with a rich and varied
diet. Fodder crops are equally important as they
– provide the additional feed
  required and thus meet protein
  requirements,
– take over the function of
  permanent grassland on entirely
  arable farms,
– suppress and control weeds and
– maintain and improve soil fertility
  (humus levels).

Legumes meet these requirements
particularly well. They provide well-
structured roughage, give high protein yields and also increase soil nitrogen levels. Long leys also provide
fine grass roots and are the only certain method of increasing the permanent humus level in soils. This offers
ideal conditions for commercial
growing of row crops, cereals and
other crops.

If the soil and the climate are right,
fodder can be largely grown as catch
crops, so that less of the available
arable land is needed to grow fodder
as a main crop.

The available range of fodder
plants is large, so that suitable
species and varieties can be found for
all soils and climatic conditions.
Lupin and serradella are particularly
suited to very light soils, Alsike
clover to damp, heavy soils, and
birdsfoot trefoil with meadow fescue

Meadows and pastures provide the ideal basis for supplying farm animals with a rich and varied diet.

to relatively dry sites.

In cropping sequences, perennial
clover-type crops usually follow cereals, whilst fast-growing annual fodder plants are grown as second crops.
Almost all are considered good preceding crops for row crops, cereals
and oil plants as they generally increase humus and nitrogen levels,
improve soil structure and tend to be
deep-rooted.

Within-crop and inter-crop plant
compatibilities require attention, especially with sunflowers, flax, red,
Alsike and black medick, sainfoin
and peas.

Fodder plants are frequently grown
as undersown crops and make special
demands on cultivation in so far as
the seed tends to be small and needs
a fine, firm seed bed; this should be
as free from weeds as possible as
growth tends to be slow in the juvenile stage. In difficult conditions,
open drilling (without cover crop)
may be the best method, as cultivations can then be adapted to the special needs of the crop.

With regard to soil fertility, all fodder plants, with the exception of serradella and yellow and blue lupin,
need dependable supplies of lime and
phosphorus. Non-leguminous plants
(crucifer family, grasses) usually
need high nitrogen levels. Cover
crops grown with legumes may need
timely applications of manure, if possible well rotted farmyard manure.

Seed quality must be high even for
fodder crops. Poor quality results in
incomplete, stunted crops, the nega-

tive effect being particularly marked in long-lived crops. The field will be left in poor crumb, with nutrient levels low, full of perennial weeds, and yields will be low.

Extensive leys with partly bought-in seed will be increasingly fouled with weeds in later years, mainly curled and broad-leaved dock (*Rumex crispus* and *R. obtusifolius*). It is easy to see why farmers are increasingly producing part of their own seed from fodder plants.

In the past, the origin of small-seeded fodder plants was most important, for the provenance had to suit the site to give good yields. 'Franconian lucerne' or 'Wuerttemberg red clover' were widely known for top quality. Propagation for seed would be done in the districts from which the names derive or in sites offering similar conditions. Farmers knew which grew best and gave persistently good crops in which location.

Drilling technique also adds much to the result. Fodder plants are given a good start by suitable cover crops, especially cereals, for stubble of reasonable length provides cover from drying winds, strong sunlight and impact from heavy rain.

Cereals suitable as cover crops are listed below in order of preference (Renius 1978).

Winter crops
1) Rye provides the best conditions as it gives little shade and is harvested early.
2) Wheat is slow to develop in spring and can be harrowed a number of times. This provides a good seed bed and protects the juvenile stages of the undersown crop.
3) Barley tillers in autumn and has

therefore produced dense cover by spring. The risk of lodging is also greatest. The advantage lies in the early harvest.
4) Rape ranks about the same as barley.

Spring crops
1) Early maturing wheat varieties are the best cover crop as they are resistant to lodging, let the light through and are drilled early.
2) Barley needs relatively little water and clears early. The tendency to lodge may be a disadvantage. Vigorous clovers may grow through if drilled too early; drilling should be delayed until the barley is at the four-leaf stage. If this coincides with a regular dry period, another cover crop should be chosen.
3) Oats are perfectly suitable as a cover crop if early maturing, even if they do come last in this list.
   · Growth tends to be dense and this may inhibit the undersown crop. On dry sites, the high water consumption of oats may cause problems, so that clover and oats should be drilled at the same time in this case.

Red and white clover and Alsike do well if drilled early; they may even be drilled into light snow cover, providing the soil is not frozen. Lucerne (alfalfa), black medick and sainfoin need warmer conditions and should not be drilled before the end of March.

Early clearing crops provide the best conditions for oversown crops, especially a mixture of vetches, peas and oats grown for silage.

The following grasses are particularly suitable for autumn drilling with winter cereals. They are listed

For sowing technique, see also pages 124 and 125.

crop	seed rate (kg/ha)	sowing time
Persian clover	15–20 (O)	April
+ annual ryegrass	+ 10–15	
Egyptian clover	30 (O)	end of April/mid-May
+ annual ryegrass	+ 5	
serradella	40	mid-May
red clover	15–20 (20–30)*	spring–August
+ Italian ryegrass	+ 5–25 (15–25)*	
lucerne	15–18	mid-April/mid-August
black medick	20	March–July
Alsike clover	8–10 (3–5)**	spring–August
white clover	10	spring
sainfoin	140–160 (U)	spring
white melilot	20 (U)	spring to early September

O = open sown;   U = undersown   * tetraploid;   ** as part of mixture

in descending order of late drilling tolerance (Renius 1978):

   timothy (*Phleum pratense*)
   creeping red fescue (*Festuca rubra* var. *genuina*)
   meadow fescue (*Festuca pratensis*)
   cocksfoot (*Dactylis glomerata*)

If timothy is drilled early with winter barley, the plants may start to shoot in spring, resulting in loss of yield and problems with harvesting the cover crop. Creeping red fescue may be grown on all soils for green manuring or mixed with timothy and meadow fescue, which is not very competitive, in permanent leys. Timothy grown in a mixture with fescue or cocksfoot needs to be resown in October. Clovers and other grasses and herbs are drilled in spring at an angle of about 35° to that of the winter crop. Any soil preparation that is needed may be done with weed harrow or roll; rolling after drilling is an advantage.

Drilling depth is low with most clovers and grasses, but drilling is still preferable to broadcasting by hand or machine as it ensures that the seeds are covered with a fine layer of soil and seedlings are protected from drying out.

Ridging must be avoided when using a mechanical hoe. The small elevations in the soil present a serious problem when haying and cutting for silage.

Seed baths also benefit small seeds, but some species tend to go mucilaginous. It is therefore necessary to check the seed repeatedly when applying the liquid, using less or discontinuing the operation in case of doubt. When the seed is spread to dry, it may be necessary to turn it more frequently.

Horn manure applications encourage growth to a marked degree and contribute a great deal to the success of undersown and stubble-sown crops.

When horn silica is applied to the cover crop, this must provide sufficient leaf mass to protect the young clover and grass seedlings from

Table 46. Seed rate and sowing times for clover-type fodder plants grown as main crops.

valerian	birch pit concentrate	wild camomile	yarrow
maize	phacelia sunflowers	all legumes marrowstem kale oil radish rape turnip rape mustard turnip	fodder rye grasses

**Table 47.
Seed baths for fodder plants.**

being wetted, as their growth may be inhibited. If this is not possible, the silica preparation should be sprayed at a later date.

Annual clovers

Persian clover (*Trifolium resupinatum*) originated in Iran and Afghanistan; it is only in recent years that it has been more widely grown in our latitudes. It is not winter hardy, but high quality cultivars tolerate late frosts reasonably well. Persian clover does well in soils that have a good supply of lime, but it prefers the better sites.

Rapid and vigorous growth means that whilst not suitable as an undersown crop with cereals it increases the fodder value of green fodder mixtures. Silage from these has an excellent protein/starch ratio which gives it special value as a feed for dairy cattle.

Persian clover grown on its own and cut after full flower is eaten greedily by the animals and will give high milk yields. Feeding young Persian clover on its own is not advisable because of the risk of scouring and bloat. The solution is to mix the clover with fast growing annual rye-grass (*Lolium multiflorum* var. *westerwoldicum*). In sufficiently

warm and wet weather conditions Persian clover can be cut up to five times.

Applications of horn silica when the crop is hand high and about a week before utilization will reduce the risk of bloat and improve growth. Dense crops cut a number of times will suppress creeping thistle and other persistent weeds within one growing year; they also have a high preceding crop value for row crops and spring cereals.

Egyptian clover (*Trifolium alexandrinum*) has similar properties to those of Persian clover. It originates from the Mediterranean region and is sensitive to late frosts. With both species the provenance of the seed is important. Only multi-cut cultivars produced in Europe, mainly Portugal, should be used. Egyptian clover has a lower crude protein and dry matter content than red and Persian clover. Cattle find it palatable, but it is only useful as green fodder.

An early cut encourages aftermath. Weed suppression and preceding crop value are slightly less than for Persian clover.

Serradella (*Ornithopus sativus*) will grow in slightly acid, slightly sandy and almost boggy soils if there is sufficient water. It does not like excessive lime or dry conditions. The varieties grown in our latitudes are sensitive to temperatures below –6 °C and therefore not winter hardy. Undersown or stubble-sown serradella produces tender, non-woody green fodder suitable for soilage, silage, grazing and green manuring.

Mixed with Alsike and white clover and undersown, or with yellow lupin, millet or mustard and stubble-sown, it may be expected to give a good yield.

Perennial clovers

Red clover (*Trifolium pratense*) is used on its own or with perennial ryegrass mainly over a two year period. Timely undersowing with suitable cover crops will usually still allow one good cut in the first year, with two or three cuts the following year.

Very loose (boggy), light (sandy) and poorly drained soils are not suitable. In the right site, red clover gives high yields for a variety of uses. Grown on its own it is mainly used as green fodder. For silage or hay it has proved useful to mix it with Italian ryegrass (*Lolium multiflorum* var. *italicum*). It likes to be shallow sown and is therefore better drilled after the cover crop. In areas with dry periods in spring it needs to be drilled as early as possible, best of all in winter rye.

The best time for mowing is before full flower. Good strong roots will help overwintering. Lush foliage by the beginning of winter, on the other hand, results in winter injury; late utilization is therefore important. The crown from which the shoots grow is drawn close to the soil as the tap root contracts in autumn, so that the plant is well protected in winter. If leaves have been left covering the crown, the plant may begin to rot under snow cover, resulting in missing plants and slow development in spring.

Tetraploid red clover mixed with tetraploid ryegrass is very winter hardy and gives excellent yields. Aftermath capacity even in relatively dry sites, weed suppression and good legume tolerance have made this a popular crop. It grows on well into autumn, which makes it a better preceding crop for spring crops or row crops than for winter wheat. Careful ploughing is needed or it will grow through again, being vigorous and winter hardy, and interfere with the following crop.

Lucerne or alfalfa (*Medicago sativa*; hybrid lucerne = a cross of blue-flowered *M. sativa* and yellow-flowered *M. falcata*), the queen of fodder plants, was called a 'child of the sun' by Rudolf Steiner. In the warm sun of the Mediterranean, in southern France, it allows maximum yields with seven cuts. Protein yields can be very high, twice as high as for red clover, four or five times as high as for oats or a poor meadow.

Ideal conditions are warm, permeable loess, as deep as possible and rich in lime, or warm weathered limestone soils. Lucerne follows a weed-free row crop, either under a cereal cover crop or open drilled.

Yield and the period of utilization depend greatly on the timing and number of cuts. Timing depends on:
– the stage reached by the buds and shoots developing on the root collar (rhizome). These will be the aftermath and must not be cut. Care must be taken therefore not to cut too late or too deep;
– storage of carbohydrate reserves in the root, which happens at full

Red clover will give high yields in most sites except those that are very dry in summer.

flower. The crop should therefore only be cut at this time.

Final utilization in the year should be such that sufficient assimilates can be stored. This means that the last main fodder cut should be done no later than mid-September.

Spring cultivations are harrowing after drilling in the first year and after this grubbing to loosen the top soil, in areas where there is a risk of late frosts after the first cut. In the year when the lucerne is ploughed in, the operation is followed by a drilling of annual ryegrass. The fine roots of this leave a good crumb structure, the lucerne roots having got the middle and subsoil into first class condition. The preceding crop value of lucerne (alfalfa) is enhanced by this method.

Black medick (trefoil) (*Medicago lupulina*) is a species of lucerne but is annual or at most biennial. It demands a lot of lime, but even shallow, cold and stony weathered limestone soils will suffice. As a low-growing species, black medick is mainly undersown for green fodder and green manuring.

Alsike clover (*Trifolium hybridum*) holds a position midway between red and white clover as regards the colour of its flowers and growth characteristics. It nevertheless ranks as a species in its own right. True hybrids of red and white clover are not possible.

Alsike clover will still manage quite well in cold, wet sites where red clover does not thrive. Only dry, lean or hot soils are not suited. Alsike clover is only grown on its own for seed, as yields are low and bitterness makes it unpalatable unless mixed with other fodder. Given to horses, it may cause severe skin in-

flammation.

The most important use is in leys. It is self-compatible and not very susceptible to clover stem rot, which is why it is used in place of red clover in sites where this is at risk.

White clover (*Trifolium repens*) has multiple uses and is highly adaptable. It is essentially a grazing plant and as such persistent; what is more, frequent mowing and grazing actually enhance development.

White clover grows on practically all sites, from wet bogland to dry sandy soils. It does best on fresh to moist sites, but adequate atmospheric humidity will suffice. Here the large-leaved tall varieties of white clover grown with perennial ryegrass (*Lolium perenne*) give high fodder yields. Trials done in England have shown that protein yield was equally high for perennial ryegrass grown with 30% of white clover and no mineral fertilizer and grown without clover and given 600 kg/ha of nitrogenous fertilizer.

White clover is winter hardy, self-compatible and usually grown for three or four years; aerial runners and self-seeding frequently give it almost unlimited persistence.

Crimson clover (*Trifolium incarnatum*) is mainly known as part of the Landsberg mixture (see page 216). It is the fastest growing clover species and ready to cut in spring two or three weeks before red clover if grown for more than a year. Winter damage is frequently due to late drilling (after 15 August) and lack of firmness in the soil.

The species does well anywhere except in extremely wet and cold soils, and in boggy and lean sandy soil.

Birdsfoot trefoil (*Lotus corniculatus*) is an undemanding persistent

Grown in suitable sites and efficiently utilized, a crop of lucerne (alfalfa) will give top quality yields for several years.

legume. It is winter hardy, stands up well to grazing and cutting and tolerates relatively long periods of dryness. It is rarely drilled as a pure crop in Central Europe, probably because local varieties are not suitable for this. On the other hand it is common in pasture and meadow seed mixtures and in ley mixtures for dry sites. Relatively high proportions in a ley ration given to dairy cows will benefit milk fat levels.

A close relative, **greater birdsfoot trefoil** (*Lotus uliginosus*), prefers really damp sites. It merits more frequent inclusion in permanent leys for damp and wet areas, for it is winter hardy, persistent and tolerant of shade. Grown under the right conditions and in sufficiently high proportion it enhances the normally low fodder value of such leys because of its high protein content.

Sainfoin (*Onobrychis viciifolia*) loves warm, dry calcareous soils. Unlike *O. montana* and *O. arenaria*, which demand a lot of lime, sainfoin is no more demanding than lucerne and will also do well in shallow lime, chalky and marly soil. Even sandy soils will do, providing the subsoil contains marl. The species does not grow in wet, cold and impermeable soils nor in almost boggy ground. It needs less warmth but more light than lucerne, especially when young. Undersown sainfoin will therefore do best if drilled between the rows of the cover crop on the light-well principle, i.e. following emergence of the cover crop which is grown in rows spaced at 25 cm. Sainfoin is sensitive to late frosts in its juvenile stages and is therefore not drilled as an undercrop until after the beginning of April. Drilled as a pure crop after a winter catch crop on suitable sites it will give good results if drilled as

late as the end of May and beginning of June.

The crop is extremely sensitive to grazing and cutting in the rain or with rain soon following. The hollow stubble rots easily and the whole crop perishes.

Sainfoin has a strong tap root and almost equally strong lateral roots; these branch widely before they also go down, penetrating fissured rock with a dense network of fibrous roots. The plant takes possession of the soil as it combines the properties of widely branching red clover roots and the more deeply penetrating roots of lucerne (Kraus 1914). The roots are reddish brown to sulphur yellow; the woody root bark with its cork layer is well protected from water loss due to evaporation, so that sainfoin is extremely resistant to drought conditions.

Two types are grown. The single-cut, late-flowering type will give one good cut at the end of full flowering and then remain in the rosette stage. The double-cut type flowers earlier and is cut when it begins to flower. It is highly sensitive to premature or late cuts and must be given time to grow between two utilizations. Otherwise vitality and yield will go down and grasses will quickly take over.

Sainfoin provides excellent, palatable fodder, with higher yields than lucerne on soils where lucerne is near its limit.

The crop will persist longer if about 18 t/ha of composted manure are applied every two years. Sainfoin is not merely useful but also truly handsome as a plant. On poor, shallow and stony calcareous ground, the rose pink field, alive with the hum of bees gathering nectar, is a delight to the farmer's eye. It is one of the best

Birdsfoot trefoil cultivars available in the USA give good fodder yields on heavy soil in dry sites not suited to lucerne (alfalfa).

Balanced rations with plenty of variety prevent fertility and other health problems in farm animals.

preceding crops for cereals, grasses, roots and tubers and its very presence in arable land will make all cereal crops more fruitful. Sainfoin should therefore be much more widely grown. Yields may be slightly less than with other legumes, but this is made up for by the beneficial, harmonizing effect on the whole farm.

White melilot (*Melilotus alba*) is a pioneer plant. It improves sandy, shallow and dry soils that have adequate lime by producing a large volume of dry matter and because of its great capacity for dissolving minerals. The high coumarin content means that it cannot be used for fodder, and it also grows woody quite early. It suppresses weeds completely.

Leys

Well managed meadows and pastures are an ideal most easily achieved on arable land with rich mixtures of clovers, grasses and herbs. Apart from high fodder quality, these are also of great benefit to soil fertility.

Unbalanced mixtures, e.g. red clover and ryegrass, or lucerne and false oatgrass, will give high yields, especially of protein, but they will never equal the fodder value of mixtures rich in species. The latter also leave more root residues, with a more lasting effect on soil structure and humus levels,
– due to specific root activities,
– due to differences in ability to dissolve minerals, and
– due to the differences in mineral composition and concentrations in the plant matter which are the result.

Richly varied and well balanced rations are vitally important for farm animals. It has been shown that dairy cattle given unbalanced rations, e.g. lucerne hay and beet and turnip leaf silage, develop fertility and other health problems that are difficult to overcome. Cows allowed to graze in pastures rich in herbs and fed with hay and silage from meadows and leys containing many species have been found to be more fertile and stable in health. Many grassland herbs contain high levels of trace elements that help to prevent deficiency diseases if available in the right proportions. Selected herbs should therefore be added to fodder crop mixtures.

The following points need to be considered when devising clover, grass and hay mixtures:
– soil and climatic conditions, especially water supply during the main period of active growth,
– intended use as pasture, for cutting and grazing, or cutting only,
– intended use as hay, soilage or silage,
– intended period of utilization,
– qualities and requirements of individual fodder plants.

To find out which are the best mixtures for a particular farm, farmers need to have detailed knowledge of the properties and requirements of different plant species and varieties and to make careful observations of wild plants natural to the site.

When a carefully devised mixture has been drilled, development over subsequent years needs to be monitored so that necessary changes may be made to later mixtures, taking account of legume compatibilities. A clover, grass and herb crop should contain about 45% of clover, 45% of grass and 10% of herbs.

With long leys it is important that plenty of good fodder is produced not only in the first but also in later years. Consideration therefore needs to be given to the persistence of the species included and also to their ability to compete against weeds.

Table 48 gives the most important qualities of commonly used grasses.

It is impossible to give standard formulas for suitable mixtures, for every site is different and the number of potential mixtures almost equals the vast variety of sites. Successful drilling therefore depends on an accurate knowledge of local conditions and especially the microclimate. Site adapted plants are chosen that as far as possible are harvest ripe at the same time, mutually compatible, and complementary as regards nutrient requirements, ability to dissolve minerals and root space requirements. They should also provide palatable fodder of rich variety and high nutrient value. The choice is difficult as there are so many varieties. With rich mixtures, the components may be expected to be to some extent complementary. Tables 43, 48, 49 and 50 provide some useful information.

Table 50 gives figures for the relative seed quantities required.

The drilling method is that described in the chapter on re-seeding grassland.

The duration of a ley determines the extent to which permanent soil fertility is improved. Two or preferably more years create excellent conditions. It will however be necessary to maintain a dense crop for the whole duration. This depends on

– using the right kind of mixture,
– a well-prepared seed bed (free from perennial weeds) and
– weather conditions.

A period of two or at maximum three years is generally best, as this allows the good preceding crop effect to be brought to bear more quickly and more frequently.

Should conditions prove unfavourable so that a newly drilled crop fails, it is better to plough the field and drill a mixture of short-lived fodder plants such as Egyptian and Persian clover. The same applies if bare patches appear early or the field is fouled with weeds.

The best method of manuring long-term fodder crops is to apply a good quantity of well-rotted composted manure to the preceding crop or prior to drilling in late summer. Repeat in the second year of utilization. Depending on the type of mixture used, an application of dung liquor would benefit a mixture with a high proportion of grass. In clover areas it is better used on other crops. An application of composted manure and dung liquor before ploughing will enhance the long-term preceding crop effect.

In his book *The Clifton Park System*, which was published at the turn of the century, Robert H. Elliot described the effect of adding herbs to the mixture. He worked with a rotation of four years of arable alternating with four years of grassland. A special feature of the system was the addition of five herbs with good root development to the ley mixture:

chicory (*Cichorium intybus*)
salad burnet (*Sanguisorba minor*)
yarrow (*Achillea millefolium*)
parsley (*Petroselinum crispum*)
wild parsnip (*Pastinaca sativa*)

Table 48 ▷
(pages 204 and 205)
Key characteristics
of some grasses

name (botanical name)	habit	life	time of coming into after 1 April (days)
sheep's fescue (*Festuca ovina*)	bottom grass compact tufts	perennial	15–39
meadow foxtail (*Alopecurus pratensis*)	top grass loose tufts	perennial	24–26
creeping or red fescue (*Festuca rubra*)	bottom grass with stolons	perennial	39–49
smooth meadow grass (*Poa pratensis*)	bottom grass with stolons	perennial	37–48
swamp meadow grass (*Poa palustris*)	bottom grass loose tufts	perennial not long-lived	63
cocksfoot (*Dactylis glomerata*)	top grass compact tufts	perennial	44–59
perennial ryegrass (*Lolium perenne*)	bottom grass	perennial dense tufts	46–71
meadow fescue (*Festuca pratensis*)	top grass loose tufts	perennial	50–57
Italian ryegrass (*Lolium multiflorum*)	top grass loose tufts	annual or longer	52–61
false oatgrass (*Arrhenatherum elatius*)	top grass loose tufts	perennial	52–55
yellow oatgrass (*Trisetum flavescens*)	middle grass loose tufts	perennial	52
hybrid ryegrass (*Lolium hybridum*)	middle grass compact tufts	biennial or longer	58–63
timothy (*Phleum pratense*)	top grass loose tufts	perennial	62–92
tall fescue (*Festuca arundinacea*)	top grass	perennial	59
fiorin (*Agrostis alba*)	middle grass loose tufts	perennial does not compete well	69–72
annual ryegrass (*Lolium multiflorum* ssp. *gaudini*)	top grass	annual not winter hardy	71–79

recovery	site requirements climate	soil	uses
moderate	all sites	light also dry	pasture green manuring
good	damp, fresh	not too light	meadow
excellent	all sites, incl. harsh climates	all, incl. wet	pasture
good	all sites	all, except wet, heavy	meadow and pasture
good	damp	damp, wet	meadow and pasture
excellent tolerates dryness	damp	all, incl. light	grazing none too frequent
excellent	high rainfall	all damp soils	pasture, frequent grazing
good	high humidity high rainfall	medium to better quality	pasture, sensitive to overgrazing
excellent	high humidity high rainfall	almost all	winter catch crop
good	warm, not too wet	well structured rich in lime	not for grazing, not to be cut too often
good	dry, warm	permeable rich in lime	pasture and meadow
good	high humidity	almost all	winter catch crop leys
good	fresh and damp	medium to good	pasture
moderate	wet and cold	heavy, cohesive	early mow pasture
moderate to good	wet, cold sites	damp	pasture
excellent	damp	high in nutrients cohesive	alternative to clover

a) As main crop

dry sites not suitable for red clover and lucerne	sites suitable for red clover and lucerne	damp, cool sites, cold soils
black medick	red clover	Alsike clover
birdsfoot trefoil	lucerne	birdsfoot trefoil
sainfoin	Italian ryegrass	timothy
cocksfoot	false oatgrass	meadow fescue
Hungarian brome		

b) For grazing, perennial ryegrass and white clover must be included.

c) Intended period of utilization

stubble sown	18 months	2½ years	long-term
red clover	red clover	Alsike clover	lucerne
Alsike clover	Alsike clover	birdsfoot trefoil	birdsfoot trefoil
white clover	black medick	(or lucerne)	sainfoin
black medick	Italian ryegrass	white clover	white clover
serradella	timothy	timothy	timothy
Westerwold's ryegrass	cocksfoot	cocksfoot	cocksfoot
	meadow fescue	meadow fescue	meadow fescue
	false oatgrass	false oatgrass	false oatgrass

Table 49. Selection of mixtures (Klapp 1951)

The complete mixture was as follows (kg/ha):

cocksfoot	12.5
tall fescue	6.0
oatgrass	6.0
hard fescue	2.5
dogstail	1.2
yellow oatgrass	1.2
late-flowering red clover	2.5
white clover	2.5
Alsike	2.5
kidney vetch	4.0
chicory	5.0
burnet	10.0
yarrow	1.2
parsley	1.2
wild parsnip	1.2

Having gone through the rotation twice, Elliot was able to grow arable crops (twice each row crops and cereals in the four years) without the need for mineral fertilizers, and achieved excellent yields. The lesson to be learned from this is that a rich and varied mixture of site-adapted plants including suitable herbs makes all the difference to the soil. Again, duration is a factor, one-year leys being considered unsuitable.

The system has been used at Talhof farm since 1951, suitably modified for poor, shallow weathered Upper Jurassic limestone and an extremely harsh climate. In over thirty years, the humus level of the arable soil has risen from just below 1% to

		purity %	germinating power %*	competit- iveness**	amount of seed kg/ha		
					A	B	C
false oatgrass	*Arrhenatherum elatius*	87	77	I			50
cocksfoot	*Dactylis glomerata*	91	85	I			20
Italian ryegrass	*Lolium multiflorum*	96	90	I			20
perennial ryegrass	*Lolium perenne*	96	90	I			30
meadow foxtail	*Alopecurus pratensis*	72	70	II		29	33
Hungarian brome	*Bromus inermis*	92	85	II		41	47
yellow oatgrass	*Trisetum flavescens*	72	70	II		23	27
fiorin	*Agrostis alba*	90	87	III	7	9	12
meadow fescue	*Festuca pratensis*	95	90	III	45	60	75
creeping fescue	*Festuca rubra*	92	87	III	25	33	41
reed grass	*Phalaris arundinacea*	93	75	III	15	20	25
timothy	*Phleum pratense*	95	88	III	12	16	20
swamp meadow grass	*Poa palustris*	91	87	III	15	20	25
smooth meadow grass	*Poa pratensis*	91	86	III	15	20	25
hybrid lucerne	*Medicago varia*	95	85	I			20
red clover	*Trifolium pratense*	96	87	I			20
black medick	*Medicago lupulina*	94	82	II		23	27
birdsfoot trefoil	*Lotus corniculatus*	95	81	III	20	26	33
large birdsfoot trefoil	*Lotus uliginosus*	94	81	III	10	13	17
Alsike clover	*Trifolium hybridum*	95	87	III	15	20	25
white clover	*Trifolium repens*	95	87	III	12	16	20

*   Good averages
**   I = tends to displace components rated II and III
      II = will displace or be displaced, depending on circumstances
      III = at risk from more vigorous components
A   In mixtures containing group III species only.
B   In mixtures containing group II and III species only.
C   In mixtures containing group I–III species.

4.5%. The resulting improvement in soil structure has increased the apparent depth of working from 4–12 cm to 6–24 cm. The soil is clayey and heavy, but it is possible to use a three-share plough coupled to a 37 kW (50 hp) tractor to a depth of 24 cm moving at a good pace.

Cutting needs to take account of the type of mixture and climatic conditions. The same seed mixture will produce growth of different composition on different soils and even with-

in the same year. Dry weather, for example, will encourage lucerne, birdsfoot trefoil, cocksfoot and oatgrass, wetter weather red, Alsike and white clover and meadow foxtail.

Cutting times will depend on the maturity of the constituents. Mixtures with a high proportion of lucerne and sainfoin at the juvenile stage will not tolerate cutting back, whereas open-sown Persian, Egyptian and red clover can be cut back if fouled with weeds. They will

Table 50. △
Seed list for
mixtures
(Klapp 1951)

grow all the better afterwards, as they have more light, air and warmth and there is no competition for the available water.

Leys should never be cut too short, as some species are sensitive to this. The resting period before the final autumn cut should be long enough to allow sufficient carbohydrate to be stored in the roots.

The first year after drilling the first cut should not be too early to avoid suppression of slow-growing plants.

As to cultivations, very loose puffy soils will need rolling. More thorough work with harrow or grubber should be limited to pure lucerne (alfalfa). A planker is used after compost applications and to deal with mole and vole hills.

The biodynamic sprays are used as for grassland.

Long leys need to be ploughed up in early autumn 2 1/2 or 3 1/2 years after drilling. This is the best time as regards weed suppression, resting the soil and accumulation of nitrogen and root mass. Both nitrogen levels and root mass are highest in autumn. Ploughing offers the opportunity of deepening the crumb layer. Final utilization is immediately followed by an application of farmyard manure. The land is then ploughed deeply, using a skim coulter. The beams should be at as much of an angle as possible so that sufficient warmth and air can enter the soil and chemical conversions are accelerated.

A long ley with clovers, grasses and herbs contributes a great deal to the continual improvement of soil structure and fertility.

**Table 51.
Ley mixtures used at
Talhof farm (kg/ha).**

For two or three-year leys

red clover	1	sweet vernal grass	2	common meadow grass	2
lucerne	4	cocksfoot	2	creeping fescue	1
white clover	2	timothy	4	yellow oatgrass	2
sainfoin	10	false oatgrass	2	caraway	1
black medick	2	meadow fescue	2	lesser burnet	8
birdsfoot trefoil	8	Italian ryegrass	2		
kidney vetch	1	perennial ryegrass	2		

Long-term leys

red clover	1	cocksfoot	2	perennial ryegrass	4
lucerne	2	timothy	4	creeping fescue	1
white clover	4	false oatgrass*	4	yellow oatgrass	2
sainfoin	20	meadow fescue	2	caraway	1
birdsfoot trefoil	10			lesser burnet	8
kidney vetch	1			chicory	3
				parsley	1

* omitted if for grazing

Soil conditions vary enormously (soil numbers ranging from 16 to 59) and the mixture is always specially adapted to the condition and location of the field (slopes facing north, south, east and west).

28

29

30

31

Seedlings are grown in a cold frame (29).
Bush tomatoes (28) produce well-flavoured
sun-ripened fruit. Nettles are specially
grown to make the biodynamic preparation (30). Pasque flower and pot marigold
(31, 33) are medicinal plants; goat's rue
(32) is a legume that helps lactation.

32

33

34

35

The benefits gained from the bees that pollinate the flowers cannot be overestimated. It would be good to see bee hives again on many farms. The bee house needs a wind-protected site, ideally above a water vein (34). Merely abstaining from the use of herbicides in baulks and hedges will create better conditions for bees. 36: Experimental bee unit (Tuebingen University) in unsprayed baulk. Wood ant heaps are protected against damage from both humans and animals (35).

36

Non-leguminous fodder crops

Non-leguminous fodder crops are not much grown as main crops, unless roots grown for fodder are included in the category.

Mixtures of pulses and cereals may be grown twice in succession in a vegetation period to control weeds. Some fodder plants also give high yields if grown as a second crop on some sites – above all maize for silage, sunflowers, swedes and marrowstem kale.

Maize (*Zea mays*) growing has seen an explosive increase over the last 20 years. Mechanization is easy, productivity in relation to labour is high, ensilage is straightforward, the material is specially suited to fattening beef bulls, dry matter yields are high and selective herbicides can be used.

A sensible amount of maize in a cropping sequence helps to cover feed requirements and make rations more varied. The proportion should not appreciably exceed 10% of the arable area and 15% of the dry matter in feeds.

On heavy soils it is best to apply rotted farmyard manure or well-fermented liquid manure to the catch crop. No time will then be lost with manuring after harvesting that crop and the soil is not exposed to pressure. On lighter soils maize can also do with manuring in spring. An application of well-humified compost after drilling the maize will give better growth, with the soil warming up more quickly. The compost also encourages root development so that juvenile growth will be more rapid. An additional application of dung liquor will stimulate growth further.

Weed control is easier and the danger of birds eating the grain is

Maize yields are definitely increased by repeated applications of horn silica.

reduced by using a ridging tool immediately after drilling. The seeds are then at a depth of 10–14 cm and difficult for rooks and pigeons to reach. Several brisk passes with the weed harrow will deal with germinating weeds, letting the young maize plants develop undisturbed. If potatoes are also grown it is advisable to use the same row width for both crops, so that implements only have to be set once. If this method is used, cultivation is as for potatoes; for level sowings it is as for beet. Flame weeding has also proved effective.

Before hoeing the crop for the last time when it is 40–60 cm high, white clover or black medick may be sown by hand or with the fiddle. If successful, the undersown crop will cover the ground densely by the time the maize forage harvester and trailer are used, greatly reducing damage especially in wet weather. Successfully undersown maize makes a good preceding crop, leaving a well structured crumb rich in root material.

Maize reacts well to repeated applications of horn silica; yields may be increased to a remarkable extent.

Sunflower (*Helianthus annuus*) is less demanding in all respects than maize is. The growing period is shorter, weeds are quickly suppressed, fodder yield is high and the soil is left in a good crumb state.

Sunflowers respond well to large amounts of farmyard manure. Seeds only ripen in exceptionally warm areas in our latitudes. The crop is therefore grown mainly for green fodder and silage.

Winter catch crops make excellent preceding crops, sunflowers being sensitive to frost, so that they cannot be drilled until just before or after the 'Ice Saints' (12–15 May). They may be stubble sown after winter rape, winter barley and early-maturing winter rye, peas and spring barley.

Densely drilled crops have thinner stems and this increases the fodder intake of animals. It has proved a good idea to mix a small-grain field pea in with the seed. If cut when the sunflowers are in full bud, or about a quarter are in flower, this mixture is more palatable to cattle than pure sunflower; it can also be used for silage.

The first application of horn silica is made just before the leaves close up the rows.

Marrowstem kale (*Brassica oleracea* convar. *acephala* var. *medullosa*) will provide green fodder right until winter sets in, for it will tolerate temperatures down to –10 °C. The green fodder period can thus be extended by several weeks. It will also provide soilage for two or three more weeks if bundles of it are placed in the gateways of barns or along the outside walls of buildings and protected with plastic sheeting and bales of straw. Marrowstem kale is added to maize during ensilage to balance the protein content. Farmyard manure applied to the preceding catch crop or before planting or drilling must be well rotted down, otherwise pests may become more of a problem. About 800 g of seed will be enough to grow seedlings for the optimum

number of 90,000 or 100,000 plants per hectare. Drill in beds in April, six to eight weeks before planting out; this will provide vigorous seedlings for planting as soon as the preceding crop has been harvested.

Cultivations are as for swedes until the rows have closed up.

The first application of horn silica is made as soon as this has happend.

Italian ryegrass (*Lolium multiflorum*) will rapidly produce a large bulk of herbage, but requires high nitrogen levels if grown on its own. This is only done in exceptional cases – to fill gaps in clover fields due to winter damage, or on farms with a high percentage of stock where good use has to be found for the resulting manure. Its main use is in combination with red clover in leys of one year or eighteen months. In longer leys it will displace most other species and leave large gaps in subsequent years, since it often does not survive a second winter. Italian ryegrass prefers fresh, light or cohesive soils and a climate that is not too harsh.

Annual ryegrass (*Lolium multiflorum* var. *westerwoldicum*) grows more rapidly than Italian ryegrass, producing mature seed in the year it is drilled. Always open sown and usually also on its own.

Hybrid ryegrass (*Lolium hybridum*) is a cross of Italian and perennial ryegrass. It is more long-lived and winter hardy, which makes it suitable for leys that are both cut and grazed.

Catch crops

In sites where climatic conditions permit, catch crops can play an important role in producing additional

Maize grown for silage makes a good preceding crop if care is taken to avoid pressure damage to the soil when harvesting (undersow with clover, harvest in dry weather).

crop	seed rate (kg/ha)	depth (cm)	distance between rows (cm)
maize for silage	18–52	5–7	62.5–85
sunflowers (second crop)	25–30	3–4	18–25
+ fodder peas	+50–60		
marrowstem kale	4*	1–2	30–40

* for planting, 800 g

Table 52. Seed rate, sowing depth and distance between rows for non-leguminous fodder plants grown as main crops.

fodder and green manures. Adequate water supplies are necessary if they are to succeed.

Distinction is made between spring and winter catch crops. Spring crops in particular have been grown more and more frequently in recent years to balance essentially cereal-based cropping sequences. The majority of catch crops belong to the legume and crucifer families. Plant breeding has produced a range of fast-growing varieties.

In borderline sites where harvest is late and active growth ceases early in autumn, undersowing is the only method. This may include all clovers that remain low until the cover crop is harvested, and also leys that will develop quickly once the main crop has been cleared: serradella, white clover, black medick, Alsike, white melilot and late varieties of red clover.

Serradella and lupins, too, may still be broadcast in winter rye as late as May, if rain is expected and the soil is suitable. This is done by hand or, if tramlines exist, with a spinning fertilizer distributor set high, at a time when the rye is 60–90 cm high.

The principles are the same as for main fodder crops: the field must be free from perennial weeds, a good water supply is required, and the growth and harvest of the cover crop should not be impeded.

Stubble sowing is preferable in areas where the period of active growth is sufficiently long – if the main crop is harvested early and a long, mild autumn follows – or if perennial weeds are present. Preparing the seed bed after harvest does of course mean some degree of water loss through evaporation, and extensive stubble-sown catch crops do need adequate machine availability.

Every July day gained by drilling early is equivalent to eight August days or the whole month of September as regards the production of leaf mass.

Stubble-sown crops grown to produce high-protein fodder and increase soil nitrogen levels include field peas, vetches and tares, serradella and field beans. If the preceding crops clear early, Persian and Egyptian clover and lupins may be considered singly or in mixtures.

If plenty of manure is available, sunflowers, green maize, marrowstem kale, turnips, millet, buckwheat, rape, oil radish, mustard and phacelia will also give good yields.

Winter catch crops are most certain to give good results in the majority of sites if stubble-sown in summer. Different species and varieties have different requirements concerning drilling dates. Rape, Landsberg mixture, vetches and rye, fodder rye and turnip rape (in order of their drilling dates) are most widely grown. Mixtures of Italian, or even better, hybrid ryegrass with rape, crimson clover and winter vetch are generally successful.

A special advantage of winter catch crops is that they prevent leaching of minerals, especially nitrogen, during the cold months and provide early green fodder.

Below, a brief description is given of plants other than those already described that make suitable catch crops.

Grown on lighter soils where water supplies are adequate, **turnips** (*Brassica rapa* var. *rapa*)

give high yields of palatable, milk-producing fodder that may also be used for silage. They will tolerate temperatures as low as –8 °C and produce sufficient additional growth in autumn to give yields of up to 60 t/ha.

All early clearing crops may be grown as preceding crops: green oats and peas in mixture, chitted early potatoes, winter and spring barley, winter rye and early-maturing peas. The cabbages and their relatives should be avoided.

Quick, clean preparation and drilling, shallow working of the soil and rolling after drilling create the necessary conditions for a good yield. Mechanical hoeing is also of benefit. Combines are now available for harvesting.

Afternoon horn manure applications are made when drilling and

**Table 53.
Seed rate, depth and distance between rows for some catch crops.**

crop	seed rate (kg/ha)	depth (cm)	distance between rows (cm)
turnips	1.5–2.5	1–2	25–30
oil radish	20–25	up to 2.5	25–30
phacelia	8–12	up to 1.5	15–20
summer rape	7–12	1–2	20–30
winter rape	7–10	1–2	20–30
winter turnip rape	9–12	1–2	20–30
mustard	20–25	0.5–2	15–25
green rye	170–200	2	15–20
vetches and rye:		2–4	15–25
rye	40–80		
+ winter vetches or	+40–70 or		
+ Hungarian vetch	+60–90		
Landsberg mixture:		1–3	15–25
winter vetches	25–35		
+ crimson clover	+15–25		
+ Italian or			
hybrid ryegrass	+10–20		
(+ winter rape*	+ 4)		

* Winter rape to replace crimson clover in cases of clover sickness

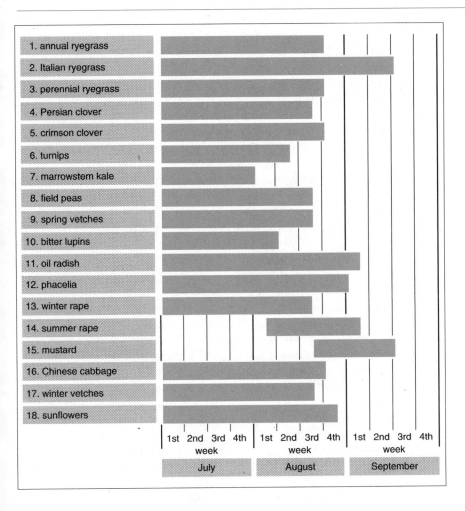

	July				August				September			
	1st	2nd	3rd	4th	1st	2nd	3rd	4th	1st	2nd	3rd	4th
		week				week				week		

1. annual ryegrass
2. Italian ryegrass
3. perennial ryegrass
4. Persian clover
5. crimson clover
6. turnips
7. marrowstem kale
8. field peas
9. spring vetches
10. bitter lupins
11. oil radish
12. phacelia
13. winter rape
14. summer rape
15. mustard
16. Chinese cabbage
17. winter vetches
18. sunflowers

Fig. 67. Favourable sowing times for important catch crops.

again when hoeing; horn silica is first applied when the turnips begin to swell, in the morning, with a second application made when the rows have closed up about three weeks before harvesting, this time in the afternoon.

If the following crop requires well manured soil, it is advisable to apply about 25 t/ha of good quality composted manure before or after drilling the turnips.

Liquid manure applied when drilling or later between rows before hoeing will directly increase yields.

Oil radish (*Raphanus sativus* var. *oleiformis*) has been grown more frequently in recent years, mainly in sugar beet growing areas, for it is inimical to beet cyst nematodes. It is one of the oldest oil plants of Asia but is only used for fodder and green manure in Central Europe.

Being a long-day plant, oil radish will tolerate late drilling, right into the first ten days of September (see Fig. 67). It is fast growing and suppresses germinating weeds, whilst its stout tap root penetrates deep even in compacted soils. The mustard oil content rises with age, so that oil radish must be used for fodder or silage by the time the pods begin to form. Plentiful applications of liquid manure or dung liquor encourage the production of green mass.

Phacelia (*Phacelia tanacetifolia*) is a catch crop that will quickly produce large amounts of greenstuff; it makes no special demands concerning soil and climate. The only soils that do not suit are those that are very clayey, wet and inclined to form crusts. If plenty of nitrogen is available, a good yield of protein-rich fodder is obtained. Cattle will gradually come to like it if it is introduced with some skill. The plant tolerates temperatures as low as –8 and –9 °C, but is not winter hardy. It makes a good green manure, leaving the soil rich in root matter, with a good crumb structure and free from weeds. Drilling is possible until early in September.

Summer rape (*Brassica napus* var. *silvestris*) is widely grown as a stubble-sown summer crop. Drilled between early August and early September it will quickly produce high yields if sufficient nitrogen is available. Summer rape may be grown for soilage, grazing or silage. For green manuring, drilling may be at a later date, as a good root mass is produced even if the aerial parts are poorly developed.

Summer rape needs a fine seed bed and is drilled on the flat.

In areas where erucic acid free varieties of rape are grown, summer rape should be of the same kind to avoid cross fertilization with varieties containing high levels of erucic acid and glucosinolates if the crops reach the flowering stage.

Winter rape is grown mainly for oil but to some extent also as a winter catch crop. The method is the same in either case, except that earlier drilling is an advantage with the catch crop. This will yield relatively early soilage in spring and is a good preceding crop for potatoes and maize.

Even earlier green fodder is provided by **winter turnip rape** (*Brassica rapa* var. *silvestris*). This also suits relatively harsh climates and poor sites. It is drilled three or four weeks after rape. Manuring, drilling method and cultivation is as for rape.

Mustard (*Sinapis alba*) will grow rapidly if stubble-sown late and provide soilage or green manure. For soilage, the crop must all be cut before flowering begins, as it then grows bitter and becomes unpalatable. The mustard oil may also affect the taste of the milk. Yields are enhanced by generous applications of dung liquor or liquid manure and by legumes as a preceding crop. Mustard is killed by winter frosts, so there is no risk of it coming up again with the following crop.

Fodder or green rye (*Secale cereale*) is one of the most adaptable crops and will grow in almost any soil, the exceptions being extremely poor, dry sandy soils and wet and heavy clays. Drilling should be timely to allow for vigorous tillering in autumn. Liquid manure applied when drilling or on thawing snow at the end of winter will accelerate spring growth and give higher yields. Green rye will provide fodder after green rape.

Digestibility will decrease rapidly once the tips of the awns are appearing; harvest should be complete by this time, therefore, despite the fact that considerable leaf mass is produced later.

With members of the crucifer family (oil radish, rape, mustard and turnip) grown as catch crops, care must be taken that in the cropping sequence they do not come too close to other members of the family (cabbage, swedes, rape, mustard) grown as main crops; they share the same pests.

	Period of active growth required after main crop harvest	winter rape	winter barley	spring barley	winter rye	winter wheat	spring wheat	oats	early potatoes	mid-early potatoes	peas grown to ripeness	field beans
						preceding crops						
days available for growing catch crops		100	90	80	80	68	59	66	80–100	30–50	90	50
undersown												
red clover	80–100	(+)	+	+	+	(+)	(+)	(+)				
Alsike clover	80–100	(+)	+	+	+	(+)	(+)	(+)				
white clover	80–100	(+)	+	+	+	(+)	(+)	(+)				
clover/grass ley	80–100	(+)	+	+	+	(+)	(+)	(+)				
Italian ryegrass	80–100	(+)	+	+	+	(+)	(+)	(+)				
serradella	80–100		(+)	+	(+)	(+)	(+)	(+)				
fodder carrots	80–100		+	+	+							
Persian clover	80–100		+	+	(+)							
stubble-sown												
fodder kale	80–90	+	+	+	+							
millet	85–90	+	+						+		+	
green maize	80–90	+	+						+		+	
mixed legumes	75–80	+	+	+	+				+			
sweet lupins	70–80	+	+	+	+				+			
turnips	70–80			+	+	(+)			+			
sunflowers	70–75	+		+	+	(+)			+		+	
oil radish	60–75			+	+	+	(+)	+		+		
phacelia	55–65	+		+	+	+	+	+		+		
summer rape	55–65			+	+	+	+	+		+		
mustard	50–60			+	+	+	+	+		+	+	
winter turnip rape	50–70			+	+	+	+	+		+		
winter rape	60–70			+	+	+	+	+				
green rye	45–60			+	+	+	+	+		+	+	+
vetches and rye	50–60			+	+	+	+	+		(+)	+	+
Landsberg mixture	55–70			+	+	+	+	+		(+)	+	

+ well suited, (+) suited within limits

Vetches and rye need the same kind of soil and climate as pure green rye, but the fodder mixture has significantly higher protein lev- els. Drilling should be done two or three weeks earlier to allow enough time for winter vetches (*Vicia villosa*, hairy vetch; in warmer regions

Table 54. Catch crops within cropping sequences (Fischbeck, Heyland & Knauer 1975).

V. pannonica, Hungarian vetch) to develop sufficiently in autumn to be able to overwinter. Higher proportions of vetch will increase the protein level and the preceding crop value of the mixture, but the seed will be more expensive.

Landsberg mixture has the highest protein and bulk yield of all winter catch crops but also needs the longest period of active growth and a good supply of water. It consists of winter vetches, crimson clover and Italian, or preferably hybrid, ryegrass.

The relative proportions may be varied depending on soil, climate and drilling times. The total seed rate should not be less than 60 kg/ha. Drilling should be done by 20 August at the latest to avoid winter damage. The crop needs a fine seed bed prepared sufficiently early to be good and firm. It is recommended to apply composted manure before drilling, without working it in. The amount will depend on the needs of the following crop. Maize for silage, sunflowers, beet grown from transplanted seedlings and marrowstem kale require more than legume fodder mixtures. If annual weeds are likely to be a problem, the distance between rows should be increased from 20 cm to 25 cm so that mechanical hoeing is possible. The slight ridging effect is an advantage.

Lush autumn growth may be cut back or grazed with some care. This will improve the winter hardiness of crimson clover and winter vetches.

Depending on site, the best time for harvesting is between mid-May and early June.

Landsberg mixture may be used for soilage, silage or hay. A dense, vigorous stand will leave the soil in excellent crumb structure and weed free. This reduces the need for cultivation with following crops.

Crimson clover increases the risk of clover sickness in the soil and should be replaced by rape in cropping sequences with a high proportion of red clover and legumes.

Growing fodder plants for seed

As previously mentioned, growing one's own seed makes an important contribution to the farm. Fodder crops hold a central position as the link between animal husbandry and arable farming on the one hand and as the mainstay of cropping sequences on the other. A brief discussion of seed production for some fodder plants therefore follows.

Lucerne, or alfalfa, is grown in a narrow strip between two low-growing crops. Good access for light and air encourages flowering and gives higher seed yields. Two passes with the mechanical hoe, the first with protectors, will encourage seedling growth and suppress weeds. Any weeds that remain and any clover species need to be removed by hand. The crop should not be cut back. Seed is harvested in the year of drilling to keep down flower gall midges. These crops usually give maximum yields the following year because of the carbohydrates stored in the roots.

Red clover needs to be grown in dense stands free from weeds. If seed is grown for the farm's use, the presence of other clover species may be acceptable. An early first cut will encourage early flowering with the second growth. The leaf mass will be reduced but flowerheads are larger and more numerous

Fodder rye is one of the best preceding crops for carrots.

with this method. Dry, warm weather helps flowering and pollination by insects. The crop is mown when the flowers are a blackish brown. The combine may be used in dry, warm years, but in most cases it is best to cut and rack, threshing at a later time.

Black medick may be undersown together with perennial ryegrass. The crop is lightly cut for fodder or grazed in the early autumn of the drilling year. Black medick and perennial ryegrass are well matched for growth and maturity, so that they may be harvested together. The seeds are easily separated. After the seed harvest the crop may be grazed.

Alsike clover has a tendency to lodge, so that relatively dry sites must be chosen for seed growing. Seed is taken from the first cut, which means the year the Alsike clover was drilled if it was undersown into early clearing green mixtures. Otherwise conditions are the same as for red clover.

Being shade-tolerant, **white clover** may be grown with suitable cover crops even for seed. The large-leaved tall varieties are taken for seed from the second growth, small-leaved creeping varieties as a first cut. It has been found useful to graze the stand briefly as it begins to come into flower, as the flowering period is long and seed from earlier flowers is simply lost.

Crimson clover, or trifolium, cannot be grown for seed at altitudes greater than 400–500 metres above sea level. Drilling in late summer is preferable to spring drilling. The crop is normally drilled pure and without a cover crop, but may be mixed with early maturing Italian ryegrass. The seeds can be

Fodder crops are the link between animal husbandry and arable farming.

harvested together and it may be possible to cut once more for soilage.

Grasses are included in mixtures of **birdsfoot trefoil**, meadow fescue, false oatgrass or cocksfoot, or of **large birdsfoot trefoil** and marsh meadow grass to serve as supports, as both birdsfoot trefoils are unable to stand on their own. With seed grown for farm use it is sufficient to cut the birdsfoot trefoil when wet with dew once the seeds are ripe and spread it on a tarpaulin in a sunny place. Most of the pods should be yellow or yellowish brown by this time, the grain should have brown cheeks and just break on the nail when tested. If the harvest is kept protected from dew and rain the pods will split of their own accord when sufficiently dry.

White melilot tends to be more of a problem, as many seeds are lost on harvest and seedlings growing from them may seriously interfere with following crops. Seed is taken in the active growing period that follows the year of drilling.

It has proved useful to add mustard or summer turnip rape to **serradella**. The young plants are slow to develop, so that a pass with the mechnical hoe is indicated. If suitable sites are chosen, the plants will soon provide their own dense ground cover. Black medick is harvested when the lower pods have matured and again in the dew, as losses due to breaking may be con-

crop	seed rate kg/ha	row spacing cm	yield t/10 ha
lucerne	7–9	20–25	2.5
red clover	13–16 (U)	20–25	2–3
	10–12 (O)[1])		
black medick	16–20[2])	15–20	3–4.5
Alsike clover	8–10	20	2–3
white clover	9–10 (-12)	25–30	2
crimson clover	25 (-30)	20–25	6–8
birdsfoot trefoil	14–15 (U)[3])	20–25	3
	12 (O)		
large birdsfoot trefoil	12 (U)	20–25	3
	9–10 (O)		
sainfoin	90–110 (U)[4])	25–35	4–8
	70–80 (O)[4])		
white melilot	20–25 (U)	20–25	4–5
	18–20 (O)		
serradella[5])	30–40	20–25	6–7
Italian ryegrass	22–25 (U)	20	6–7
	20–22 (O)		
oil radish	14–18	20–30	1–1.5
phacelia	8–10	15–20	3–6
hairy vetch	20–40[6])	–25	5–8

U = undersown; O = open sown
[1]) if open sown in summer: 12–14 kg/ha
[2]) or 9–10 kg black medick + 15 kg perennial ryegrass
[3]) plus 20–40% of grass
[4]) 1/3 less if shelled
[5]) add very small amounts of mustard, summer rape or spring rye to provide support
[6]) in mixture with 60–100 kg of rye: sown pure, 90–120 kg (unusual) or 40–60 kg of hairy vetch and 3–6 kg of winter rape in rows 30–40 cm apart. Hungarian vetch – use 20–25% more seed.

Table 55. Seed rate, row spacing and average yields from fodder plants grown for seed.

siderable otherwise.

With **Italian ryegrass** seed can only be taken in the second year. Seed may be taken from the first cut in about early July and the second time in early September.

Oil radish for seed is drilled in the second half of April. Poor, acid or extremely dry soils are not suitable. Cool weather at the juvenile stage will improve readiness to flower; later on it is better to have warm, dry weather. A single pass with the mechanical hoe is usually sufficient; after this the plants will suppress any weeds that come up. Composted manure is preferable to liquid manures which are inclined to force growth and favour blossom rape beetle and rape flea attack.

The pods will not burst but are liable to break off, so that seed has to be harvested before dead ripe. Birds may cause major losses when drying in the swathe or on stacks.

Phacelia seed is expensive to buy

and therefore best grown at home. 1/10 hectare will yield about 35 kg of seed, enough for 3 hectares. Harvest when wet with dew to prevent loss of seed capsules. The time for harvesting is when the last, uppermost flower opens. Drying and final ripening will be rapid with the crop loosely hung on racks. Relatively large areas may be combine harvested, otherwise the crop is thrashed with a flail.

On farms where **winter vetches** are grown in quantity, it may be advisable to grow for seed by drilling with winter rye. Wheat would be more resistant to lodging and also has a more convenient harvesting date, but generally cannot be used as it is difficult to separate the seeds. The only possible combination would be wheat varieties with large, long grains and hairy vetch with its small seeds. The seeds have hard seed coats and this may cause problems in so far as dropped seed may persist in the soil and germinate later to create a weed problem. Plant breeders are looking for ways of overcoming this.

Herbs

Many plants have a long tradition as medicinal and culinary herbs. In recent years there has been growing awareness of the fact that the healing powers of nature, especially in form of medicinal plants, can relieve or cure many diseases in both humans and animals. Many native herbs and foreign spices have also returned to favour in cookery.

Herbs can be extremely helpful to domestic animals:
– added to feeds to aid appetite and

digestion, to improve hormone balance and, closely related to this, to stimulate lactation,
– as teas, compresses or in ointments to prevent and treat pathological conditions.

The biodynamic preparations make full use of the special powers of certain plants to produce compost and manure that are able to bring healing qualities, vitality and long-term fertility to the soil.

It is part of the work that is done to make each farm an individual and independent organism to grow one's own herbs and the plants needed to make the preparations. Yarrow, dandelion, oak, valerian, nettle and often also horsetail can be found in fields and woodlands. Camomile (scented mayweed) is easy to grow if not found wild. The method is to collect a basketful of seedlings from a friend's farm or garden and plant these 8 by 20 cm apart in a garden bed. Flowers produced in an area of 10–15 m² will be enough to produce tea and preparation for a 25 ha farm and its animals. Sufficient seed drops out during harvest to provide seedlings on the path beside the bed that can be grown on the next year.

A number of other herbs are also useful to humans and animals. Most culinary and medicinal herbs belong to the carrot family (Umbelliferae), mint family (Labiatae) and daisy family (Compositae). Table 56 gives information on how to grow and use some of the most important ones.

Cultivation

The herbs grown in Central Europe originated in widely different cli-

In the garden, herbs contribute to the vitality of vegetable crops and help to increase the number of butterflies.

mates, but are generally highly adaptable. Most of them like loose, humic soil in warm sites with moderate moisture, and either sunny positions (marjoram, sage) or semi-shade (lovage, tarragon). The soil is roughly dug in autumn. It is best to avoid manures that will force growth, as this reduces the scent and flavour. Well rotted farmyard manure or, even better, compost is preferable. Compost can be nitrogen enriched by adding hoof and horn chips. Dung liquor should not be applied during the period of active growth.

High standards are required for seed and seedlings. If home-grown material is not available, the best sources are other farms or market gardens well known to the farmer, or reliable specialist shops.

Table 56.
Basic data for growing and use of herbs.

name (botanical name)	growing method	space required cm (row spacing)	sowing rate g/100 m² (TGW)	time
carrot family				
angelica (Angelica archangelica)	SO p	40 × 50 (30)	15–30 (2–3)	A
anise (Pimpinella anisum)	SO a	20–25	200–250	Sp
caraway (Carum carvi)	SO p	30 × 30 (30–35)	80–100	Sp/S
celery/celeriac (Apium graveolens)	P b	25 × 30	2–3 (0.5)	Sp
chervil (Anthriscus cerefolium)	SO a	(10–15)	100	Sp
coriander (Coriandrum sativum)	SO a	35 × 40 (25–30)	2000–2500	Sp
dill (Anethum graveolens var. hortorum)	SO a	20 × 25 (25–35)	80–120	Sp/S
fennel (Foeniculum vulgare)	SO p	1st yr: (20–25) 2nd yr: 50 × 60	(4–6.5)	Sp
lovage (Levisticum officinale)	SO/D p	40 × 50	20 (3–3.5)	(Sp) A

SO = sown in open
P = plant out
St = stolons

T = top cuttings
D = division

Sp = spring
S = summer
A = autumn

As table 56 shows, many herbs are propagated from seed drilled directly in the open or with seedlings grown in seed beds and trays. With the last method, frost-sensitive annuals are planted out after 12–15 May and perennials by the end of August or early September at the latest. Seeds that germinate in the light should only have a light covering of soil. For those that germinate in the dark, drilling depth should not be more than three to five times the seed diameter.

Vegetative propagation is possible with perennial herbs. Top cuttings are taken in June, when they are firm enough, and put in slightly sandy soil or a mixture of peat and sand until roots develop. They are planted out in late summer or the next spring.

comments	part used	use
tolerates semishade	root herb	pharmaceutics fodder
needs warm climate, germinates in the dark	seed, fruit herb	lactagogue, culinary use, tea fodder
germinates in the light, bee plant, risk of voles	fruit dried stems	culinary use and fodder fodder
sowing not before March, germinates in the light	tuber herb	vegetable fodder (dried late)
	herb	culinary use, fodder
bee plant	fruit straw	culinary use, fodder fodder
bee plant	seeds herb	culinary use lactagogue, culinary use, fodder
divide roots in 2nd year	seeds whole plant	pharmaceutics, tea lactagogue, fodder
(needs singling) plant out	root herb	helps digestion fodder, culinary use

p = perennial
a = annual
b = biennial

name (botanical name)	growing method	space required cm (row spacing)	sowing rate g/100 m² (TGW)	time
masterwort (*Peucedanum ostruthium*)	D + St	40 × 40		
parsley – leaf – root (*Petroselinum crispum*)	SO a	(10–15) (25–30)	80–100 40–50	Sp
mint family				
basil (*Ocimum basilicum*)	P a	20 × 20 (20–30)	5–7	Sp
hyssop (*Hyssopus officinalis*)	P/T/D p	30 × 30	6	
lavender (*Lavandula latifolia, L. angustifolia*)	P (T) p	30 × 40	3–5 (1–1.5)	Sp
lemon balm (*Melissa officinalis*)	P/T/D p	30 × 40	4–5	Sp/S
marjoram, pot (*Origanum majorana*)	P/SO a	20 × 20 (20–25)	P: 2–5 SO: 80–100	Sp
marjoram, wild (*Origanum vulgare*)	SO/T p	(25–30)	40–50	Sp
peppermint (*Mentha piperita*)	T/St p	40 × 20		Sp/A
rosemary (*Rosmarinus officinalis*)	P p		(0.8–1.3)	Sp
sage (*Salvia officinalis*)	P/SO/T/D p	30 × 30	P: 10–15 SO: 80–100	Sp
savory, summer (*Satureja hortensis*)	SO a	25 × 20 (25–30)	50–70	
savory, winter (*Satureja montana*)	SO p	(25–30)		Sp
thyme (*Thymus vulgaris*)	P/D/T p	20 × 20	P: 3–5 SO: 15–20	Sp
daisy family				
elecampane (*Inula helenium*)	P p	50 × 50	5	Sp
marigold, pot (*Calendula officinalis*)	SO a	40 × 40	200–400 (2.5–5)	Sp

comments	part used	use
wild plant for hedges, waste ground	root	pharmaceutics, spec. healing properties
	leaves	culinary use, fodder
	herb	diuretic, vegetable
	root	colic, fresh eases pain, culinary use
sensitive to frost, germinates in light	leaf	'queen of herbs'
	herb	fodder
butterflies	herb	pharmaceutics, fodder
sensitive to frost, P: March, SO: May	leaf	pharmaceutics, culinary use, fodder
resistant	leaf	tea, pharmaceutics
	herb	fodder, large quantities; lactagogue
2–3 yr cultivation, very aromatic, seed sterile	leaf	tea
	herb	fodder
bee plant	flowers	pharmaceutics, cosmetics
mixed crops	herb	fodder
	flowers	pharmaceutics
	herb	
slightly sensitive to frost	leaf	culinary use, tea, pharmaceutics
	herb	fodder
sensitive to frost, germinates in light	leaf	culinary use
	herb	fodder
winter hardy, germinates in light	leaf	culinary use
bee plant germinates in light	flowers	culinary use, tea, pharmaceutics
	herb	fodder
root mucilaginous	leaves	culinary use
	root	pharmaceutics
	flower	tea, pharmaceutics, fodder
	herb	

name (botanical name)	growing method	space required cm (row spacing)	sowing rate g/100 m² (TGW)	time
mugwort (*Artemisia vulgaris*)	P/D p	40 × 50	(0.1)	Sp–A
southernwood, herb royal (*Artemisia abrotanum*)	P/T p	40 × 30	–	
tarragon (*Artemisia dracunculus*)	T/D p	30 × 40	–	Sp (A)
wormwood (*Artemisia absinthium*)	P p	40 × 40	(0.1)	Sp

other families

name (botanical name)	growing method	space required cm (row spacing)	sowing rate g/100 m² (TGW)	time
borage (*Borago officinalis*)	SO a	(30)	70–80	Sp/S
burnet, salad (*Poterium sanguisorba / Sanguisorba minor*)	SO p	(30)	(5–10)	Sp
chives (*Allium schoenoprasum*)	SO/D p	20 × 20 (25)	20–25	Sp/S
comfrey (*Symphytum officinale*)	St p	50 × 50		Sp–S
fenugreek (*Trigonella foenum-graecum*)	p		150	
garlic (*Allium sativum*)	p	20 × 20	cloves	Sp/S
goat's rue (*Galega officinalis*)	SO/P p	60 × 60	20–30	Sp
horseradish (*Armoracia rusticana*)	St p	60 × 30 (60–70)	560 stolons	
rue (*Ruta graveolens*)	T/P p	25 × 30	10–12	Sp
scurvy grass (*Cochlearia officinalis*)	SO p		60–80	Sp

comments	part used	use
	leaf	culinary use
	herb	fodder
seed difficult to obtain	herb	fodder, in small amounts
aroma poor if grown from seed	herb, at start of flowering	culinary use, fodder
very bitter	herb	tea, pharmaceutics, fodder in small amounts, liquor for fungi and pests
germinates in light	leaves	pharmaceutics, culinary use
needs thinning	herb	culinary use, fodder in large amounts
	herb	culinary use, liquor as fertilizer and for insect pests
	herb	fodder, medicinal for pigs, liquor as liquid manure
	herb	lactagogue, fodder
	cloves	culinary use, pharmaceutics
	herb	liquor for insect pests
bee plant, sensitive to frost, in hedges, waste ground	herb	lactagogue, fodder
	root	culinary use, pharmaceutics
	whole plant	plant around potato fields
	leaves	pharmaceutics, small amounts added to fodder
	herb	culinary use
bee plant	leaves	pharmaceutics, culinary use

Interest in medicinal and culinary herbs is growing again.

Propagation is also possible by dividing the rootstock of older, well-established plants; this is done in autumn or, with frost-sensitive subjects, in spring. The method also serves to rejuvenate stock and will result in more active growth.

Stolons of peppermint or horse-radish are collected in autumn and planted out in spring. For details see the section on growing peppermint (page 227).

Immersing roots for a few seconds in a root bath will help seedlings, root and shoot cuttings. The bath is a thinnish paste made with 2/3 clay and 1/3 cow pats, adding 2% of SPS (see page 79), birch pit concentrate and, if available, horn manure liquid.

Cultivations needed are as follows:
– weed control (hoeing, hand weeding),
– regulation of leaf and root development (watering, cutting back, if necessary shading) and
– application of biodynamic field sprays: horn manure in spring and autumn and after every harvest, horn silica during early growth and prior to cutting.

Harvesting and processing

Relatively large quantities of leaves and shoots are harvested two or three times during the summer months. The final date should not be too late, to allow the plants to recover fully before winter sets in.

Aroma and active principles are usually at their highest level when the plant is coming into flower. Herbs that have reached this stage are cut or picked on a dry day in the morning after the dew has evaporated. The method of cutting will depend on the species, as plants react to this in widely differing ways. Careful observation of growth after harvest will provide the necessary information. Herbs may be dried to preserve them for winter. After removing all soiled or yellowed parts, they are well spread out on clean cloths and left to wilt in a darkened dry and airy room. The wilted plants are tied in bunches and hung to dry in a dry place. Drying is complete when the stalks break like glass. The leaves are stripped off and stored in closed containers (preferably not plastic).

Fruits and seeds, on the other hand, are collected in the early hours of the morning or under a cloudy sky, as fewer seeds are lost in this way. The time for harvesting is when the first fruits are turning brown.

Roots are dug in dry weather. They are cleaned to remove earth but not washed, as this would reduce their keeping quality.

Flowers are collected just before they open and on dry days. Repeated collections will be necessary, as flowers open successively. Spread in a shady place in the open or in an attic room.

Tables 56 and 57 show the many different plant parts that can be used. The carrot family in particular, but other families, too, include a wide variety of species that characteristically develop mainly one part. These find medicinal use for humans and animals and help to balance biological functions.

Table 57 lists plants according to the lower (root), middle (stem/leaf) and upper (flower and seed/fruit) regions, whichever is the part used.

Growing peppermint

Peppermint is one of the most widely used highly aromatic medicinal plants. It provides a pleasant tea for family use, is used medicinally and is equally valuable in fodder mixtures. Dairy cows should only have a limited amount added to their rations, as the powerful essential oil can affect the taste of their milk.

The plants are grown on for two or three years, which puts them halfway between annual and perennial crops, and they therefore have their own place both as a field crop

Table 57.
Parts used of different herbs.

root	leaf/stem	flower/seed/fruit
carrot family		
angelica	celery	anise
carrot	angelica	caraway
celery	caraway	coriander
lovage	dill	dill
masterwort	fennel	fennel
parsley	lovage	
parsnip	masterwort	
	parsley	
mint family		
	basil	lavender
	hyssop	rosemary
	lemon balm	
	marjoram	
	peppermint	
	savory, summer	
	sage	
	thyme	
daisy family		
dandelion	mugwort	arnica
	golden rod	wild camomile
	southernwood	dandelion
	tansy	marigold, pot
	tarragon	sunflower petals
	wormwood	
other families		
comfrey	burnet, salad	elder
elecampane	chives	marsh mallow
garlic	comfrey	St John's wort
horseradish	fenugreek	
	goat's rue	
	horseradish	
	rue	
	St John's wort	

and in the garden. After two or three years a new site is chosen, renewing the plant material at the same time. Propagation is always vegetative, using the stolons. Peppermint grows best in loose humic soils where the groundwater level is not too high; it likes a warm, sunny position. Rust is liable to develop if the soil is very acid or drainage is poor. Effective aeration and mulching improve plant growth and the quality of the essential oils.

Prepare a good bed in spring and give it an application of horn manure. Place the stolons about 5–10 cm apart in rills about 5 cm deep, spacing rows at 30–40 cm. Cover with earth or mature compost and firm well or roll. Spray horn silica as soon as vigorous shoots have appeared, and repeat two or three times after this, to increase the oil content. Cut with sickle or scythe as soon as the first inflorescences appear. Drying is best done in an airy shaded place.

Care must be taken not to make the second cut too late, as the aftermath comes into flower much more quickly. The other reason is that the plants need to recover fully before winter sets in.

See also page 248: Rations for dairy cows.

Rust occurs especially if plants are left to flower for a long time, or if the second cut in autumn is late, so that the plants are weakened. Repeated spraying with horsetail when in full growth and later on the soil will prevent the fungus.

Mitcham is a specially recommended variety.

Herb fodder

Herb fodder is much easier to produce than plants for medicinal use. Expenditure is low, and less care is needed with harvesting, drying and processing.

Cut with scythe or cutter bar. Leave to wilt in the sun for one to three hours before speading out well to dry in a dry, airy attic. The herbs will go mouldy if put in a damp, airless place. Leaves do not have to be stripped off, as the whole aerial part is used.

Further processing depends on the intended use:
– for teas: chop into 2–4 cm pieces,
– to add to crushed cereal grains and for the farm's own mineral mix: grind to powder (hammer mill).

In either case, operations should be carried out on dry days and only with the dried herbs.

Animal husbandry

On the nature of animals

Like the plant world, the animal world provides a rich variety of species all over the globe. Evolution as seen in the light of Rudolf Steiner's anthroposophy gives a clear picture of the evolution of animals and of man. In the course of human evolution, different animal forms were cast off as they did not provide the right physical basis for the human soul and spirit. Human beings only assumed physical form here on earth when a physical body had evolved that would enable humanity to perform its true function.

The anthropoid apes were the species that remained flexible longer than any other; they are nevertheless still a long way from the image of man. Animal species characteristically become set in specific ways at an early stage. Human beings retain their plasticity and capacity for development for a long time. They are

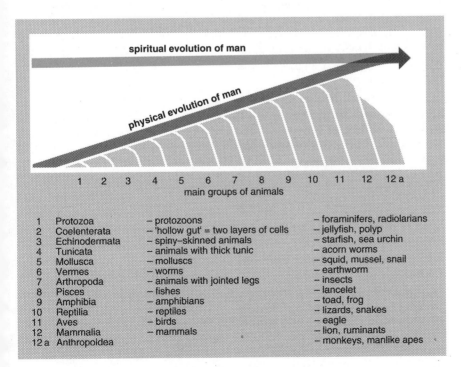

Fig. 68. Animal species separating out as human beings evolve in the course of earth evolution (Kolisko 1930).

spiritual evolution of man

physical evolution of man

1	2	3	4	5	6	7	8	9	10	11	12	12 a

main groups of animals

1	Protozoa	– protozoons	– foraminifers, radiolarians
2	Coelenterata	– 'hollow gut' = two layers of cells	– jellyfish, polyp
3	Echinodermata	– spiny–skinned animals	– starfish, sea urchin
4	Tunicata	– animals with thick tunic	– acorn worms
5	Mollusca	– molluscs	– squid, mussel, snail
6	Vermes	– worms	– earthworm
7	Arthropoda	– animals with jointed legs	– insects
8	Pisces	– fishes	– lancelet
9	Amphibia	– amphibians	– toad, frog
10	Reptilia	– reptiles	– lizards, snakes
11	Aves	– birds	– eagle
12	Mammalia	– mammals	– lion, ruminants
12 a	Anthropoidea		– monkeys, manlike apes

Among domesticated animals, the cow is most important to man.

in need of parental care for much longer than any other species and can, and indeed must, learn a great deal before they are able to think and act for themselves. Animal behaviour is set in patterns and becomes species-specific from an early age. The most serious error made by behavioural scientists is that they transfer discoveries made on animals to human beings.

The continued evolution of animal species is guided from the nonphysical world by the soul and spirit of humanity. It is not determined by any 'struggle for survival'. The sacrifices made by the third kingdom of nature enable human beings to walk upright as they go about their tasks on earth as free individuals capable of independent thought and endowed with soul and spirit.

This is why our natural feeling for animals is one of deep compassion. It is the special task of farmers to take loving care of the their livestock and also to care for wild species, providing them with the right habitat wherever possible.

In the course of evolution, animal species changed as environmental conditions changed. Every kind of landscape has its specific flora and fauna. Without the intervention of natural catastrophes and human activities, a natural balance of species develops, depending on the natural qualities and fertility of the biotope. Large herbivores usually live in

herds, some of which travel long distances in accordance with the rhythm of the seasons and their need for food.

Plants live in a field of tension between sun and earth, between the forces of cosmos and earth, of light and humus; they are tied to their specific growth site.

Higher animals live in a field of tension between drives and desires, hunger and thirst, reproduction and play, sensory functions and the urge to move; they are tied to their species-specific behaviour pattern.

Domestication of wild animals

Humanity did not really become actively involved with the environment until the ancient Persian civilization in 5000–3000 BC (Rudolf Steiner 1909). It was only during this time that the soil came to be tilled to any major extent, that crops were bred from wild plants and wild animals domesticated. Opinions differ as to the exact times and places for those early centres of civilization, but it is now generally accepted that the region of Asia Minor, Persia and India was the cradle of civilization. The Campignian culture (6000–5000 BC) moved from there through the Mediterranean countries to northern France, with methods of cultivating the soil, using a simple plough and keeping cattle.

'Cattle are undoubtedly among the earliest domesticated animals. According to Epstein (1972), Natufian finds dating back to about 8000 BC at El Khiam and Mallalah are now considered to provide the earliest evidence of domesticated cattle.' (Nachtsheim & Stengel 1977).

Dogs are generally considered to have been man's earliest companions, followed by goats and sheep, pigs, cattle and soon also cats (Nachtsheim & Stengel 1977). Except for cats, which preserve a certain independence to this day, the mammals from which our domestic animals derive all lived in herds with marked social behaviour.

Superficially it appears that the reasons for domestication were purely economic. However, a closer look at early history reveals other motives that are clearly predominant. The rock and cave paintings in Altamira (northern Spain) and Lascaux (southern France) seem to indicate that the taming and breeding of animals served ritual rather than economic aims.

The first animal breeders may well have wanted to offer the gods a peaceable bull for sacrifice that showed special beauty in shape and markings, or a ram with handsomely curved horns and a fine fleece.

The 'waste products' of breeding, meat, bone and skin, undoubtedly found uses that helped the economy.

It is assumed that donkeys and camels, water buffalo, pigeons and horses were the next to be domesticated, followed by gayal, banteng, bees and silk moths and, still within the New Stone Age, llamas and chickens. During the Bronze Age (c. 2000–750 BC) yaks were domesticated in Tibet, but it was not until the Ice Age that reindeer were tamed in northern Europe and rabbits in the south west of Europe.

Domesticated species spread rapidly through Asia, Europe and Africa, and many local breeds developed. Cattle were to be the most important

for the human race.

Cattle

The importance of cattle

Cattle are large herbivores and the most important ruminants. Their microbial digestive system enables them to convert fodder rich in crude fibre and ballast into high quality animal protein, providing food for humans.

Compared to pigs and chickens, which feed on cereals, they do not compete with humans for food. Milk and milk products are valuable foods that contain all essential components. Beef has a higher protein and vitamin A content than pork; it makes fewer demands on the liver and is therefore more digestible. Cattle utilize 'absolute' grassland (i.e. grassland not suitable for arable use) and also contribute greatly to the long-term fertility of farmland. Legumes and grass, the basic fodder plants for cattle, and cow dung with its balancing properties vitalize the soil if included in a diversified cropping sequence, improving the performance of the whole farm organism.

Breeding

The true (taurine) breeds of cattle all derive from the aurochs or urus (*Bos primigenius primigenius*). After the last Ice Age aurochs roamed vast areas of Eurasia, as far as the 60th degree of latitude and northern Africa. The last urus cow died in Poland in 1627.

True domesticated cattle are divided into humped (*Bos taurus indicus*, zebu) and humpless varieties (*Bos taurus taurus*). Zebu play an impor-

In tropical and subtropical regions, hybrids between high performance breeds and zebu are gaining in importance.

tant role in the hot regions of the earth which are their native habitat; they are highly adaptable to those conditions and resistant to infectious diseases. They do not compare to the European breeds when it comes to performance, however.

Pictures from ancient Egypt show that cattle were considered important even then and that different colours and forms existed. Assyrian records indicate that trade in animal products had reached considerable volume as early as 3000 and 4000 BC.

It may be assumed that early breeders had special abilities when it came to taming animals and assessing them for breeding potential. Later both animal husbandry and horticulture were reduced to extremely low levels until modern methods came to be developed.

Robert Bakewell, an Englishman (1725–1795), is considered to be the founder of modern domestic animal breeding. He developed several breeds of horses, cattle and sheep. In the early days he would lend proven sires to other farmers for free, the only condition being that the progeny were reared and assessed for performance and characteristics. They also had to be fed on farm grown rations. Inbreeding was important, as with all methods of producing new breeds. Fertility problems and sterility soon became relatively frequent, e.g. in Charles Colling's beef shorthorns (using Bakewell's methods).

Until artificial insemination and electronic data processing came in, breeding methods probably were the same down the ages:
– exclusion of weak individuals and those with negative characteristics,
– selection of breeding pairs outstanding for desirable characteristics.

Animals may be pure or cross bred. In the first case, both partners are of the same breed, in the second they come from different strains.

If the population (total number of individuals of a breed within a limited area) is small, pure breeding carries the risk of inbreeding, i.e. of mating animals that are very closely related. This may result in desirable characteristics being unusually good, but may also cause inbreeding depression such as constitutional weakness and low fertility. Setbacks of this kind are avoided by duly crossing two inbred lines. This results in hybrid vigour (F_1 generation with positive characteristics markedly better than those of the parents). Line breeding has proved a good method and carries considerably less risk of inbreeding problems than pure inbreeding. It consists in using the sons and grandsons of a sire with desirable characteristics as sires for the herd. An example of this is the line breeding done at Talhof farm:

The cows bred from the bull Harem (son of Hack), bought in 1961, proved very fertile and long-lived and performed well. The 14 cows reached a mean age of 13.8 years, calving 10.5 times, and in 11.3 years produced an annual average of 5408 kg of milk with 4.2% (227 kg) milk fat. In 1971 a bull from the same blood line was acquired; his name was Hassan. Cows bred from Hassan and daughters of Harem are coming up to expectation. To date they have reached the age of 9.7 years, have produced 7 calves on average, and the 7-year average of milk production is 6633 kg annually, with 4.56% (302 kg) of milk fat. Final figures cannot yet be given as some of them are still part of the herd. The mother of a bull bought in 1976

(Privat) was also descended from Hack. The cows bred from Privat and the daughters of Harem and Hassan are now in their first lactation and again promise regular fertility and good performance. The sons produced by those pairs did better on average for certification than the mean of all young bulls from Talhof.

Cross breeding uses sires from a suitable different breed with well developed characteristics (e.g. milking ability) that are either lacking or need to be improved in the maternal herd. The daughters (F_1 generation) usually prove highly successful. The repeated use of bulls of the second breed is called back crossing, the proportion of genes from this breed reaching 97% by the fourth generation. On Farm No. 6, back crossing

with a German red pied strain changed a Vorderwald herd into a German red pied one.

Modern herd book breeding with:
– artificial insemination,
– selective breeding of high-performance parents,
– performance testing of young bulls produced in this way, with reference to fleshing ability and food utilization,
– young bulls selected on 'points' for licensing and their trial use for insemination, and
– regional breeding exclusively from old bulls of known positive breeding value,

results in almost predictable annual gains in selected characteristics, e.g. a dairy breed producing c. 2.3% (120

Table 58. Examples of line breeding at Talhof farm.

Susel	S: Harem	GS: Hack		
3 Mar 62	D: Susanne			
16.5 years, 14 calves, 14.2-yr av. 5568 kg, 4.08%, 227 kg.				
Sumira	S: Hassan	GS: Haldan	GGS: Harnisch	GGGS: Hack
14 Sep 73	D: Susalie	GD: Susel	GDS: Harem	GDGS: Hack
10.5 years, 8 calves, 7-yr av. 6609 kg, 4.58%, 303 kg. Still alive.				
Birgitta	S: Harem	GS: Hack		
6 Jul 62	D: Birgit			
15 years, 13 calves, 12.7-yr av. 5734 kg, 3.98%, 228 kg.				
Biene	S: Hassan	GS: Haldan	GGS: Harnisch	GGGS: Hack
8 Apr 75	D: Birgitta	DS: Harem	DGS: Hack	
8 years (peritonitis), 4 calves, 3.8-yr av. 6166 kg, 4.96%, 306 kg.				

Priene	S: Privat	SD: Loni	SDS: Harald	SDGS: Hack
26 Sep 77	D: Biene	DS: Hassan	DGS: Haldan	DGGS: Harnisch
		GD: Birgitta	GDS: Harem	GDGS: Hack

1st class bull with only 5% inbreeding.

kg) more milk annually. At the same time infertility becomes a major reason for disposal of the cows in almost 30% of cases.

The rise in fertility problems (acyclia, poor oestrus, nymphomania, cysts, etc.) has led to a tendency to increase the number of bulls.

Biodynamic farmers will naturally keep their own sires. Frozen sperm will only partly replace the male element in the herd. One of the reasons why Talhof farm has gone in for herd book breeding is to supply certified sires for other farms that work on the same principle.

Breeding stock are selected mainly on the following criteria:
– health and constitution,
– high roughage consumption,
– sustained fertility and longevity,
– good milking quality with adequate performance,
– a solid bone structure with good legs and hard hooves.

If all heifer calves are reared, the rearing period permits selection to be made for ease of feeding, rapid growth and social behaviour. All bull calves with defects of conformation, poor maternal performance and born as a result of inappropriate service dates are immediately excluded from the breeding programme. Young bulls with character defects such as aggressiveness or failure to respect pasture fencing also fail to make the grade. Breeding bulls must have particularly well developed limbs which are at the correct angle and firmly closed hooves so that they will stand up to the demands made on breeding sires.

Longevity is no longer in demand as a characteristic, as old cows with their genetic performance characteristics have been 'left behind' in

breeding progress. Yet it is exactly these animals that have proved adaptable, fertile and healthy through good fodder years and bad, with their dung contributing greatly to the maintenance and increase of soil fertility. The farmer who has bred them has grown fond of them, and a relationship has developed that is just right for both animal and human being. Cows respond to loving care and appreciation with attachment and reliable performance.

Rearing and management of young stock

Calves

The aim is to develop the inherited characteristics of young stock, and the first precondition for this is a strong, lively, healthy calf.

Daily exercise improves the general health of cows, makes calving easier and enhances the vitality of the calf. Cows calving in a pasture or in loose housing will only segregate themselves from the herd a short time before the event. As soon as they have given birth, older members of the herd will usually make contact with the calf and its mother. This is why the calving pen should be close to the cow byre or, even better, be integrated with it, permitting both visual and physical contact. Any prolonged segregation means new battles to re-establish the hierarchy; the time spent in the calving unit should never be too long for that reason.

On rare occasions – after a difficult birth or more frequently after a first calving – cows will refuse to lick their calves down or may even buffet them severely. They therefore need to have an eye kept on them. Licking will on the one hand establish the mother-offspring relationship and on the other encourage delivery of the afterbirth and stimulate the calf's circulatory functions. Suckling is equally beneficial and speeds up involution of the uterus. Calves should be allowed to suckle for a few days (3–5) if at all possible. Later there is a risk of gorging if the cow has a high milk yield and milks easily. The same applies to high milk fat content; this may rise to more than 10% after calving in some flecked breeds and may cause scouring.

Calves should begin to suckle within three hours of being born, or, failing this, the cow should be milked for the first time and the calf given milk to drink. Calves are given four, or better six, meals on the first day, with the total volume not exceeding three or four litres. Experienced breeders will put a hand under the sucking calf's stomach and easily estimate the amount of milk that has been drunk, removing the calf in good time if necessary. High performance cows need careful watching to avoid problems for both dam and calf.

If calves are immediately fed from a bucket, the natural feeding position is best achieved by using a bucket with teats and placing it at the right height. It will be easy to change to normal bucket feeding after about two weeks. After more than two weeks it may prove quite difficult to get the calves to accept the change.

During the first days, body contact should be maintained with the calf as it drinks, for this meets a natural need. Calves remain trusting and thrive better with this method. Daily care should not be limited to correct feeding and physical care. The per-

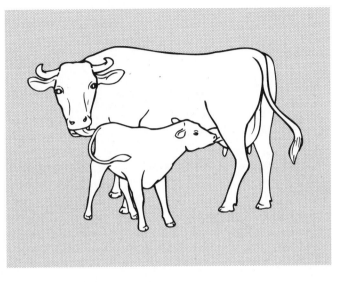

Fig. 69. Suckling cow with calf.

sonal relationship with the animal is maintained by an occasional kind word and a little pat now and then whilst work is being done in the byre. It is often imponderable things like these that determine whether animals are continually ill and there are other problems with rearing on a farm or whether all goes well.

During the first two weeks it is best for calves to stay in single pens that are not too large (2–3 m²), with wooden walls and straw on the floor. After this, several calves may be put together on straw in loose housing. They will need to be tied when given a drink, to prevent them from sucking each other.

The daily ration of whole milk is slowly increased to 8 litres over two weeks. It then remains at this level for three months. For breeding stock, it has proved a good method to continue to give whole milk in slowly decreasing amounts over the second three-month period, unless the farm itself produces fresh skimmed milk. Quite a few conventional farmers have changed back from milk equivalent to whole milk again.

Fig. 70. Calf drinking from bucket with teat.

for cows used as nurse cows immediately after first calving. The calves share a pen with the cow; good quality hay, kibbled oats and carrots when in season are fed from a place not accessible to the cow. Water should always be available from an automatic feeding bowl.

The calves are weaned after three or four months, when the place is needed by a new calf, or if the nurse cow needs to dry off. At this age, calves can be weaned in two or three days. Dry milk powder mixed into the kibbled oats may help. Concentrates are then taken more easily. Set-backs are not normally seen.

As with other rearing methods, careful observation allows any problems that may arise to be dealt with in their early stages. Lively, fit and glossy calves will be the result; the long suckling period – in spite of long habituation as domestic animals – satisfies a deep-rooted need [c. 6,000 sucking actions per day are the norm (Sambraus 1981)] and allows the animals to develop into healthy, fertile cows that will perform well.

The first cut on grassland areas that are the first to be grazed in spring provides tender hay with fine, uniform stems. This is put in racks or suspended in small bundles when the calves are three days old. The curious youngsters will soon try some, so that after a week they will usually be taking some on a regular basis. This helps early rumen development and lays the foundations for high roughage intake and utilization later on. A few days later they are given small amounts of roughly kibbled oats, prepared from naked oats if available. Cubed or ground carrots are taken eagerly from the fifth or sixth week onwards. Linseed mu-

The following method has proved effective in allowing German black pied calves to be reared in close to natural conditions:

Newborn calves feed on the dam's colostrum for at least three, better five, days before they move on to nurse cows. One of these is able to provide two to four calves with as much milk as they need.

Cows used as nurse cows are mainly cows that
– are difficult to milk,
– have had diseases of the udder. Several suckling calves provide regular and thorough massage several times daily, which is the best possible treatment after recovery from mastitis,
– are not particularly good milk producers; frequent suckling will stimulate lactation.

Nurse cows can be machine milked again in their next lactation, except

cilage made with cold water may partly replace whole milk after three months.

Water should be available ad lib. from a special drinking bowl. Rye and wheat straw makes the best litter; oat straw should not be used as it tends to go mouldy.

From about eight weeks onwards the calves are more mobile, with only 13–15 hours a day spent lying down. They may now be put in a parasite-free yard or a pasture close to the homestead for a few hours each day. After six months they may be on pasture for half the day, with supplementary rations of hay and kibbled oats. In winter calves of this age are also given good quality pre-wilted grass silage.

It is easy to make up one's own mineral mixture for calves, heifers and bulls:

100	kg calcified seaweed
50	kg basalt meal
50	kg kaolin or bentonite
50	kg wheat bran
50	kg cattle salt
35	kg herb mixture
2.5	kg homoeopathic calcium powder (Weleda)

The dose is about 30 kg per 100 kg liveweight. The rearing period ends when the calves are nine or ten months old.

Young bulls

Bull calves designated for rearing remain with the cow calves until six months old. They are separated after this because sexual drive increases rapidly at this age.

During the summer they remain in the pasture, returning for the night to their pens in the cowhouse where hay and concentrates are available.

During the winter they absolutely must have daily exercise in a yard or run. As in the pasture, up to four bulls may be put together; separation into smaller groups or tethering of individuals will only be necessary if playful fights and jumping up make the animals too restless.

Basic rations are best hay, grazing in summer and grass and clover silage in winter. From the age of six months, they are also given kibbled oats, barley and wheat, or bran mixed three parts to one with linseed meal, ad lib. It is important to see that the trough is always quite empty before more concentrate is given. The proportion of oats is increased if the animals are to gain in height, the proportion of barley if they are to be more compact.

Kibbled field beans or peas fed to calves and to young and old bulls may cause limbs and joints to grow soft and spongy; they should therefore only be given in very small amounts. Linseed mucilage with a little skimmed milk is given daily from a bucket. (The animals would suffer thirst rather than drink from an unfamiliar container during certification and at auction sales. They will then take only little roughage because they are thirsty, with the result that the animals stand there looking gaunt and miserable, are given poor ratings and do not find enough buyers.) Apart from this, water is made available in water troughs during the rearing period. Fodder sugar beet or, even better, carrots make a valuable addition as they improve the digestibility of rations.

Nose rings are fitted about two or three weeks before the animals are sold. This is always done with only one of the two animals in a double pen, so that the other can operate the

Daily exercise in open air and sun is essential for all animals. Calves are put to pasture or in a paved yard for a few hours daily from about 8 weeks onwards.

Every change in feeding and management must be introduced gradually.

automatic drinking bowl. After two weeks they will have got used to the ring and feed and drink as before. This is also the time when they are taken to pasture or into the yard on a halter, to get them used to it.

Care of the hooves is specially important. Badly cared-for feet will easily cause poor limb posture. From five months onwards, regular inspections should be made every four or six weeks, cutting back as required. The animals may then be expected to have firm, healthy hooves and good limb posture. The final care operation on hooves should be done not less than four weeks before an auction sale.

The character and good temper of fully grown bulls depends very much on the treatment they have had when young. Patience and friendliness combined with firm handling give reassurance and make the animals peaceable, so that there will be no accidents later on.

Heifers

The transition from calf rearing to keeping as heifers is usually made between nine and twelve months of age. During this period, rations of best hay, carrots and concentrate are gradually changed to the extensive rations for heifers. The move to new housing is made in suitably mild weather conditions.

During the summer the one and two year olds remain in paddocks well away from the homestead that are best managed as rotational grazing. Additional second class hay or fodder straw are only added to the rations at times when the weather or the season make the grazing inadequate. The grazing material should not be too young physiologically when the animals are moved to a pasture, so that it contains adequate amounts of crude fibre. Young livestock need relatively large quantities of this to meet nutrient requirements. With their digestive systems thus 'trained', they will later be able to eat large quantities of best basic rations and give good milk yields.

Adequate water and mineral salt mixture supplies should always be available in the pasture.

For the winter feeding period, deep litter housing with a paved yard has proved useful. Given plenty of space, different age groups will manage well together providing they are separated at feeding times. Feeding racks that can be adjusted to different heights will serve the purpose.

In areas where the climate is not too harsh, open housing is ideal for young stock. The Talhof lies in 'Swabian Siberia', but doors to the yard remain open at temperatures above −20 °C; they are only closed at night when the temperature goes below this. Frost does no harm if the litter is deep enough. Warm and damp housing on the other hand makes animals more susceptible to infections. Hardened stock will go out into the yard in all weathers, even in sleet and freezing rain.

Open housing calls for heatable drinking troughs, so that water will always be available. Winter rations consist of pea and good quality oat or barley straw, second class hay and smallish amounts of silage.

group	feeding intensity		insemination rate at first service	replaced because of infertility
1	normal	100%	1.43	46%
2	high	140%	2.14	50%
3	low	65%	1.25	28%

A study to establish the effects of feeding intensities at this stage was done on relatively large herds in Denmark and the USA. The results were as follows (Johannsen *et al.* 1966):

First service was at the same time, irrespective of different levels of development. Group 3 (low intensity) showed some weakness, and Group 2 (high intensity), given the same rations after calving, gave the lowest milk yields.

The study neglected one important principle. If transitional feeding had been introduced in good time before calving, gradually increasing the ration until normal rations were reached, the weakness in Group 3 would not have occurred.

If harm is to be avoided, the basic rule with all kinds of animals and all management systems must always be: *Changes in feeding and general management must always be gradual.*

With cattle, the flora of the rumen needs several days to adapt to a change in diet, e.g. from hay and silage to greenstuff. Heifers are therefore treated just like dairy cows in spring, when they are given the usual roughage ration and gradually put out to pasture more and more or, if kept indoors, given smallish amounts of soilage.

The timing of first service depends on the breed and other factors.

Physiologically speaking, first calving should only occur when the change of teeth is almost complete. Second dentition is however not complete until the animals are between four and six years old. Modern varieties mature relatively young, so that it is no longer possible to wait that long. Minimum weights of c. 330 to 400 kg, depending on breed, must however be reached before first service.

If first service is too late, the non-return rate (percentage of animals that do not come into oestrus again after first service) will be low and the percentage of those not in calf relatively high.

Considerable demands are made on heifers in calf, for they are still growing and so is the embryo. After calving, they have to meet modern standards for high milk performance whilst still growing, soon to be followed by a second insemination and development of a second calf.

Pregnant heifers need to adapt to different feeding and management as dairy cows, and it is best to make the changes about four months before they calve for the first time. Again it will be necessary to proceed slowly and organically so that depressions may be avoided.

General well-being may occasionally be reduced with the change of teeth. Cattle also suffer from toothache and will chew as little as

Table 59.
Different feeding intensity for heifers from one year old to first calving.

possible in that case. Observant stock people will provide the animal in question with foods that are easier to digest: fine hay, bran, which may be steeped in hot water, and tender soilage or silage.

Dairy cows

General management

The cow has been a symbol of fertility from time immemorial. A healthy herd of long-lived high-performance animals reflects a well-functioning, balanced farm organism.

Wild animals know how to react out of pure instinct. Domesticated animals have progressively lost some of their instincts.

Careful management must take the place of those instincts. In the past, it was based on tradition and intuitive understanding. Both of these have largely gone today, with economic and labour aspects largely determining management methods. On the other hand behavioural science has also provided detailed information on the behaviour of different animal species.

Most domesticated animals are gregarious with well-developed social behaviour and a keen desire to move. Management should be such that each individual is given every opportunity for species-specific behaviour.

In the light of present-day knowledge, summer grazing and tethered housing with straw litter in the lying places and exercise space in winter provide the best conditions for dairy cows to be given individual care and opportunity for species-specific behaviour.

Figures 71 and 72 show the ideal solution for new farm buildings, with tethered housing for feeding and milking, roofed deep-litter area and open yard for other times. The system permits the animals to move freely and follow all essential behaviour patterns, and also allows individual observation and care.

The yard surface should be paved, non-slip but not too rough, and easy to clean. All traffic routes, doors, gates and narrow passes must allow space for animals to give way to those of different rank. The width of doors should be such that either it is clearly possible for just one cow to

Fig. 71. Tethered housing with covered lying space and open yard. Farm No. 8 (see pp. 24 and 25) (from a drawing by the architect Rennert 1983).

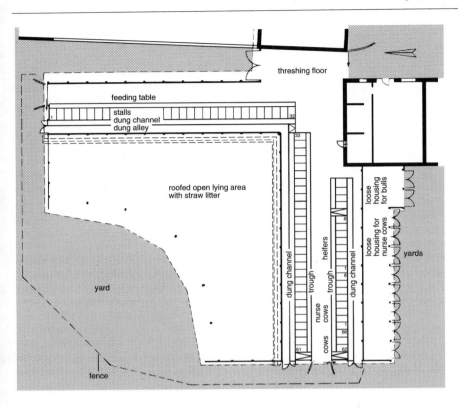

threshing floor

feeding table

stalls
dung channel
dung alley

roofed open lying area
with straw litter

yard

fence

dung channel

nurse cows trough

heifers

cows trough

dung channel

loose housing for nurse cows

loose housing for bulls

yards

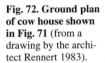

Fig. 72. Ground plan of cow house shown in Fig. 71 (from a drawing by the architect Rennert 1983).

pass or there is space for several of them to go through; otherwise wrangling may cause injuries. Slatted floors in cowhouses seriously reduce the ability to follow normal behaviour patterns. Blood adrenalin levels doubled in mast bulls compared to those kept in deep-litter loose housing or in tethered housing, with a marked reduction in time spent lying down and resting (Andreae 1978), clearly indicating the persistent stress caused by slatted floors.

Wooden-style housing offers special comfort as heat losses are reduced and humidity is well controlled, providing suitable ventilation has been established.

Breeding cattle are comfortable at temperatures between 0 and 20 °C and a relative humidity of 60–80 %. Well functioning natural ventilation systems, e.g. air inlet at the level of the eaves and outlets in the roof ridge, are preferable to mechanical ventilators, which involve continuous noise. Motors will of course have to be used if heat is to be conducted elsewhere. Air should enter the inlets at a rate of 2–2.5 m/sec; in winter, air movement in the vicinity of the animal bodies is ideally at 0.2 m/sec, compared to velocities of up to 0.6 m/sec to prevent stagnant heat in hot weather.

Wrong indoor climatic conditions make the animals more susceptible to disease. Not only plants, but animals, too, need adequate light to prevent deficiency diseases. Bovine tuberculosis is due to poor capacity for light metabolism. Ultraviolet radiation is largely filtered out by window glass and rickets will develop if insufficient exposure prevents adequate vitamin D production in the skin.

Visual disorders, especially night blindness, susceptibility to bacterial infections and poor blood supply to mucous membranes are frequently connected with vitamin A deficiency. Until recently it was thought that vitamin A given by mouth or injection would cure this, but it has now been established that animals must produce part of their own vitamin A from carotene (provitamin A = precursor). Foods rich in carotene and direct sunlight are essential to the animals' health.

Cows lie down in such a way in pasture that they do not have to inhale each other's breath. This must be taken into account with feeding tables used from opposite sides.

Grooming of the cows and regular hoof care are most important. Apart from cleanliness being important for milk hygiene, grooming also furthers the relationship between cows and humans, as the animals like the procedure. The task should not be neglected in tethered housing. In loose housing, yards and pasture animals are able to take care of themselves if suitable provision is made (scratching posts and brushes, $1^1/_2$ metre tree trunks and small groups of bushes). It is part of the social behaviour of cows that partners of equal rank provide comfort and groom each other by licking inaccessible places on the head and neck. Observing this, one gets the impression that animals, too, have 'friendships' and feel 'affection'.

They depend entirely on humans when it comes to care of the hooves. Three or four weeks before they go on pasture and again immediately after the period out on pasture hooves should be checked and trimmed. Modern hoof-care stands and single-handed angle files with flexible disc files of different grain sizes make the work much easier.

Breeding bulls need hoof care every six to eight weeks, as reluctance to serve is frequently connected with hoof problems or painful joints resulting from these. If the animals have got used to the procedure when young, the job presents few problems.

Pregnancy and calving

Fertile cows are expected to calve annually. Certain principles have to be followed to avoid problems and prolonged intervals between calvings.

In healthy cows, milking should stop 40, or at most 60, days before calving. Drying off is therefore best done seven weeks (c. 50 days) before the expected calving date. Cows that calve earlier will have been dry for the minimum period, those that calve later will not exceed the maximum period.

The 'Kraftborn system' has proved efficient if done correctly and if udders are healthy. The day before the chosen date, the cow is milked out completely in the morning and not milked in the evening. The following morning, all four quarters are carefully examined to see they are healthy, using indicator paper to check the pH and the California mastitis test. If the condition is satisfactory, the animal is milked out completely, after which the teat openings are treated with an iodine dip and closed up with clean milking fat.

Cows whose daily milk yield is more than 12 kg when drying off are given dry food only and limited water for two days. According to Schaumann (1980), 500 g of

A good method of dealing with hoof injuries is to glue a wooden sole to the healthy part (special 2-component glue). This relieves the strain on the injured part and accelerates healing.

Glauber's salt dissolved in water and given two days before drying off will avoid the risk of mastitis.

If the cow has had mastitis during the last lactation period, a prophylactic infusion of 15 ml of Laseptal (Schwabe) or Pyrogenium (Schaette) into each quarter after the final milking, observing strict cleanliness, will help to prevent inflammation during the dry period.

During the dry period, udders should be examined very gently at relatively long intervals. Any inflammation that is found requires treatment by an experienced vet, homoeopathic if at all possible; if untreated, the cow's general condition may be seriously affected and, as with the use of antibiotic drying-off preparations, it may prove more difficult to get her in calf during the next period of lactation.

Dry cows are given the same rations as all other members of the herd. In summer, they return to pasture two or three days after drying off. Apart from the above udder examinations, they are treated as usual. During the winter feeding period, they are not given any meal for 10 days, after that they have 1–3 kg like all other cows. For the last two weeks 1 kg of meal is replaced by 1 kg of wheat bran; crushed linseed may be given in addition.

If the calf is in the normal position, cows usually require no help with calving. It is nevertheless advisable to keep them under unobtrusive observation. Assistance should only be given by experienced personnel who know their limits exactly and will call the vet in good time if required. Assistance must be limited to cows who will not manage on their own. Maximum cleanliness is imperative with any intervention. The animal's genitalia and the assistant's hands and arms need to be thoroughly washed with hard soap. Lack of cleanliness during a birth may be responsible for later fertility problems.

After normal calving, the cow is treated as usual, except that half the meal ration is replaced with wheat bran for the first ten days and care is taken not to feed anything liable to increase lactation to a major extent. After this, the cow goes back on normal rations.

After a difficult birth, the animal stays indoors for a few days, or is taken by itself to a calf paddock for hours at a time. Rations consist of fine hay and small quantities of good quality silage, with a twice-daily drink made with linseed mucilage and bran soaked in hot water.

It has been found that parturition, delivery of the afterbirth and regeneration of the uterus are helped by injection 12–15 ml of Metrovetsan (a proprietary product manufactured by Dr Wilmar Schwabe containing *Sepia* 4x and *Pulsatilla* 2x) four and two weeks prior to calving and again after calving. The day after, 20 ml of Calendula/Eucalyptus comp. (Schaette) diluted with an equal amount of hot boiled water may be carefully instilled into the uterus using a sterilized thin flexible tube. This, too, has a beneficial effect on everything happening in the genital area and hence on fertility.

As a rule, the normal cycle is rapidly re-established. After a normal birth and postpartum period healthy animals will normally be in oestrus 21 days after calving. They may be served again 9 weeks after calving, i.e. when in oestrus for the third time. Cows are then physiologically ready to produce a new calf, calving once a year. In problem situations it is gen-

When a cow needs help with calving, lack of hygiene may cause fertility problems later on.

erally recommended to inseminate when the animal is in oestrus around the 40th day post partum, as cows get pregnant more easily at that time. This may appear good advice at first sight, but experience has shown a definite connection between early insemination and the short reproductive life span one sees today. A better method is to deal with the causes of existing infertility problems. These are largely connected with management systems that do not allow for daily exercise in the light and open air and with feeding.

Feeding and performance

The original wild cattle probably lived in lowland deciduous forests and savannah-type open plains. Apart from grass, they would feed on leaves, herbage and fruits.

Cattle are able to convert high-fibre roughage into high-quality animal protein and adequate amounts of this type of food must be made available to prevent diseases and fertility problems.

For good yields and good health cows must be in the habit of taking large quantities of food rich in ballast. Such habits are established by management and feeding when rearing the animals. A dairy cow weighing 630 kg should take 16–20 kg of dry matter (DM) per day; this will enable her to produce the required yield from rations suitable for ruminants.

A vital prerequisite is to offer palatable rations with plenty of variety. Care must be taken to meet the dairy cow's need for absolute regularity by strictly adhering to feeding times and the sequence in which different components are presented.

High dry matter content of varied, well-structured and species-specific rations ensures longevity, fertility and health, while maintaining high milk yields.

Any change in rations, even from poorer to better quality, must be gradual. The ruminal and intestinal flora needs 10–14 days to adapt to changes. Particular care is needed with the change from winter rations given indoors to summer grazing in spring, and the other way round in autumn, situations that are always fraught with difficulty.

Full winter rations are maintained as the cows are gradually taken to pasture instead of into the yard for increasingly longer periods. Starting with a period of one hour, the time spent in the paddock is increased by half an hour each day. Grazing starts when the sward is about 10 cm high, moving rapidly over the areas. After two weeks the animals stay in the paddock all day between feeding times. With increasing sward height, indoor rations are gradually reduced, starting with the succulent feed. It is advisable to add some coarse hay reserved from the first cut of the previous year to the ration. In mild weather the cows can then also stay out overnight. Altogether the changeover should take four to six weeks.

Grazing areas would have to be 25% larger than required to ensure that the cows can have all the feed they require. Strip grazing with balancing rations given at milking times will prevent the loss of a quarter of the available green fodder. Depending on the type, composition and physiological maturity of the available grazing the animals are given coarser or finer hay and later also soilage from fields and meadows. Again it is important to avoid abrupt changes. If balanced rations are given, it is not generally necessary to feed cereal or legume meal during the summer feeding periods, though it may be advisable to give 2–3 kg of meal to animals with very high milk yields to prevent metabolic disorders.

The composition of rations for autumn feeding requires great care and attention, as the energy value of grass is greatly reduced by that time. This is also the time when high-protein catch crop fodder becomes available. Hay or good-quality fodder straw added to the rations will prevent scouring and reduced milk fat levels. Special caution is indicated with fast-growing cabbage family species such as rape and mustard. These should not be cut in advance or left in swaths or heaps for any length of time, as this means a risk of nitrite poisoning. Turnip tops, too, should not be given on their own as their raw fibre content is low at 12%. They need to be balanced by adding sufficient hay or much-wilted silage to provide 40% of the basic food requirement. Fresh matter given to dairy cows should not be in excess of 40 kg per day.

The transition to winter housing is the spring transition in reverse. Part of the green fodder is increasingly replaced with good-quality fodder straw or hay. About four weeks before the proposed date for winter housing, the cows stay indoors overnight. The longer green fodder remains part of the ration the better. Grass and clover mixtures from areas due to be ploughed in, catch crops and marrowstem kale as well as turnip tops may be used.

November and December are a difficult time for animals that have been used to full-time pasture during the summer. As the days are rapidly getting shorter and the sun often does not penetrate the dense mist for days on end, free movement tends to be greatly reduced. A small store of carrots is helpful at this point. A few

High-protein catch crops fed when the energy concentration of grass is decreasing in autumn need to be supplemented with hay or good-quality fodder straw.

kilograms a day will enhance resistance to disease.

Winter rations should also be rich and varied. The need is met by good-quality hay and pre-wilted silage made from greenstuffs grown in leys, mixtures of legumes and cereals and in meadows. Root crops added to the ration will improve basic fodder intake by 1–1.5 kg of DM. More than that increases the danger of acetonaemia (diabetes) in animals that are at risk, especially after calving; the same applies to silage with high butyric acid levels.

Smallish amounts of maize silage (between 5 and a maximum of 10 kg/day/animal) may also be given to dairy cows.

At this point, brief reference should be made to silage and hay making, as these make up the greater part of basic rations.

Hay is the most important basic ingredient for species-specific feeding. Drying under cover greatly improves the quality. Cold air ventilation is usually adequate, but solar power now provides a good energy source, so that heated air can be used in suitable plant. Drying times are significantly reduced by the simple measure of increasing the air temperature by 5 °C, reducing dependence on the weather.

Grass for both hay and soilage is

Concentration per kg	hay	grass and clover silage (37.5% DM)
digestible protein	75 g	40 g
starch equivalents	390	210

Table 60. Hay and silage samples from Talhof farm.

cut early in the morning. If a flail harvester, crimper or similar machine is used, the crop is brought under cover in the late afternoon of the same day in good weather conditions. If heated air is used, pre-drying to 45% water content is adequate, with losses due to fragmentation reduced. Cold air drying plant are charged with greenstuff pre-dried to 30–45% of moisture level, and in this case, too, losses will be minimal. Unlike clover and lucerne (alfalfa) grown on their own, mixtures of the two with grasses are preferable not only from the point of view of nutritional physiology, but also for drying, as the necessary pre-drying level is reached more quickly.

Finger-wheel rakes have relatively low peripheral wheel velocity and are therefore gentlest, especially when putting the hay in swaths prior to bringing it in. Another advantage is that they can be used to turn small swaths, so that it is not necessary to drive over the pre-dried material. On

the other hand, greater care is needed when operating these machines (Heuma, Spinne, Orion) than with p.t.o.-driven machines such as rotary tedders and turners because there is a risk of wrap-around and stringing. The best possible method is probably to use a rotary tedder when the grass is quite fresh and then the finger-wheel machines to make, turn and windrow small swaths.

A blower and telescopic distributor is best used to distribute the pre-dried material in the drier; this reduces the need for manual labour, with less compression due to treading. Driers with solid outer walls can be filled to a height of 4–6 metres without the need for air shafts. A grating with an inlet wedge will be sufficient.

Good pre-wilted silage requires considerable experience, high technical capability and suitable silos. Good-quality lactic acid fermented fodder is produced even with high-protein grass and clover or legume and cereal mixtures if these are ade-

Table 61. Mean values for 8 hay samples and 3 grass and clover silage samples from two biodynamic farms using the new NEL method.

Constituent	hay	grass and clover silage
crude protein % of DM	12.97	15.8
crude fibre % of DM	24.67	24.3
crude ash % of DM	10.08	9.3
digestibility %	67	68.1
gas production ml	48.4	46.0
crude protein (g/kg)	92.2	93.0
starch equivalents	478	540
NEL	5.46	5.85

Winter rations

Hay: 70 g digestible protein, 380 SE, equivalent to 4.63 NEL
Grass and clover silage (35% DM): 40 g digestible protein, 204 SE, equivalent to 2.17 NEL

Quantity	fodder	DM (kg)	dig. protein	SE	prot.:starch	NEL
16 kg	silage	6	640	3264	1:5.1	34.72
12 kg	hay	10	840	4560	1:5.4	55.56
2.5 kg	peas/cereal	2	326	1808	1:5.5	18.25
Total		18	1806	9632	1:5.35	108.53
Minus maintenance requirement			330	3300	1:10	36.80
			1476	6332		71.73
Sufficient for kg milk with 4.5% fat			22.70	21.83		21.28

Summer rations

Hay: 70 g digestible protein, 380 SE, equivalent to 4.63 NEL
Grazing (strip grazing): 22 g digestible protein, 117 SE, equivalent to 1.24 NEL

Quantity	fodder	DM (kg)	dig. protein	SE	prot.:starch	NEL
70 kg	grazing	14	1540	8190	1:5.3	86.80
4 kg	hay	3.5	280	1520	1:5.4	18.52
Total		17.5	1820	9710	1:5.35	105.32
Minus maintenance requirement			330	3300	1:10	36.80
			1490	6410		78.52
Sufficient for kg milk with 4.5% fat			22.9	22.1		23.29

quately pre-dried to 35–50 % of dry matter. It is important to fill silos rapidly, pack the material down well and use air-tight covers.

Under these conditions it is possible to produce palatable, healthy, lactic acid fermented basic food with high nutrient concentration in the dry matter and the right structure for ruminants. In theory and from the physiological point of view it would also be possible to use thoroughly pre-wilted soilage as the sole basic food. In practice it has been found that cows given top-quality pre-wilted silage still like to eat 2 or 3 kg of hay after they have had their fill. It is therefore better to make up a ration in the inverse ratio, i.e. $^2/_5$ silage and $^3/_5$ hay.

With 16 kg of pre-wilted grass and clover silage containing 35 % of DM (0.55 t/m³), silo space required per cow for the winter feeding period (200 days) is c. 6 m³. This makes up one third of the total ration.

Fodder analysis can only be done on a small proportion of the total; this will however also provide some information relating to the part not analysed. Table 60 gives the 10-year average figures for hay and silage

Table 62.
Rations for dairy cows on Talhof farm. Figures based on repeated weighing and analysis of fodder.

samples from Talhof farm analysed in collaboration with the regional government and ministry of agriculture in Germany.

The actual 10-year average yield from 26.3 cows was 6045 kg of milk with 4.50 % fat content, i.e. 272 kg of milk fat. The yield from basic fodder is just under 5000 kg of milk, that from home-produced concentrates well over 1000 kg.

To maintain mineral metabolism, dairy cows are given 155 g/cow/day of a mixture produced on the farm. The composition is as follows:

  200 kg cattle salt
  200 kg calcified seaweed
  100 kg bentonite or kaolin
  100 kg wheat bran
  100 kg basalt flour
   75 kg herb mixture.

The herb mixture is made up as follows:
  40–50% stinging nettle
  25–15% fennel, goat's rue, leaf hay
  c. 35% calendula flowers, dill, wild camomile, chervil, coriander, caraway, marjoram, lemon balm, peppermint, sage, yarrow flowers, thyme, hyssop
  c. 2% mugwort, lovage, rue, wormwood.

Leaf hay is produced from birch leaves and young shoots of ash, field maple, spruce, hazel, lime and willow.

Field maple and lime are especially good for fertility, whilst the others generally enhance vitality and constitution. Leaves and young shoots for leaf hay are gathered before St John's tide (24 June), that is, before the midday point of the sun begins to move downwards again. The material is dried in the shade or in a drier, chopped in a chaff cutter and then

Poisonous shrubs such as laburnum and pea-tree are not suitable for leaf hay.

ground to a coarse powder in a hammer mill. 5% of the powdered herbs may be added to cereals before they are crushed, but not to the salt mixture. The animals find these improved mixtures very palatable. The herbs contain trace elements and essential oils that stimulate vital functions, especially with regard to hormone, vitamin and enzyme metabolism, which contributes greatly to the cows' fertility and health. Herb mixtures of this type are also commercially available in Germany.

Foods and nutrition – general considerations

Basically distinction may be made in animals between the sphere of neurosensory activity (with its centre in the head) and the sphere of metabolism and locomotor activity, with the rhythmical system mediating between them (respiration and blood circulation, lung and heart). Anyone who is willing can see these systems in animals, much in the way previously described for plants.

Rudolf Steiner spoke of them when he discussed the feeding of animals in 1924.

Foods that are part of the root region of plants act specifically on the neurosensory organization of animals, foods from the leaf region on the respiratory and circulatory organization, and foods from the flower and fruit region on the mechanisms of metabolism and locomotion. Both metabolism and rhythmical processes are involved in milk production, which is why any deviation from the customary rhythm will immediately reduce milk yields.

The balance between protein and starch is an important aspect of rations. Excess protein or lack of energy may cause profound disorders in the animal's vital functions. For dairy cows, the protein:starch ratio is 1:10 for maintenance and 1:4.6 for milk production. Combined in a single ration, these give a ratio of 1:5.4.

Roots

Carrots, beetroot, parsnips and sugar beet are particularly suitable for young stock. A powerful inner sensory activity monitors organic development and growth in general at this age. When conditions permit they also show greater liveliness than fully-grown animals. Foals, calves, piglets, fully-grown horses and some poultry (chickens and turkeys) depend a great deal on roots.

Mangels, turnips and swedes are not true roots and mainly show a tendency to grow round and plump. They should therefore only be given to adult animals, especially to promote milk production. Quantities should not be too large, however. The principal consumers are dairy cows, suckling sows, mares, ewes and nanny goats.

Potatoes are to some extent a special case. They develop in the root region without being part of the root system, as they are enlarged stem elements. This makes them unsuitable for young stock, particularly as the plant belongs to the deadly nightshade family and produces the poisonous alkaloid solanine in its green parts. Given raw in small amounts, potatoes will encourage milk production, whilst steamed potatoes help fat stock to put on weight.

Leaf

The primary fodder crops for dairy cows and sheep and within limits also for dairy goats come under this heading. Young leafy material with its low crude fibre content is also good for breeding sows.

The following are provided as grazing, soilage, silage or dry fodder: clovers, grasses (except for late 1st cut), legumes, fodder plants such as rape and mustard and also turnip tops, carrot tops, green maize and sunflowers cut before flowering.

The stem connects the root with the flowering and fruiting region, usually with some foliage included. Stem fodder consists of 1st cut of grass for hay and green cereal plants, sunflowers when in flower, millet grass and marrowstem kale. Depending on the time when cut (early for milk production, later for developing young stock), these provide the ideal basic fodder for all ruminants and horses. The last in the list, marrowstem kale, is however mainly used for dairy cows, dairy sheep and suckling sows.

Flower, seed, fruit

Foods derived from this part of the plant encourage metabolic and reproductive functions and provide energy for external and internal movement activities in the animal organization. The group includes:

Cereal and leguminous grains, linseed, oil seeds and also maize when it is past the milky stage of ripeness. Oats are for all young stock and for horses. Pigs and chickens prefer barley and wheat as well as some rye once they are used to it and maize in different stages of ripeness; these an-

Carrots are important as part of growing rations.

imals may also be given small amounts of the leguminous grains pea, field bean, vetch and sweet lupin. Uncooked leguminous grains promote milk production and fertility functions; when steamed or boiled they provide energy for work and help fat stock to gain weight.

Some types of fodder do not entirely fit those categories.

The seed coats of all seeds have an important role to play. Bran as the outer part of seed and embryo is rich in vitamins. It particularly helps the development of the fetal membranes and is therefore given to pregnant animals.

Herbs and medicinal material come from all three regions of the plant. Characteristically, their active principles are produced in a region that lies between plant and animal nature and include alkaloids and essential oils. Medicinal actions cannot be ascribed to individual constituents as a rule, but depend on the specific composition as a whole. Once again the root sphere acts on the neurosensory organization, the leaf sphere on the rhythmical system and flower and fruit on metabolism and limbs.

Herbs make food more digestible and correct imbalances in the ration; dispositions to certain diseases can be overcome. Strictly speaking they are not fodder in the proper sense.

The same applies to cattle salt, which nevertheless plays a vital role in nutrition. Its main function is to channel the different nutrients to the right part of the organism. If wool sheep do not get the salt they require, wool quality and quantity are reduced. The coats of horses and cattle grow dull with salt deficiency, the horny substance of hooves and horns gets brittle and is apt to crack, and blood supply to mucous membranes

Steam sterilization of pipeline milking installations avoids the risk of detergent residues.

is poor. In the wild, animals often travel long distances to salt licks or lakes to meet their needs. Farmers need to take care that deficiency does not develop.

In a balanced farm organism, livestock numbers are determined by the amount of fertilizer required by soil and plants and the fodder requirements of animals. In contrast to intensive animal keeping, this allows for individual care to be given to each animal. Human beings find their inner life enriched through such a personal relationship to animals.

Milk

All efforts to manage and feed the animals in accordance with their natural needs will be in vain unless extreme care and attention are given to milking and dairying methods.

The first precondition for wholesome milk of good flavour is to keep milking times and methods and the milking order as regular as possible. Any change or upset in the daily routine will reduce milk volume and constituents. Fat and lactose levels serve as indicators in this case. Milk is one of the most valuable foods but also one of the most sensitive. Extreme cleanliness must be observed during milking, storage and any processing. The cows themselves, the people who work in the milking parlour and dairy and all equipment must be meticulously clean. The water used to clean milking machines must meet the established health standards. The use of soaps, detergents and disinfectants requires special attention and caution. Rinse with plenty of plain water after using them. A method that has proved effective is to flush milking machines and pipes with water heated to 75 °C for 20 minutes, rinse with cold water and air-dry immediately before milking starts.

Rubber parts of milking machines that come in contact with milk need to be changed at least every six months.

Milk from sick animals, even if treated with medicaments that do not require a waiting period, should be given to older calves or pigs.

If the above directions are followed conscientiously and in detail, and care is taken with the management and feeding of the dairy cows, then milk is one of the most important basic foods. Taking it regularly, one can to some extent sense and share in the experience of the variety of tastes provided by pasture and hay that include many herbs in the cycle of the year.

Horses

Horses (*Equus ferus ferus*) are solipedes and typical steppe animals. They have only one, relatively small stomach, but the colon and above all the appendix are so highly developed that large quantities of roughage can be taken at a time. The earliest signs of domestication go back to c. 3500–3000 BC in sites in Europe and Asia north of the Caucasus. Horses rapidly formed personal bonds with humans as they were used for hunting, travel and in battle. It was only much later that they achieved importance as draught animals in agriculture, though little used for that purpose today.

Small breeds such as the Hafling may be used as draught horses for the cultivation of row crops, to weed harrow and harrow fields and for ridging and hoeing; their value lies in the fact that they do little damage to the soil. Through their dung, ideally mixed with that of other animals on the farm, they contribute something of their specific nature to the whole farm organism.

Management must take account of the needs of this active, intelligent animal. Work horses are extremely undemanding: deep litter open housing with two alternate yard areas of adequate size is perfectly adequate. Another form of species-specific housing is loose boxes with a floor area of 12–15 m² and a minimum height of 3 metres and automatic drinking bowls, and a yard or paddock. Originally a herd animal, single horses depend on the company of other farm animals or humans; without it, they get bored and lonely and may develop vices.

Sound hay from a first cut made when reasonably mature, oats and good straw provide the basic ration. Carrots and fodder sugar beet are favourite foods. A 'carrot diet' given twice a year to horses that are properly managed in all other respects helps to keep worm infestation under control. 1–5 kg of oats per day, given whole or freshly crushed, should meet energy requirements depending on the work to be done. Hay and good-quality fodder straw should be given to prevent colic. In summer the basic foods are forage grass and soilage that is not too young. Whilst the new coat is growing, horses should be given linseed mucilage and wheat bran steeped in boiling water as a once-daily drink for six weeks. A lump of rock salt should be accessible.

Horses turned out to graze daily

Hafling and Fjord horses are excellent for light cultivation work; they demand little by way of care and feeding.

need no grooming, which in fact could be harmful as the grease on the under coat has an important skin protective function. Stabled horses need daily grooming with a body brush, not a currycomb, as here, too, grooming should not be too intense.

Cleaning out the hooves requires special care. After work on clayey or sticky soils, the hooves need to be scraped with a blunt implement and if necessary washed and greased before taking the horse into the stable. Shoes have to be renewed every six to eight weeks, even if still firmly in position. If this is not done, the growth of horn causes faulty position of the limb and ultimately leads to painful diseases.

Breeding and rearing

Foals may be offered hay and crushed oats from the second week onwards, though their dam's milk continues to be the main food. If they are to be put to use early (age over two years) the dam needs to be fed well, as the birth weight should double within a month. Foals will only achieve such rapid growth if given plenty of milk. It is better, however, to wait until they are three years old, in which case the birthweight only needs to double in two months. Iron deficiency will be no problem if foals can be put out to pasture in their first days of life. If pasturing is not possible, special iron preparations must be given prophylactically.

Hay racks should be adjustable in height to avoid back problems.

Depending on other demands made on the dam (new pregnancy or work), suckling continues for five or six months. Weaning can be done from one day to the next if the foal has been apart from its mother for sever-

al hours each day for some weeks previously. The mare must be kept on short rations during this time, with water also limited if necessary. After weaning the young horses are given 2–3 kg of oats and a little hay to supplement the grazing. Carrots are much liked in winter and may also be replaced with sugar beet or fodder sugar beet.

Yearlings will normally manage on good-quality grazing and mineral supplement.

Energy food is only given again when the horses are used for breeding, riding or as draught horses. The amount of oats or ready mixture given will depend on the work required.

Pigs

Domesticated pigs belong to the genus of true pigs (*Sus*); they are cloven-hoofed ruminants. It is assumed that current breeds all derive from a single wide-spread wild variety. Two species of this are the European wild boar (*Sus scrofa ferus*) and the Asiatic wild pig (*Sus vittatus*). Domestication probably started between 10,000 and 6,000 BC in China, around the Baltic and in the South and South East of Europe.

European wild boars can still be found in the wild today and may indeed cause considerable crop damage. Their life style is characterized by extensive migrations, probably the reason for their survival. Sites where damage has been caused by one and the same group within 48 hours are sometimes 40 or 50 km apart.

Pigs need much space for their well-being, with large family units to

Pig dung, being cold and wet, makes a good supplement for cow dung on warm, light soil. Areas with this type of soil are therefore particularly suitable for pig keeping.

satisfy their social needs. Modern pig breeding has produced animals that are totally unsuited to near-natural rearing and management. The heat-insulating layer of peripheral fat has been bred out, so that the animals have to be kept in heated houses. The capacity for temperature regulation has also been lost on the whole, and the pigs are much more susceptible to stress.

Certain conditions have to be met if these animals are to be integrated in the farm organism. The first point to be considered is site conditions; pig dung is not suitable for cold, damp areas, so that it is better not to keep pigs in that case, or only a small group to utilize organic waste material. On the other hand pig dung is extremely useful added to cow dung for light, warm soils. That is also the type of soil where quality potatoes with good flavour do well, so that damaged and small tubers are available as a basic pig food. Large herds of grain-fed pigs compete with humans for food and are therefore not acceptable in terms of world food supplies. A reasonable number of pigs, fed mainly on waste material and any produce that is difficult to utilize for other purposes, contribute to make farm management rational and economic.

Breeding and rearing

Robust, healthy breeding sows with thriving offspring do best in single huts of straw bales and wooden boards in sufficiently large paddocks. To be successful, pigs have to be adapted to such conditions from an early age and should ideally come from intensive breeds or lines. If sufficient land is not available, loose housing with straw-covered floors

Pigs need ample space for accommodation and exercise to maintain the large family units that satisfy their social needs.

and yards of adequate size is preferable to the tethered housing that is so wide-spread today.

Paddocks and yards must meet the following requirements:
- sound fencing with no risk of injury, e.g. wooden poles, if necessary with an electric wire relatively close to the ground,
- constant supply of clean drinking water,
- shelter from strong sunlight and extreme weather conditions,
- separate feeding places for piglets and sows, with solid flooring easy to keep clean,
- mud wallow for body care and for cooling down in hot weather; this is cleared and filled with new soil once a year,
- At least in yards, a rooting corner with grass turves or humified cow dung compost.

If pigs are to be kept in groups of several breeding sows with boar and piglets until weaned, adequate space is needed and the animals must be used to each other. Ranking order is usually maintained unless new breeding sows join the group. Suitable protection for the young must be provided in farrowing units. Sows usually take good care of their young in the above-mentioned straw huts and rarely lie on them. The person in charge of the animals must ensure that farrowing can proceed undisturbed; monitoring is necessary if farrowing pens are used.

Restless sows or piglets suggest inadequate milk supply (agalactia). The causes of this are hormonal imbalance, underdeveloped teats, mastitis and sickness in the sow. Veterinary help must be sought immediately. The normally obligatory iron injection can be avoided by making composted cow dung, soil from around nettle roots or from grass sod available to piglets from the first day. They will quickly get used to eating glumeless oats or barley and having a taste of their mother's green fodder. The digestive system of pigs and especially suckling sows is not well adapted to roughage; they need greenstuff that is easily digestible and low in crude fibre, and silage made of the same materials in winter. A mixture of crushed oats and barley, peas, wheat and herbs is added to this.

After eight weeks piglets have usually reached the stage where they can manage without their mother. Skimmed milk or buttermilk given for two or three weeks when weaning makes the transition easier. Housing with straw-covered floors and a suitable run is also best for store pigs. Separation into breeding and fattening pigs comes at the age of 10–12 weeks.

Breeding animals are not taken from first litters but from the third or fourth litters of good sows. Females are selected on the following criteria:
– health,
– lively, wide-awake temperament,
– good build, slightly above litter average,
– skin with good blood supply, with pink colour showing through,
– glossy, medium coarse, dense bristle coat,
– tail very curly,
– absence of abnormalities and
– at least seven pairs of regularly developed teats.

Depending on race and intensity of management and feeding, gilts are ready to be put to the boar at 7–9 months and a minimum weight of 90 kg. At this point the final selection of breeding animals is made and they are put in groups that should not be changed after this, to avoid fights to re-establish ranking order.

Gilts are moved to the paddock or house where they are to farrow when half-way through their pregnancy. Short but adequate rations ensure an easy birth and a healthy litter.

Fattening pigs

The carcase quality demanded by consumers and the meat processing industry – meat:fat ratio, relative proportion of desirable parts, meat quality – has encouraged breeders to produce the modern early-maturing but highly susceptible pork type pig. At the same time consumer demand for pork from animals kept under near-to-nature conditions is rising and this agrees with the aims of biodynamic pig farmers.

Fattening may be done under similar species-specific conditions as for breeding pigs: straw-covered floors indoors and several hours daily spent in the yard or paddock, with rations made up of farm-produced material such as potatoes, greenstuff or also fodder sugar beet, bran and crushed oats, barley and peas steeped in hot water, with herbs added. The meat:fat ratio is somewhat narrower with animals kept in this way, but the meat is juicier and has more flavour than pork from modern pigs.

Daily outdoor exercise has been shown to have definite value also for fattening pigs.

The animals are much more contented and less susceptible. Fattening does take a little longer, but consumers are prepared to pay slightly more. Nor should we forget that dung from these animals has a better consistency and a more vitalizing effect on the soil.

Flocks of sheep have an important function in the maintenance and care of cultivated landscapes.

Sheep

Sheep (*Ovis ammon aries*) were among the earliest animals to be domesticated and derive from wild sheep (*Ovis ammon*). They are true herd animals, the size of the herd being considered a measure of family wealth in the past.

The total number of sheep in the world is approximately the same as for cattle – just under a thousand million and rising. This does not, however apply in Central Europe. Sheep are an important element in agriculture because they are undemanding and provide valuable wool, wholesome meat and rich manure.

Sheep make a major contribution to the maintenance and care of cultivated landscapes in industrialized countries. The special character of juniper heathlands and the poor hillside areas in the Swabian Alb region and Lueneburg Heath would soon be lost if sheep did not graze there, for woodland would soon take over. Too many sheep on the other hand may cause severe damage, causing whole areas to be denuded (karst).

A herd of sheep can benefit a farm considerably. Sheep dung has 'heating' qualities that warm and loosen heavy, sticky soils. Other uses are the utilization of poor grassland a long way from the homestead, roadsides and waste areas and carefully regu-

lated grazing of winter proud growth (e.g. winter barley or Landsberg mixture in autumn, winter rye in spring). Efficient folding on slopes that do not take vehicular traffic will improve soil fertility even on difficult sites.

Management and feeding

A trained shepherd is a definite advantage for larger flocks. Smaller groups can be included in the general work programme, though this takes some effort. Airy wooden housing with straw-covered floors and opportunities for partitioning off some areas for lambing ewes and their lambs should be available in winter and for the hot part of the summer. Draughts must be avoided, but the temperature should not be too high (12 °C is the ideal). The house should be in a central position relative to the grazing areas and have a solid-floored yard area. Indoor space required for a ewe with lamb is 1.5–2 m^2; yearlings, wethers and unmated ewes need 0.7–1 m^2.

Compost preparations have to be added to the dung in good time and it needs to be moistened at intervals to produce good composted manure, for sheep dung tends to heat up and grow mouldy, resulting in high nitrogen and carbon losses.

The Texel is a good breed for keeping in paddocks, but other breeds adapt very quickly.

Additional rations if required are good-quality straw from grain legumes (pea, vetch and lentil), cereals (oats and barley) and grass-seed production. Older lambs and suckling ewes may suitably be given smallish amounts of hay and crushed cereal grain and also small portions of pre-wilted silage when in pasture.

Rams are given additional concentrate shortly before and during tupping time. Young rams can safely serve 3 or 4 ewes, older rams 4–6 ewes a day without taking harm.

Adequate water and mineral mixture (the same as that given for cows) should be made available.

Care of the feet is important and should be done three times a year. Attention also has to be paid to external and internal parasites, with the necessary treatment initiated in good time.

Milk sheep

East Friesian milk sheep can assume the function of dairy cows in market gardens. They become very attached to people and respond to tender loving care, even rams becoming sociable and peaceful.

Fertility is extremely high (above 200%) and they normally give birth to twins and sometimes triplets. Good ewes produce over 1000 kg of milk with 6–7 % of fat and 5% of protein. To avoid undue emaciation, they must be provided with good-quality and abundant pasture or be given additional soilage or pre-wilted silage and also hay, fodder beet and crushed cereal or legume grains. In addition to milk and lambs, a ewe will produce about 4.5 kg of long,

Excessive numbers of sheep or goats have caused large areas to be denuded. If numbers are right and the herd is properly managed, they contribute much to meeting the demand for wool and feeding the world.

somewhat coarse wool per annum with 66% pure wool content.

Sheep husbandry as an integral part of farm management not only offers economic benefits but also rounds out the animal world's contribution to the farm organism.

Goats

Goats (*Capra aegagrus hircus*) are probably the most independent of domestic animals, despite the fact that they are also among those that have been domesticated longest. Their original home was the dry desert shrubland in the highlands of the Near East.

To really understand goats, one must have seen the way they keep their balance on the narrowest of rock ledges at altitudes of over 300 metres, stretching their slender necks to reach a specially aromatic herb. Highly strung, always on the lookout for something new, they move among the rocks all day looking for the best and most aromatic leaves and tips of branches they can find. They will only return to the mountain hut for milking at night if they are sure of being offered a special treat and above all a full salt lick. If the stable has been cleaned out in the meantime and a litter of fine dry leaves, straw or unusable hay put down, their milk is a delight to drink, provided the goat keeper keeps himself and the milking equipment scrupulously clean.

It is easy to see from the above what has to be done to have contented goats – an almost impossible goal – and delectable milk. Cleanliness, a good variety of aromatic fodder and good opportunity for exercise are the main requirements. The billy goat is out of place in the milk goats' stable, though he may go with the herd and play his pranks during the day.

During the period of active plant growth, goats prefer shrubby pasture areas. With some patience they can be made to accept being tethered, with the stake moved several times a day, if no single suitable area is available. They will merely need an additional $1/_2$ kg each of hay and concentrate made up of equal parts of bran and crushed oats and peas.

During the winter when they are kept indoors, goats should be let out into the open air for several hours each day. This also provides an opportunity for cleaning and airing the house, cleanliness being a precondition for palatable goat's milk. Winter rations for adults goats are 1–2 kg of hay and the same amount of roots, grass silage, or clean kitchen waste, plus $1/_2$–1 kg of the above concentrate. Goats like frequent small meals, so that the ration is best divided into three meals daily. Kids are given whole milk for six weeks and then skimmed milk for the same period (2 litres a day). If the weather permits, they can go out to pasture when just a few days old. Female kids can be served for the first time at nine months. Goats need to be dry for 5–7 weeks before kidding, to allow them to gain the strength they need for kidding and the next lactation period.

The food requirement of a goat is one tenth that of a cow. Kept under the right conditions she will produce almost a third of the volume of milk produced by a cow.

The feet have to be taken care of several times a year to ensure healthy limbs.

Properly managed, fed and cared for, two mountain goats will ade-quately meet the milk and milk product needs of a family of four. A UN-ESCO study has shown that the people of the Third World can only be provided with sufficient protein and fat by increasing the goat population.

Poultry

Pigeons and some ducks are the only poultry still capable of proper flight. Turkeys, chickens, domesticated ducks and geese can only fly for very short distances.

Poultry differ considerably from other domestic animals in anatomy, food requirements and digestive system. Foods are broken down rapidly and intensively in a process close to inorganic chemistry; the dung is acrid and practically mineral. Chickens have the greatest economic significance of all in poultry farming.

Chickens

The domestic chicken (*Gallus gallus* f. *domestica*) is descended from the red jungle fowl (*Gallus gallus*) and was domesticated in about 2500 BC in India. Chicken protein is important in human nutrition, being easily digestible and of high quality.

The economic boom and increased buying power after the Second World War created a powerful demand for eggs and poultry meat. The ultimate

Chickens range freely in their native steppes; batteries and cages fail to meet their needs.

outcome of this was battery chicken keeping which, however, does not meet the animals' needs. Chickens are used to roaming widely in the steppes and like any animal need to be able to move freely in light and air. Biodynamic farmers therefore always give preference to near-natural free-range systems.

Management and feeding

Poultry numbers are essentially determined by the volume of cereal waste; the quality grain being used for human consumption. A laying hen eats about 45 kg of grain including wet mash a year, so that 10 ha of food quality cereal (wheat, rye, naked oats and barley) will just about maintain 100 chickens.

The birds cannot go out of doors in winter weather as the combs will freeze and the chickens become snow-blind. Housing must therefore provide adequate space. Three chickens require a minimum of 1 m² floor space. Windows need to be 1/5 the area of the floor space; they should face south and be high enough to allow the winter sun to reach every corner of the house. Five hens need 1 metre perch space and one open nest; with trap nests one needs one for every three hens. A sand bath and a reasonable area with composted cow manure for scratching are to be recommended.

One hectare of open run is sufficient for 300 laying hens and their offspring or 400 hens without young stock. Parasite problems are avoided by having twice the area available, to be grazed one year and cut the next. Chickens only eat very young greenstuff, and it has proved effective to let calves, pigs and horses graze with them during the main growing

period, as these will keep the sward short.

In summer, each hen is given 50 g of wet mash in the mornings and 50 g of grains in the afternoons. In winter they have 100 g of wet mash in the morning and 30 g each of wheat, germinated oats and carrots, beetroot or vegetable wastes. Sea-shell cake and poultry grit are provided ad lib. Wet mash is made with equal parts of crushed oats, barley and peas, adding 10% of herb mixture and hayseed with a high proportion of clover leaves. Mix with skimmed milk or whey. Low fat curd cheese and fresh clean drinking water should always be available. The number of eggs laid per annum can be increased by adding 4–6 g of fish meal daily. Good layers will then produce 230–245 eggs a year.

Breeding and rearing

The correlation between high laying performance and good fattening properties is negative, so that lightweight laying breeds are preferred for egg production. Trials of many years' duration have shown white Leghorns to be particularly suitable (Johannson, Rendel & Gravert 1966; Hutt 1958, 1965). Compared to other breeds, Leghorns had
– a better constitution,
– lower food consumption per kilogram of egg material,
– a higher vitamin content in the eggs of birds given the same rations,
– lower vitamin requirements,
– a higher shell content and therefore shells less liable to break,
– greater resistance to infectious diseases, especially during rearing and
– reduced susceptibility to rickets.

White Leghorns are good foragers and layers, which makes them the breed for free-range keeping.

Labour policies usually mean that farmers buy pullets of hybrid stock. With natural breeding the problem is to find breeding cocks of different stock so that inbreeding is avoided. Inbreeding trials running for 14 years at the University of Minnesota showed that laying performance went down by just under 10 eggs annually for every 10% increase in the inbreeding coefficient, with hatching ability down by 4.4% and sexual maturity delayed by six days. As the degree of inbreeding increased, defects also increased compared to non-inbred chickens: curvature of breastbone, twisted beak and cleft palate. It is therefore absolutely essential to get new breeding cocks every two years, particularly as their fertility decreases markedly in the third year. One cock is needed for every 15–20 hens.

For a four-year mean cycle, 120 hatching eggs from proven layers or ten to twelve broody hens with 11–13 eggs each are required for every 100 hens. Experience has shown that naturally bred hens are more robust and have greater vitality than those bred artificially and will live longer, while maintaining a good laying performance.

To keep labour requirements within reasonable limits, natural breeding is best done in special brood hen units. These should be fairly close to the farmstead to avoid too much time being lost 'on the way'. Nests should be partitioned from neighbouring ones with boards so that the hens do not upset each other. Facilities for shading the light are needed, as the hens will stay on their nest better in the dark.

Eggs from good hens should be stored in a cool, dark and frost-free place and turned once daily (the date stamp is on top one day and underneath the next). The eggs should weigh between 53 and 68 g, be normal in shape, with the shell free from defects, and be not more than 10 days old when put under the hen.

A brood nest is made by cutting a large turf, placing bricks around it, padding the small hollow with hay or fine straw, and surrounding this with a firmly twisted plait of straw. If the ground is still very cold in spring, it is advisable to warm the turves in good time by putting them in a heated room.

Once a hen is well established on china eggs, the slightly warmed brood eggs are put under her in the evening. Once a day, always at the same time, she is let out into the run, which has a sand bath, and fed outside with maize, wheat or barley but no mash or oats. Broken eggs and droppings are removed from the nest during this time. After just under half an hour the hen is allowed back on the eggs.

Eggs are candled whilst the hen is out in the run on the 7th and 14th days. Infertile eggs are easily distinguished from fertile ones; they can be boiled and fed to any chicks that have hatched. Hatching occurs on the 19th to 21st day. Eggs with unpecked shells are floated in water at a temperature of 38–40 °C. Live chicks will cause the egg to move actively. Whilst hatching is in progress, empty shells are removed at intervals and new chicks are put in a warmed padded basket. When all have hatched they are returned to the hen.

Feeding is the same as for artificially hatched chicks. The brood are given fairly coarse wheat meal and from the fifth day onwards a mixture of soft curd cheese (quark), coarsely grated carrots, chopped dandelion,

For breeding, new cocks of different stock are needed every two or three years; otherwise inbreeding will seriously affect performance.

nettle or lettuce leaves. They are given weak herb tea to drink, using camomile, peppermint and wormwood in turn. To prevent rearing problems, two tablespoonfuls of *Arsenicum album* 7x are added to every litre of the liquid.

The hen and her chicks are allowed to go outside from the third day onwards. From now on she will take care of her brood and not only all the children in the neighbourhood but adults, too, find that wonder never ceases each time they are able to see this very picture of life and fertility.

Pullets are ready to lay at five or six months. To avoid a change of housing during the laying period, they are moved to a thoroughly cleaned hen house about four weeks beforehand.

Other poultry

Geese and **ducks** may be kept if ponds or lakes are available. Some breeds of duck are considered good snail eaters and grassland has reputedly been cleared from liver flukes by flocks of ducks eradicating the snail species (*Limnaea trunculata*) that acts as intermediate host. Ducks can also be very useful in market gardens by eating many of the snails and slugs.

Turkeys need good-size runs but are good brooders. If hens prove unreliable, a turkey hen will take 20–30 hens' eggs, depending on size. They are rather clumsy and may step on the newly hatched chicks, so that it is necessary to keep them under observation when the chicks are hatching, removing the new chicks to a warm place of safety if necessary. Later on the turkey hens will look after the brood with great care and skill, effec-

If health problems are dealt with early, expensive long-term treatment may not be needed and there is often no need to call the vet.

tively protecting them from predators.

Bronze turkeys are a somewhat lighter breed and particularly suitable for extensive grazing. Given a sufficiently large area, ideally with some woodland included, they need little additional feed.

In conclusion, mention must be made of **pigeons**. They can cause serious damage to field crops, but can also be a help by feeding on small weeds and weed seeds. Pigeon dung is particularly useful for supporting phosphorus processes in the soil and encouraging plants to flower. The same applies, through in lesser degree, to chicken and turkey dung.

Animal health and ill-health

With human beings, the term health is used to define a 'state of complete physical, mental and social well-being, with every individual his own standard in this respect.' (Brockhaus 1958)

'Animal welfare depends essentially on vital processes taking their course undisturbed in a species-specific and behaviour-adapted way.' (German Animal Protection Legislation).

Plant growth is said to be healthy if uptake of matter (salts) through the roots is in balance with production of matter (sugar) in the leaf under the influence of the sun's light and heat.

Soil health depends on balanced, site-adapted interaction between minerals, organic matter and moisture on the one hand, and air, warmth and soil organisms on the other. Soil health and plant health are intimately connected. It may be necessary to

hardening deficiency hypofunction want	balance **health** harmony	dissolution excess hyperfunction surfeit

consider a sick plant on its own in order to diagnose the condition. The cause and potential treatment can only be found by taking account of all the factors involved – soil life and structure, cultivations, manuring, cropping sequence, and so on. Recovery will depend on changing these rather than treating individual plants.

Animals have an inner life, and normal progress of the species-specific life pattern depends mainly on management and feeding. Imbalances in either will often cause all stock to fall ill.

With human beings, balance and harmony in life play a role in connection with sickness and health and so does individual destiny.

Health is not a fixed, stable state but a state of equilibrium held in tension between hardening and dissolution, deficiency and excess, hypofunction and hyperfunction, desire and surfeit.

On a farm, the health of the stock is indicative of the harmony that exists between the different life spheres, the balance achieved in management and feeding, and the relationship between humans and animals. Persistent or recurrent serious illnesses indicate the need for a thorough review of the whole farm organization. Extensive soil analyses, sometimes also blood tests, and the advice of experienced people, veterinary surgeons and professional colleagues will often provide the solu-tion in such difficult situations.

Occasional problems are always bound to come up and have to be dealt with. In recent years, veterinary surgeons have shown increasing readiness to consider natural and homoeopathic methods of treatment. Mutual trust and respect between farmers using natural methods and a veterinary surgeon who thinks and works out of the biological situation as a whole make a good basis for therapy. With sufficient experience and careful observation it is often possible to take simple measures in good time and avoid more serious problems requiring prolonged treatment. Below, a number of well-proven preventive and first aid measures* are given for the different types of animals.

With all animals, injections should be given subcutaneously (under the skin) or intramuscularly (into muscle) close to the focus of the disease, using the finest possible needles. Drops may be given by mouth with the help of plastic syringes used without needles. For larger amounts of fluid use a wine bottle with a long thin neck. Care must be taken to see that none of the liquid gets into the wind-pipe, as this may cause pneumonia.

Fresh wounds are treated with compresses moistened with arnica essence or dry wound powder (Arnica/Echinacea comp., Weleda) or arnica ointment dressings. Sprains, swellings and strains are treated with

*For further information see e.g. Spielberger & Schaette (1983).

mud packs kept moist by alternately putting on arnica and comfrey essence. At the same time give *Arnica* 3x drops by mouth or *Arnica* 5x by injection.

Older injuries that have become inflamed are treated with compresses moistened with dilute calendula essence or echinacea extract (e.g. Echinacin, Madaus).

Interdigital bacillary necrosis (foul-in-the-foot) is frequently cured by applying cotton wool soaked in tincture of iodine as a dressing. *Silicea* 10x is given by mouth to enhance the effect. Wood tar is applied to mechanical injuries of the feet.

General disorders with no evident cause – loss of appetite, poor digestion, etc. – are best treated in the first place by giving 0.7 litres of hot strong coffee or 100 ml of warmed Coffea prep. (Schaette). This can do no harm and has often proved effective.

Resistance may be enhanced by acid therapy. 60 ml of fruit vinegar per CU given once daily for an extended period will inhibit inflammation and help to prevent 'multifactorial disease' (problems caused by several unfavourable factors coming together, e.g. shipping fever). Similar effects may be achieved by spraying or vaporizing Kapff's acid or Sabona stable acid. In many cases it is sufficient to put out shallow dishes containing these acids.

Both internal and external inflammations are effectively controlled with injections of Lachesis Argentum (Wala), Laseptal (Schwabe) or Pyrogenium comp. (Schaette). Inflammatory conditions always put a strain on the liver; this can be dealt with by also giving injections of *Flor de piedra* 4x and *Chelidonium* 4x, or 20 drops of the same given per CU

Coffea preparatum ad usum veterinarium (Weleda/Schaette) is a medicament made from coffee based on a formula given by Rudolf Steiner. Its indications are wide, especially for cattle, horses and chickens.

three times daily by mouth.

Virus infections and vaccines

Cattle often react violently to vaccination against virus diseases. In extreme cases, vaccination against foot-and-mouth disease (FMD) may cause the death of susceptible or weak young stock and abortion in cows. Insurance may compensate for financial losses but the animal, reared with affection, is missed from the herd. Abortion may be followed by long-drawn-out fertility problems, so that a valuable breeding cow is not available. Calves born in the weeks following vaccination frequently show poor vitality and are susceptible to endemic diseases of the rearing period.

Good contact maintained with the local vet usually makes it possible to find out if this type of vaccination is planned. The farmer can then give a 6 ml injection of Viruvetsan (Schwabe) per CU eleven days and one day prior to vaccination as a prophylactic measure. The same preparation given in combination with treatment for inflammation has proved effective in preventing secondary bacterial infection in animals suffering from virus diseases such as swine influenza and shipping fever.

Rearing problems

Weak offspring are sometimes born in November or December, usually due to metabolic disorders, vaccination or virus disease of the mother. Scouring, joint-ill, white scours and spastic conditions may become endemic, affecting almost all young stock and causing severe losses. The following treatment has been found effective in such cases:

Pregnant mothers are given half a

teaspoonful of *Calcium carbonicum* 4x daily for three months prior to giving birth, and weekly injections alternating between Vitavetsan (Schwabe) – which must be given subcutaneously to avoid inflammation – and *Chelidonium* 4x, 6 ml in each case.

The calves are given colostrum five or six times on the first day, the first time in their first hour of life. 5 ml of Viruvetsan is injected immediately they are born, and nonspecific immunostimulants on the 1st, 3rd and 5th days (e.g. Duphamun for calves and piglets – Duphar B.V., Amsterdam, Holland). Non-specific immunity is achieved by

– increasing phagocytosis, the process by which certain cells in the body absorb and destroy pathogenic microbes,
– enhanced interferon production (interferon is a substance produced in the body that inhibits the multiplication of viruses in living cells; it is effective against a number of viruses, and many viruses that occur in animals are sensitive to interferon),
– stimulation of the lymphopoietic system, so that immune reactions are enhanced.

From the fifth day onwards, young animals are given daily oral doses of *Flor de piedra* 6x and *Arsenicum album* 6x, with 4 ml of Viruvetsan and Vitavetsan injected once a week in alternation. Once the chain of infection has been broken, therapy can be gradually scaled down and discontinued with the calves, foals and piglets that follow.

Diseases of the udder

Highly acute febrile mastitis devel-

oping within a few hours generally requires veterinary treatment. The udder is milked dry every 30 minutes until the vet comes, lightly massaging in Udder Balsam (Schaette) afterwards. Subcutaneous injections of 15 ml of Laseptal or Pyrogenium comp. every four to six hours should be continued even if conventional veterinary treatment is given. 20 drops of *Aconitum* 4x, *Asa foetida* 4x and *Phosphorus* 6x are given hourly in rotation. Liver therapy is given in addition.

Chronic mastitis calls for careful long-term treatment. The udder is milked dry after the day's milking has been done. The affected quarter is massaged for 15 minutes with Udder Balsam, Pollen Comb and Honey Ointment (Wala) or homemade udder ointment (see below), finally instilling 15 ml of Pyrogenium comp. or Laseptal into the quarter via the teat canal. This must be preceded by careful disinfection of the tip of the teat, and a new sterile disposable syringe with sterile disposable plastic tip must be used on every occasion. The treatment is supplemented with the above treatment for inflammations and with 20 drops of *Pulsatilla* 5x/*Phytolacca* 3x aa (aa = in equal parts) given three times daily by mouth. It is usually possible to reduce instillation to one treatment daily after a few days and soon stop it altogether, whilst the massage and the drops need to be continued for some time.

All quarters must be completely clear before such cows are dried out. After the milking, 20 ml of Laseptal is instilled under sterile conditions into each quarter via the teat canal; then the tips of the teats are disinfected and closed up with scrupulously clean milking fat.

The homoeopathic method given here for the treatment of mastitis is usually more successful, with longer lasting effect, than conventional treatment with antibiotics, sulphonamides, etc.

Weleda Massage Balm massaged in when milking gives rapid relief with severely swollen udders after calving. In addition 20 drops of *Apis mel.* 4x are given twice daily by mouth.

The following home-made udder ointment has proved highly effective: Soak 250 g each of calendula flowers (pot marigold), lemon balm leaves and dried marjoram plants for 15 minutes in 250 ml of alcohol; add the whole to 10 kg of melted unsalted lard, boil up briefly, and leave on a low heat for 30 minutes. After 20 hours, heat the mass and press it through a densely woven linen bag to remove the plant residues. Store the ointment in glass jars.

Fertility problems

Fertility is not normally a problem if animals are suitably fed and managed. The relationship between performance level and fertility is entirely due to environmental conditions. Johannson has done extensive studies and concludes that 'there is nothing to indicate genetic correlation between high performance and low fertility' (Johannson/Rendel/Gravert 1966).

In the same way, no genetic link has been found between ovarian cysts and milk yield, though it is established that ovarian cysts are hereditary. Cows with cysts produce small amounts of endocrine oestrogen and this increases the milk yield. One-sided selection for high milk yield and continued breeding from cow families with increased incidence of cysts will give rise to such apparent connections. These families should not be continued, as they are liable to perpetuate low fertility.

The following treatment may be

Cows with a hereditary disposition for ovarian cysts should be excluded from the breeding programme and especially from being the mothers of breeding bulls.

used to support the reproductive functions in cases of periodic or occasional problems. A number of medicinal preparations based on the pasque flower (*Pulsatilla vulgaris* or *Anemone pulsatilla*) are available, all of them medicinal in the genital sphere. One of these is Metrovetsan (Schwabe); used in conjunction with Vitavetsan it provides effective prophylaxis. Animals at risk are given 15 ml each of the two preparations by subcutaneous injection four and two weeks before the birth and again when giving birth.

Since this procedure was introduced at Talhof farm, the only cases of retention of the afterbirth have been with multiple births and even then only rarely. Metrovetsan encourages rapid involution of the uterus and improved blood supply to the pelvic organs and mucous membranes. Purulent discharges are a thing of the past, except after difficult births. The cows are certain to come on heat again 21 days after calving, so that they are served again and generally become pregnant 63 days after giving birth. About a week before they are served, animals with very high milk yields are given another 12 ml each of Metrovetsan and Vitavetsan by injection, and 12 ml of Oestrovetsan (Schwabe) nine days after insemination. Oestrovetsan promotes reproductive functions and also contributes a great deal in the treatment of lack of sexual appetite (anaphrodisia) and excessive sexual appetite (nymphomania). In cases of occasional cysts, 20 drops of it may be given three times daily to support the usual treatment.

Except after difficult births, inability to rise after a birth is usually due to unbalanced feeding and the mineral deficiencies that arise from this.

The disposition for this is increased if the animal is dry for too long or milked too early. The condition is usually cured by improving the energy:protein ratio of feeds. Animals at risk are given 20 drops of *Phosphorus* 6x and *Chelidonium* 3x and half a teaspoonful of *Calcium carbonicum* 3x daily for six weeks before calving and some time afterwards. If the cow is calving in tethered housing, coarse gravel covered with straw may be put down in the area of the hind legs to reduce the risk of slipping when an attempt is made to get up.

Digestive disorders

Persistent scouring, bloat and constipation are the commonest problems in this sphere.

Any scouring that is not due to an error of diet requires careful attention. Worms and intestinal parasites are frequent causes; they are diagnosed by examining the faeces and treated accordingly.

Immediate actions to be taken if there is scouring are to withhold food, give 100 ml of slightly warmed Coffea prep. and 2–4 litres of camomile (scentless mayweed), oak bark or blackberry leaf tea.

Chronic bloat can often be dealt with by giving cud from healthy animals or 2–3 litres of fresh fluid from the rumen, which can be obtained from the rumen of freshly killed animals at the slaughter house. It has to be transported in thermos flasks as it must not get cold.

Constipation usually occurs in conjunction with foreign body problems or severe, highly febrile illness. The vet must be called immediately in such cases.

The more balanced the relationship

Meadows had such a rich flora in the past that they were a paradise for insects. The use of synthetic fertilizers has brought drastic changes in this respect.

between care of the soil and manuring on the one hand and fodder growing and animal husbandry on the other, the better is the health situation on a farm. Visits from the vet and the use of powerful conventional drugs will then be limited to rare emergencies.

Bee keeping

Agriculture has changed enormously in recent decades. Small farmers have had to go and work in industry as their land was no longer financially viable and has been swallowed up by large establishments. Animal husbandry has either been given up altogether or limited to one type of animal to rationalize feeding and management. As a result, fewer people are needed to farm larger areas with a limited number of crops, using large machines to do operations like manuring, cultivations, sowing, plant protection and harvesting at a brisk pace.

Not the smallest flower dares appear among the vivid green crops. Herbicides used to keep the roadsides clean have caused the last of the flowers to disappear. Meadows that used to be a paradise for the insect world show horrifying changes in their flora thanks to the use of synthetic fertilizers. Once the dandelions have flowered, grassland offers little interest and variety to insect eyes.

There was a time when farm tracks, minor roads and pastures were lined with fruit trees or fruit-bearing hedgerows and country roads were bordered with lime trees, chestnuts, maples and false acacias. In the hot midday sun they gave welcome shade for country people, stock and draught animals as well as anyone taking a country walk. Farms got the fruit they needed almost incidentally. Those were golden days for the insect world and especially bees, who found an abundance of food and in return provided humans with honey to eat and wax for the candles used on festive and ritual occasions.

Honey bees are the most important of the animal species that feed on plants and at the same time pollinate them to stimulate fertilization; only bumble bees are to some extent comparable. Honey bees are domesticated creatures; they cannot survive in the long term unless given proper care. In the past they were part of the farm stock just as much as cattle, horses, pigs, sheep and poultry, all of which produced valuable manure that formed the basis for rich and varied plant growth and permanent soil fertility. Bees provide human beings with honey, wax, propolis and bee venom. They pollinate flowers and thus ensure plentiful production of new seed, at the same time cross-inoculating flowers with yeasts, which helps to improve the flora in the intestine and rumen of cattle as well as their fertility.

Bees finely disperse a small amount of venom over a plant before they gather the nectar; this stimulates growth and helps to maintain variety in plant life. In his *Nine Lectures on Bees* Rudolf Steiner called this a further gift to the world of nature.

Extremely small amounts of ant

venom have the same effect in woodland; the ants distribute this over the ground and it promotes the humification of pine needles and therefore soil fertility. These processes are a kind of aromatic fertilization; they benefit all vital functions in the natural world.

It is generally assumed today that there are enough insects to pollinate plants, so there is no need to keep bees. However, the life rhythms of most other insects are geared to high summer, and their populations are still low in numbers during the spring flowering period.

The queen bee usually overwinters with the workers. Colonies that were in good condition by the end of the year will be strong and healthy if given the right care and the spring climate is good. Such a colony will have about 5000 bees available to visit the first flowers, with the number trebling as summer approaches.

A comparison with bumble bees reveals quite striking differences in life pattern. Bumble bee and wasps' nests are empty in winter, as only the queen overwinters. When no more food is available in autumn she will crawl into a crack in a wall, a hole in the ground or a pile of dead leaves and hibernate. When the weather gets warmer in spring she wakes up and starts to look for food. Having found an area where sufficient pollen and nectar are available, she will begin to build a brood place for the new colony. A bumble bee queen is therefore able both to build the first cells for stores and the brood and to look after them. The first females to hatch will then take on these functions, with the queen then devoting herself entirely to breeding. Multiplication is very slow, with the colony numbering merely a few hundred by high

Environmental deterioration in woodlands and open country is partly also due to the reduction in bee keeping.

summer. These small numbers are the reason why one usually only sees single individuals visiting early flowering plants.

The pollination of spring-flowering plants is therefore largely taken care of by bees that have overwintered; these live to an age between five and seven months because they have not expended all their energies on looking after the brood in autumn. During the summer the workers, who carry out different activities in the hive and later visiting flowers, only live for five to seven weeks. The colonies are much larger then and responsible for pollinating about three quarters of all flowers.

Only honey bees, which were domesticated in very early times, store honey and thus provide one of the most valuable foods and medicinal agents.

Bumble bees have a much longer proboscis and visit the flowers of broom, different clovers and vetches and also field beans, honey bees being unable to reach their nectar. Unlike honey bees, bumble bees can be observed gathering pollen and honey from early morning till late at night even if the weather is extremely cold and stormy. In cool springs, fruit trees therefore depend on them for pollination, with yields correspondingly reduced.

It is evident from the above that adequate conditions have to exist or be created for both these insects.* To provide a better basis for their existence, it is advisable to use every opportunity to plant fruit-bearing hedges and grow bee plants. Flowering plants may be included in cropping sequences as either a main or a catch crop. Examples are oil crops, fodder sunflowers, phacelia, buckwheat and many legumes. A pleasing delicate scent comes from a flowering field of peas, with the busy bees filling the air with a pleasantly soothing hum.

With cereal crops, it is good to grow sainfoin or white deadnettle around the edges, or even sow cornflowers among the cereals. This will attract honey bees and bumble bees to the cornfields, and yields will generally be higher.

Integrated plant protection methods will also increase honey flow. The following even more so: If roadsides and field margins are mown three or four weeks before pollen and honey providing crops (field beans, peas, fruit, oil radish, rape, mustard, vineyards, meadows, etc.) finish flowering or are harvested, honey bees and bumble bees will find new flowering plants such as white clover in these areas and also many plantain species, ensuring at least the supply of pollen.

In a trial done with this method at Tuebingen University (Bauer 1985) honey flow improved to such an extent that bee colonies could be kept stationary again. After the first year (1979) there was no further need for summer feeding, compared to colonies kept on a control farm where summer feeding had to continue.

Flowering plants should always be sown along roadsides and hedgerows and in wasteland to enrich the landscape. In a few years bees will begin to thrive much better; at the same time numerous other useful insects and butterflies will make these flowering oases their home. Bees and flowers belong together; both are 'children of the sun'. The other heavenly bodies – e.g. the planets and the moon – also have subtle influences on these sensitive creatures. Apart

*The literature relating to bees is extensive. Suggestions for bumble bee breeding may be found in *Lebendige Erde* 1978: pages 20 ff. and 69/70 (not in English).

A biodynamic farm is not really complete without a few bee colonies.

from the moon, the two inner planets Mercury and Venus probably have the greatest influence on the life and work of bees.

Matthias K. Thun observed that pollen availability persisted for a long time with Venus in Aquarius, Gemini and Libra, whilst honey flow was persistent and of high yield with Mercury in Leo and Aries. His findings have been published.

On a biodynamic farm, grazing and sire keeping are normal for all types of animals kept, and a few bee colonies form part of the whole. Providing the flowers they need and caring for these faithful friends adds much to the quality of life for the human community on the farm and at the same time helps to maintain the basis for the life of all natural kingdoms on this earth.

Dealing with acute radioactive contamination

After the incident at Chernobyl extensive areas were subject to variable degrees of radioactive fallout or washout. As there is always a possibility of this happening again, the most important points to be considered and the methods to be used are given below.

Stock must immediately be taken indoors from yards and pastures and well washed down with uncontaminated water if at all possible. Keep doors and windows closed if possible. Have filters available to insert in ventilator intakes as the occasion arises. They need to be disposed of in the prescribed way after use.

Nuclides with a short half-life will decay rapidly – within hours or days. During this period of maximum radiation children and animals have to be kept indoors, and adults must wear protective clothing that can be washed down if they leave the house to do essential work.

During the first three weeks, any uncontaminated feedstuffs that are available should be used. If contaminated material has to be fed, add 40–50 g of Montigel (a specially prepared bentonite formulation) per 100 kg of liveweight to *every* meal given to all domestic animals, either added to succulent feed or mixed with molasses, moistened crushed cereals or the like. This will cause caesium 134 and 137 to be largely eliminated in the dung, keeping contamination of milk and meat to a minimum. Montigel has to be added until uncontaminated feedstuffs are available.

It is important to provide sufficient minerals. Approximately 5 g of *Silicea* 10x per 500 kg of liveweight given once a day for several weeks will help to maintain vitality. All other known and proven methods to enhance health and vitality should be implemented and closely followed.

Landscape management

Elements of landscaping

Biodynamic farming involves more than the cultivation of land that has agricultural use, for the productivity of a farm is also partly determined by the landscape organism to which it belongs. The first things to come to mind are damage caused by storms, radiation, drought and drainage problems, pollution and so on.

Responsible farming communities make it their task to keep an eye on and care for all verges, margins and other areas not absolutely essential for economic use (damp depressions, hedges, dry outcrops of rocks, roadsides, ditches, trees and shrubs growing in fields), so that these may make their own contribution to farm health.

In addition to maintenance of residual areas and wetland biotopes and the establishment of cascades and Flowforms, the planting of hedges is an important landscaping element.

Hedge planting

Situational analysis involves the compilation of all important natural, economic, management and social data of the farm. Detailed information on the local micro-climate provides a starting point. Inspection walks through the seasons help to fa-

miliarize the farmer with the qualities of the different areas within the property:
– areas exposed to wind pressure and excessive cold air currents,
– denuded rocky outcrops,
– areas in the vicinity of street traffic with no protection,
– areas that are difficult to drain,
– bare areas due to geological faults (parallel and step faults),
– shrubless areas bordering on banks and shores, ditches that are quickly overgrown and outfalls,
– trees and shrubs growing far apart in fields with no wooded links between them,
– steep slopes with risk of erosion,
– areas with neither woodland nor hedges,
– shallow ground going waste,
– residual strips between roads and field tracks,
– areas suitable for fruit growing but lacking protection.

All these may be considered for planting hedges, trees and shrubs, providing these will not have a negative effect on the landscape and there are no other objections.

Relationships with adjoining areas up to a distance of 3 km need to be taken into account. Qualitatively different decisions may have to be made in areas with similar or variable land use, in river valleys, marshes and in

Every cultivated landscape develops into a site-specific organism that must not be disturbed by alien form elements.

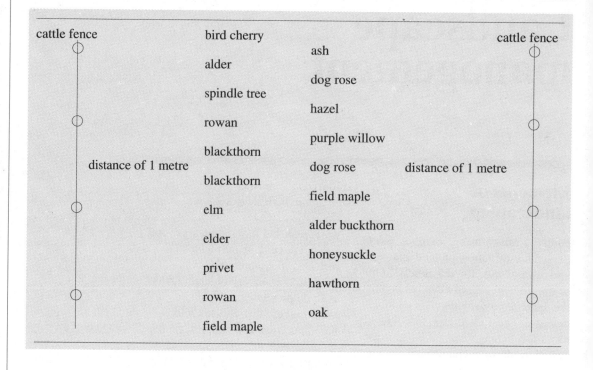

cattle fence		bird cherry			cattle fence
			ash		
		alder			
			dog rose		
		spindle tree			
			hazel		
		rowan			
			purple willow		
		blackthorn			
distance of 1 metre			dog rose	distance of 1 metre	
		blackthorn			
			field maple		
		elm			
			alder buckthorn		
		elder			
			honeysuckle		
		privet			
			hawthorn		
		rowan			
			oak		
		field maple			

Table 63. Design for a hedge on medium soil.

hill country, so that hedges blend harmoniously with the landscape.

The aim of planning is to make hedges fit in well with existing features such as woodland, trees and shrubs, railway and motorway embankments, farms, bridges and rows of houses. The end result may be a network of enclosed cell-like areas. The sizes of the individual 'cells' will depend on the general terrain and on the degree to which the main crops are sensitive to wind or shade.

Taking all this together and considering the farm's cropping sequence and the ratio of arable to grassland, it is possible to arrive at the optimum size for cells with controlled wind conditions.

The suggestions made below relate to specific situations and will illustrate the points that have been made.

In coastal marshes and extensive lowland and highland plains (e.g.

near Munich), cells that are one or two kilometres in diameter will reduce wind impact by about 10%, which is generally adequate. Marshes used as permanent grassland are wind stable; hedges merely serve to provide protection from harsh weather conditions for stock. The farmstead can be protected from storm damage and the monotonous landscape enriched. Germany's extensive lowland plains with loess soil are not exposed to problematical perpetual winds, and in high-lying inland plains serious wind damage never occurs if the water supply is adequate, despite large areas of open arable cultivation; some of the more demanding special crops are an exception.

Hilly areas need carefully planned wind protection. Special crops can be grown on their valuable south-facing slopes if hedges are used to create small-size cells. Slopes facing east and west need to be examined for areas liable to erosion. Here particularly good results can be achieved by utilizing all crests and ridges for hedge planting. Trough valleys can be partly cleared of night frost areas by running hedges parallel to contour lines but leaving the circle open at the lowest part. In this way, cold down-draught air flows off outside and the inner pool of cold air can drain away.

River valleys have to be considered individually. Use of hedges along river banks is almost always under the control of river boards and cannot be changed. With good quality water resources getting lower and lower, it would be essential to take special care of shallow banks, planting coniferous woods that are 30 m wide at least in some parts and keeping residual old river beds rubbish-free. On slopes, hedges are ideally placed along step faults; this will create different but internally consistent climatic zones such as river

meadow level, lower slope, upper slope and plateau. Parallel hedges can be grown much closer together if they are at different altitude levels than if they run down a slope.

In mountain areas, wind protection is not really the point at issue with hedge growing. Depending on local conditions there are additional functions that require entirely different spacing, such as protection from melting snow water, snow control, natural fencing, securing of roads, regulation of solar radiation and protection from avalanches and rock falls. Hedges are frequently more efficient than woods in this situation. Establishing them may be extremely expensive but is nevertheless impor-

North German plain
Hercynian mountains
large river valleys - Rhine, Danube, etc.
rugged mountain areas at higher altitudes
areas where wide plains border on mountain slopes

Table 64.
Large area terrains in Germany

Table 65.
Wind sensitivity of agricultural crops (rising scale).

1) permanent pasture in coastal areas
   litter meadows on marginal soils
   leys of several years and low-growing green manure mixtures
   catch crops and fodder mixtures, root crops
   oats, barley, maize, wheat, rye
   field vegetables, strawberries, asparagus, endive
   isolated fruit trees and cider fruit
   soft fruit, rhubarb, herbs for teas

2) highly selected fruit varieties:
   hazel, cherry, apple standards, pear, low-growing apples, plums,
   peach, walnut, sweet chestnut, vine

3) special vegetables and salad plants:
   kitchen herbs, various medicinal plants, artichoke, pumpkin, courgette,
   cucumber, tomato, peppers

4) plants for transplanting and heeled-in woody plants:
   cut flowers, plants grown for seed that have wind-borne seed, cuttings for
   tree nurseries and herbs.

Fig. 73.
A dense hedge caus-
es turbulence.

Fig. 74.
A loose hedge re-
duces wind velocity.

tant in this case. It usually is beyond the means of farmers or gardeners, however. The regional association, water authorities and other bodies may take responsibility for this type of protective hedging, with farmers planting supplementary hedges on their own land, taking the above guidelines into account. The hedges may be put along field tracks, for example, along cascades, faults and boundaries.

Special care is needed in areas where level land borders on slopes because of geological faults; such areas mark the transition between different forms of use. Hedges can be a major help here because of problems in water control. The right

choice and use of trees will consolidate the slope for a long time to come. Hedges provide for drainage of excess ground water and afford secure and lasting protection of springs and regulation of melting snow water. Where they protect northern slopes they help to make the drop of temperature less marked in case of night frosts; on southern slopes they help to prevent denudation.

Steep precipices in gravel pits, dredger holes and broken banks cause turbulent overfall winds in danger zones. The harmful effect can be reduced by planting in such a way that extreme differences in height are compensated by using aerodynamic forms and transitional strips that will

Fig. 75.
Protective zone well
above ground if
trunks are bare.

Fig. 76.
Extremely dense
hedges act like walls.
Turbulence is pro-
duced.

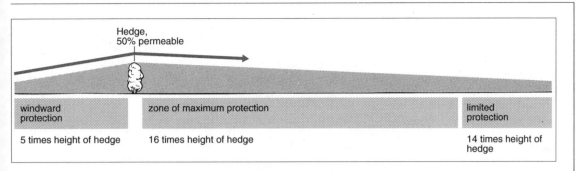

windward protection	zone of maximum protection	limited protection
5 times height of hedge	16 times height of hedge	14 times height of hedge

let the wind through. The tallest trees and shrubs should always be positioned next to any lesser depressions that may also be present. If the soil is thin on a hilltop, earth walls two or three metres in width, created before planting – by ploughing if no other way is possible – will certainly be of benefit to plant growth and for a long time.

Figures 73–80 demonstrate the effect of hedges as well as possible design errors.

Some rules for hedge cultivation

1) Integrate hedges in the landscape, making sure they do not appear as isolated lines in open country.
2) Provide baffles in field access sections that are in the prevailing wind direction.
3) To avoid wind jets at ground level do not allow animals to strip stems.
4) Design hedges in multiple rows, using single rows only where this is not possible.
5) The distance between hedges should be more than 25 times the planned height after ten years.
6) Use largely native plant species; foreign trees and shrubs do not have an accompanying fauna and flora such as insects, mammals, fungi and herbs.

7) Always grow mixed hedges; avoid monoculture.
8) Plan the final height to match the width of the headland.
9) Obtain plants from regions with similar local conditions, or at least not from regions with better soil and a milder climate.
10) Encourage dense branching by cutting back and trimming over several years.
11) Flame treat undesirable undergrowth.
12) Use the biodynamic field sprays.
13) Renew and restore existing hedges such as pollarded willows and old overgrown hedges, e.g. in a three-year programme.

Many farmers still feel hesitant about planting hedges as they are afraid of undesirable effects. Any

Fig. 77.
Effect of hedge that lets 50% of wind pass through.

Fig. 78.
Hills with much exposure to wind need three hedges to reduce wind; position, height and distance must be planned for the three hedges as a whole.

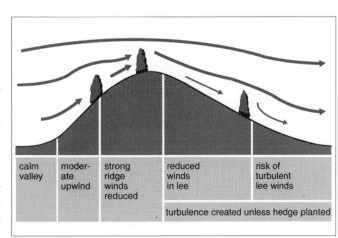

calm valley	moder-ate upwind	strong ridge winds reduced	reduced winds in lee	risk of turbulent lee winds

turbulence created unless hedge planted

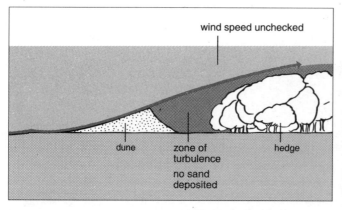

wind speed unchecked

dune   zone of   hedge
              turbulence
              no sand
              deposited

**Fig. 79.
Dune form devel-
oped to windward of
shrubs.**

such effects would be due to errors in planning and planting.

In mountain areas a hedge put in the wrong position may prevent the cold air that has accumulated overnight from running off. Cold air pools are created that may suppress some crops which previously could be grown. The daily average temperature is reduced by 1–2 °C on the north side of a hedge. Arable fields and garden areas that are shaded by hedges cannot be cultivated until two to four weeks later in spring. The distance of a hedge from a crop should therefore equal its planned height.

If areas to be used for haying are in the lee of a hedge, increased dew levels may make drying considerably

more difficult within a distance of up to six times the height of the hedge. In this case the hedge should not be planted. If this should interfere with the necessary creation of a cell system for the area, a very open hedge could be grown in this section, or half of the hedge thinned at regular five-year intervals.

In areas where rye is grown, hedges must be open to prevent wind turbulence on the leeside, which would cause lodging (single-row hedges).

The composition of hedges growing next to permanent special crops must take the special needs of these crops into account. Hedges can have an influence in so far as crops attract specific animals and plants. Dead leaves and needles may also increase soil acidity. Fields of vegetables should therefore not have spruce, beech or poplar hedges next to them.

In reducing wind velocity, hedges filter out all kinds of airborne particles, rather like a comb. These are deposited on the windward side over a distance of 1.5 times the height, and on the leeside over a wider zone, up to 12 times the height, with some tailing off. In addition to humus, clay, dust and even sand grains, the wind carries spiders, ants, aphids, beetles and other creatures.

Hedges placed too close together have an undesirable effect because of these filter functions. Along roads with hedges on both sides, snow piles up to four times the height of actual snowfall. Icing up and slippery wetness are also many times greater in autumn and spring in this case. In Germany, snow piles up especially along roads going north, whilst wetness and icing are severe in those going west.

Possible reductions in yield in

**Fig. 80.
Dunes created by
flexible and rigid ob-
stacles.**

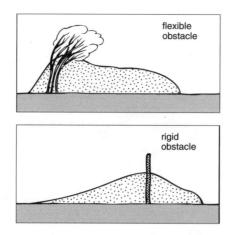

flexible
obstacle

rigid
obstacle

neighbouring crops due to the roots of hedges can be dealt with. As a rule such losses occur only over a distance equal to the height of the hedge. Apart from this, hedges do not cause losses, the exception being plant species with unusually powerful root development.

Hedges that are to stay narrow and exactly within the planting area are best planted on a bank that is at least 40 cm high and a good metre in width, with a ditch of 20 cm depth between them and field crops that is kept clear by running a plough along it every two years.

Broad strips as dense as forests are expensive to plant and maintain but provide little shelter from wind because they cause turbulence. A density similar to that of fruit plantations on the other hand does not lift the air and cause turbulence but lets it pass through, reducing velocity by about 30%. Protection may therefore also be provided by fruit plantations enclosed in a single-row hedge.

Annual or summer hedges grown because of difficult conditions have the disadvantage that they only reach an adequate height in June, when the problem winds of spring have gone. They will provide visual screens and create warm spaces for special summer crops and sensitive vegetables. The above-mentioned disadvantage can be reduced by sowing sunflowers, hollyhocks and Jerusalem artichokes in mid-September. They will start to grow early in spring and be three weeks ahead of spring-sown plants.

With the exception of yew, conifers are not suitable for hedges, as they will not produce new growth if cut back after ten years. They grow on continuously until they come to a standstill and thin out at the base.

The negative effects of this mean that they have to be topped and finally taken out altogether. The yield of wood is small, more or less equal to a middling brushwood harvest. Soil utilization is unbalanced, so that the soil easily becomes acid and sustains few species. The wind protection effect is always inferior to that achieved with deciduous species.

Hedges from cuttings

On medium and also immature soil, shrub hedges can be grown from cuttings of willow, dogwood, honeysuckle, mountain currant, privet, poplar, roses and spindle tree in sites that are not too exposed, though they will need some attention during the first year. The method is as follows. Between mid-November and mid-March cut shoots the thickness of a pencil to the length of a pencil using sharp rose secateurs, with a clean oblique cut below a bud at the base and a straight cut 2 mm above the tip of a bud at the top. In well-prepared ground, make holes with a sharpened spade handle at 25 cm intervals, at a depth equal to the length of the cuttings. Having put a cutting in a hole, firm it by treading sideways, so that only a centimetre shows at the top and no obvious air spaces are left in the soil. The row of cuttings must be kept clear, especially during the first year. Standards should have been planted at not less than 2 metre intervals beforehand.

Trees and other shrubs than those listed above should be several years old when they are bought from a nursery.

Planting a hedge

After normal preparation of the

With new hedges, planning must take account of agricultural crops grown in the area.

Hedges are best planted in autumn, postponing till spring only if weather conditions are unfavourable.

ground, sow an actively growing ley mixture. Apply the horn manure preparation in the evening. In mid-September, cut the sward for soilage or for later use as a mulch. Clear the stubble with cultivator harrow, rotary hoe or disc harrow, leave for at least three days, and loosen or plough deeply; let the crumb settle until planting time. A further evening application of horn manure preparation is recommended.

When buying hedge plants for open country, choose plants that are at least three years old and in two sizes. Nearer to the homestead and well protected from grazing animals and excessive weed growth, two-year-old propagated shrubs or willow, dogwood and privet cuttings may also be used. Autumn planting is the preferred method; planting is left till spring only if conditions are very wet, or with permanent frost or early high snow cover. Birches are the exception, for they are only sure to take if planted in spring at the time when the first leaves begin to appear. Until then the planting hole is left open to the frost.

To permit rotary cultivation, the distance between rows needs to be the width of the cultivator plus 20 cm, i.e. a total of about one metre. Distances within rows depend on the final size of individual plants. Alder, poplar, hawthorn and elder will need slightly more space than privet, roses, spindle tree or alder buckthorn for example.

Having selected suitable standard holdovers, make planting holes for these at eight to twelve metre intervals. Holes need to be quite deep and wide especially in heavy soils and in sites without topsoil. The beneficial effect of moving the soil persists for years, and the traditional dimensions of 80 by 80 cm and 60 cm deep are no exaggeration. Put in the stake so that it is to the windward side and fill the hole to the point where the roots will be at the same level relative to the surface as before. Poplars are the exception in this case; they may be placed at the very base of the deep hole. Modern varieties will thus be up to 60 cm lower than before.

Fill the hole in layers. After the first layer shake the stem vertically to allow the finer soil particles to slip through between the fibrous roots, with the coarser particles on top. Firm well with a boot, but from two sides only so that the rest stays loose and allows for respiration. Mix the upper 25 cm of soil used to fill the hole with some of the surrounding soil to avoid an abrupt transition between the two. Before the final layer is put in, firm with a boot from the other two sides, ending with a slight mound of earth. The stake must not extend as far as the crown and should be three fingers' width from the trunk. Tie as high as possible, making a figure of eight so that the tie crosses over between the two. Suitable ties are coconut fibre rope or ready-made modern ties. The prevailing wind should push the trunk away from the stake.

Lop-sided crowns indicate poor quality plants; it means that the nursery did not plant at the correct distance. When planting such specimens care must be taken that the same side faces the sun as before. Bark formation differs on the sunny and the shaded sides.

The following should be noted when transporting trees and shrubs from the nursery:

– Transport on an overcast day, expose roots to light only when loading and cover immediately with opaque tarpaulin or coarse hessian sheets.
– Make sure roots are not exposed to draughts when on the road.
– If the work has to be done in sunshine, position the plants so that the branches face the sun and the roots get minimum exposure. Keep a hose with spray-head handy.
– Arrange the work schedule so that goods that have arrived in the morning are planted by midday; then follows a second batch, to be planted by evening.
– If everything has to be collected or delivered in one go, prepare for heeling-in beforehand. Place the tied bundles close together at an oblique angle and put soil between them and on top, watering in well. Keep moist at all times.
– Heel in smaller species first, so that planting can start with the taller species.
– The site for heeling-in should be in half shade and protected from wind, but also close to the planting site.

A further method to ensure healthy development is to plant at a time when the soil is in the right condition, the weather is mild and dewy, and cosmic conditions are also right. If using Maria Thun's *Annual Sowing and Planting Calendar*, give preference to the planting days of the month and avoid doing the work on unfavourable days.

Root baths will help woody plants to settle, especially if container-grown. If small numbers of a single species are to be planted, the following radical method used in peak planting season will stimulate healthy active growth:

– Tear open the peat ball around the roots or cut the container felt almost all the way and wash out the peat.
– Cut away all but three to five branches and remove all lateral branches from these.
– Make up a root bath and immerse the ball for 15 minutes.

The bath is made up with
– one part bentonite and clay rock dust
– two parts basalt rock dust
– one part cow pats
– 1% SPS (see page 80).

Mix in large tubs with sufficient water to get the consistency of runny honey. Dilute the mixture again as it thickens whilst roots are dipped.

Basalt dust may be replaced with diabase rock dust, lava or primary rock dust of various origin providing they are rich in trace elements and so finely ground that no granules are felt between the fingers and the material only feels slightly rough when rubbed firmly against a surface. Half the granules should have a particle size of 0.005 mm and less, the other half not above 0.05 mm. Fine rock dusts like these, including bentonite, have a laminar crystalline structure. Like the organic components of cow pats, their biological and biochemical activity enhances vital functions, so that healthy growth is encouraged in woody plants.

Make up sufficient root bath to take care of all the other plants as well. Plants without root balls are only dipped for 2 or 3 minutes. It is a

Trees and shrubs for planting should come from nurseries with similar site conditions. Container plants are less suitable for organic growers.

good idea to dip not just the roots but the stem and even the branches of dog rose, for example. Before dipping, cut back roots and branches; trim injured roots back cleanly, with the cut surface facing downwards.

Cut branches back in a way that establishes a good balance between them and the remaining roots. Main branches should be cut above a bud, reducing all new growth to one third. Remove lateral and weak branches completely if necessary. Such severely cut back plants will grow into large, healthy specimens within five years, in contrast to a hedge where the plants have not been cut back.

Management and colonization of hedges

Little work is required in the first year. Sow grassland seeds between rows, inspect to see that hedge plants have taken, check for dryness, pests and weeds and tighten loose ties. If the ground is dry, tillage is preferable to watering, giving several applications of the horn manure preparation. Wild herbaceous plants need to be kept shorter than the woody plants, and thistles should be prevented from seeding. If insect pests appear in relatively large numbers, adequate control is achieved by spraying with a concentrated cold extract of bitter herbs steeped for 24–48 hours and then diluted with five parts of water, adding 5% of rock dust. If there is a serious problem, spraying once each in June, July and August will be sufficient. Concentrated dusting with rock dust is the best method of treating aphids. If mildew, grey mould and other fungi are a serious problem, spray with the above cold extract. A few percent of cowpats stirred in water or quicklime serves

as a sticker and enhances the effect.

The work required in subsequent years is variable. Hazels are not cut back until the leaves are out, i.e. the following May or autumn, when the moon is descending. Plants that have not taken well are cut back sharply, making sure the best buds remain as terminal points. The cut with the secateurs should be 2 mm above the growing point. Use a scythe to cut herbaceous growth in autumn, leaving the cut plant material in place. When the hedge has been well colonized with grass and clover, melilot or mugwort, tansy, tall grasses and nettles, an occasional cut and mulching will be all that is required. Repeated rotovation or hoeing are the best method of controlling creeping thistle, broad-leaved dock, common orache, gallant soldier (Kew weed), bindweed and square-stalked willowherb where these become too well established.

Gaps are made up in the second year. The hedge is now also included in the biodynamic field spray programme with both preparations. In the third and later years, large shrubs and trees are pruned to help them to reach the desirable height at a good pace. Strong shoots are encouraged, weak lateral shoots cut away. With hedge maple, blackthorn, hawthorn and privet, annual shoots are cut back to about a hand's width above the branching point. This will encourage them to branch densely right down to ground level, providing shelter and accommodation for birds and other animals.

If there are established trees and shrubs in a nearby field, subshrubs like raspberry and blackberry will often appear of their own accord after some years in hedges of more than one row that contain many

To grow dense and have a long life, hedges need protection from being eaten by wild animals; they also require some care, as described on this page.

species. The same applies to perennials from related families. If some important species fail to appear, they can be helped to do so by transplanting some from neighbouring woodland, which should be done from the third year onwards. Melilot can be sown and ivy needs to be planted.

In hilly areas, a double-row mixed hedge is best and offers most variety. The profile is jagged due to the difference in height between taller standards and lower shrubs of variable height between these. When this type of hedge is planted on a slight bank, properly orientated relative to the prevailing winds, in exactly the right place and connecting with other woods or hedges, it helps to create sound environmental conditions that benefit the whole farm. This type of hedge gives maximum protection from strong winds. Useful spiders and insects migrate to it and multiply in remarkable numbers. Alder buckthorn will provide food for the caterpillars of the brimstone. Hedgehogs, shrews and weasels are attracted. Cut brushwood should always be left in small heaps between the rows to help these creatures. Once the hedge has reached a reasonable size, leaf hay (see page 248) can be cut for cattle, to be fed dry in winter. If wood stoves should come into use again, hedges yield more wood than woodland over a period of decades (hedges make the equivalent of 8–10 cubic metres/ha of solid wood new growth annually from their fifth year onwards, forests only 5–8 cubic metres/ha.

Dunnock, yellowhammer, redbacked shrike, robin, linnet, willow warbler, chiffchaff, whitethroat, lesser whitethroat and our glorious goldfinch will once again be able to find nesting sites. If additional nesting boxes are provided, tits, too, will be attracted. Wrens will return to build their globular nests in humid banks.

In areas where the landscape opens out, 1.5–2 metre high poles can be set up even in new hedges, with a cross bar fitted at the top to provide perches for buzzards on the look-out for mice; kestrels will also use them on overcast days. This will greatly reduce the risk of voles gnawing their way through the roots of the hedge plants.

Barberry acts as an alternate host for wheat rust, buckthorn for oat crown rust, spindle tree for black bean aphid (wintering of eggs), honeysuckle and rowan for cherry fruit fly, St Lucie's cherry for fire blight and both hawthorn and blackthorn for a number of fruit pests. These host plants are controlled by legislation and should not be planted near the crops concerned.

On the other hand it has frequently been found that, except in specially disastrous years, such 'dangerous' neighbours do not increase the risk. So far there appear to have been no reports of plantations having to be cleared because of serious pest problems originating in hedges. There are however many reports that all these problems decreased when hedges were grown; where they did not decrease, the plantations as such were found to be faulty.

Hedgerow soils have a rich flora of fungi, ensuring that the number of useful fungi in the fields does not decrease. Spores discharged at the height of summer keep providing new generations, so that the losses caused by large modern farm machines are soon made up.

With the exception of fruit scab and some air-borne rust fungi, the

Some hedgerow plants may act as intermediary hosts for pests. Attention must be given to legal requirements in this respect.

spread of harmful fungi is reduced if sufficient beneficial fungi are present in the soil.

Fungus growth can be encouraged in hedges by putting in large and small branches of wood and letting them rot. Beech and oak branches are best for the purpose. It is always a good idea to have plenty of English oak in hedges in areas where harmful fungi threaten to be a problem. Shredded oak bark spread on the ground will serve as a preventive measure where necessary.

Tits are particularly useful in field vegetable, potato and root crops. To attract them to field hedges, set up posts with nesting boxes at a height of two or three metres. The hole for the birds should be about 29 mm in diameter and face south-east. An unbroken hedgerow should extend to within a metre of it. These wooden or wood cement nesting boxes need to be checked and cleaned in autumn. They will be used as sleeping quarters for the winter if sufficient food is available in the area. A gravity feeder is easily made from a plastic bucket with fitted lid. Drill a hole of 3 cm diameter in the base and tie a second lid so that it is 2 cm below the base. The contents, with a high proportion of sunflower seeds, are gravity-fed to the rim as the birds feed. Roofing felt with an overhang may be put on top to be held in position by the bucket handle for protection when it snows. The food will last for several weeks. The feeder should be suspended so that it cannot be reached by field wood mice. One will be sufficient for 400 metres of hedge or an area with twelve inhabited nesting boxes.

It is also possible to do something for the few surviving woodpeckers and treecreepers. Mix warmed beef tallow with wheatgerm and spread on

Verticillar cuts, nesting holes and feeding places make hedges a paradise for a number of useful bird species.

the weather-protected side of older trunks, especially also in orchards and fields, and tie a flower pot filled with the same mixture next to this in such a way that the birds are able to climb from the trunk into the inside of the pot as the inside is gradually hollowed out.

In hedges adjoining large orchards and soft fruit plantations it may be worthwhile to fix slightly larger nesting boxes with 70 mm wide oval holes three metres above ground level, as they may attract a pair of hoopoes. These birds need fairly large areas of pasture with loose soil and many worms in the vicinity.

Open-fronted nesting boxes for spotted flycatchers, redstarts and wagtails are out of place in hedges. Put them in damp woodlands for spotted flycatchers and on house walls and in rock clefts for redstarts and wagtails. Small cavities in heaps of stones within hedges may serve the wheatear, but are also visited by weasels and martens.

Aquatic and wet biotopes

The value of a hedge as biological compensation for unbalanced field crops is much enhanced if creatures are able to find drinking water in the vicinity. This can be achieved in a number of ways:

1) An outfall ditch may be widened into a semicircle to provide a watering place for stock and wild creatures such as insects, birds and small mammals.

2) A depression in pasture or arable land that tends to become waterlogged can be developed without becoming an impediment to field work. Deepen and line it and

plant a few clumps of wetland plants around the edge.

3) Another method is to block off one collecting channel to a drain in the corner of a field. Dig a trough of 5–10 m² area, line it and create a shallow bank on the south side. Plant wetland plants and possibly also purple willow and hemp agrimony.

4) Streams with straightened and re-inforced banks cannot be used by animals for drinking and birds for bathing. It would be necessary to widen part of the stream, as under 1). Rushes, live willow cuttings tied in bundles or turves forming a cellular pattern with plants in the crevices will secure the edges of this small artificial valley. The sun should be able to reach it often.

5) Existing ponds need to be im-proved if surrounded by high banks or palisades or if there is access to pedestrian traffic all round. One method is to make the bank marshy in one place, anoth-er to make an island or a peninsu-la with earth and again plant wet-land plants. A good time for doing this is in late autumn, so that the pond will be colonized by amphibians, water beetles, drag-onflies and other insects in spring, which in turn will attract more birds. In exceptional cases, a wide board may be placed so that it forms a shallow slope.

6) If the ground will not hold water so that lining with clay will not suffice, plastic lining may have to be used.

7) If none of the above are feasible, a wide trough supplied with rain water from the roof of a field barn may be provided with float-ing boards to serve as a drinking

Wetlands are areas of surplus. Their absence impoverishes cultivated land.

place for insects and a bird bath. If no such provision is made, blackbirds and starlings will per-sist in attacking strawberries and cherries.

Wet biotopes

For almost 200 years, major land im-provement work has consistently in-volved drainage, regulation of rivers and accelerated surface drainage. The resulting drought conditions have in-creased to an alarming degree. In spite of this, crops originating in re-gions of Central America with a hot-ter climate and humid soil, such as maize, are successfully grown on a large scale in Europe.

The sprinklers that are commonly used on sensitive crops in dry sites means additional water consumption through evaporation and a reduction in ground water levels. This appears to make it possible to manage with-out the damp riverside conditions. On the other hand, the extreme weather conditions seen in June and July in recent years have clearly demonstrated the serious disadvan-tages of reduced surface water.

No one would wish to see a return to old-time shooting parties, success-ful as they were. Yet the fact that species such as snipe, curlew, lap-wing, stork, ruff, black grouse, sand-piper, little ringed plover, garganey and shoveler have become rare even without being shot indicates that, with wetland areas greatly reduced, there is no food to spare for these birds. Generally speaking, crops can

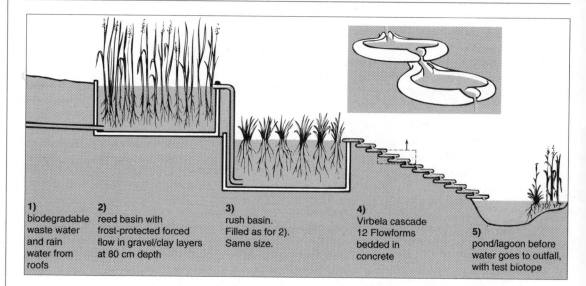

1) biodegradable waste water and rain water from roofs

2) reed basin with frost-protected forced flow in gravel/clay layers at 80 cm depth

3) rush basin. Filled as for 2). Same size.

4) Virbela cascade 12 Flowforms bedded in concrete

5) pond/lagoon before water goes to outfall, with test biotope

Fig. 81. Biological water treatment with Virbela cascade (Virbela Institute).

only be grown with the help of fertilizers today. Wet biotopes are zones of surplus life; yet cultivated land is impoverished when they are no longer in existence.

Wet areas re-established as part of a progressive biotope management scheme offer no immediate advantage; they cost money and require labour. In the long term, however, the principle should be not to feed the crops but to vitalize the soil. Increased soil fertility gives higher yields that represent a true surplus which can be taken to the cities without depleting the land. The same principle should apply to wet sites. Every kind of biotope will progressively deteriorate unless it is regenerated and given proper care.

The volume of water that leaves the farm must equal that which comes into the farm. All water really should be better in quality when it leaves the farm than it was when it was tap water or 'natural' water polluted by industry. Waste water should go through on-site treatment on farms and in small settlements. Biological treatment systems will at the same time feed regenerated wet areas. The large herbaceous plants growing in such a habitat will provide food for greater numbers of wild creatures, whose dung enhances life quality. 'Cells' of increased vitality are created that enrich the ordered farm organism, and the conflict between cultivated and waste land is overcome and transformed into a mutually supportive relationship. This enhances vitality in all spheres, creating a rich basis for human life even in the age of technology.

Artificial spring-fed slopes

The natural spring-fed slopes of the past can be imitated in a system that allows the safe biological treatment of domestic waste water. Such an additional wet area provides an additional biotope for the above-mentioned birds which have become rare today.

The basic principle is as follows. Waste water runs on a broad front into the base of an 80 cm deep, lined basin. This is filled with a mixture of gravel and clay, with reeds growing in it. The area required is 10 m²/person. The water runs over the edge of the basin into a lower basin in which sedges are growing. Depending on the degree of pollution, a third basin, which can also be charged from below through frost-protected pipes, may be included. The water from the basins is improved further by going through a cascade of Virbela Flowforms before it is discharged into small and large ponds or outfall ditches. A rich flora and fauna develops around the system.

A rich wetland area can be created on any farm by consistently channelling all rainwater from roofs to a low-lying area. One part of this should have sufficient depth to prevent it from ever drying out, which is easiest to achieve with a triangular ground plan. Each of the three banks may then slope at a different angle. The combined utilization of rain water from roofs and waste water is a fundamentally new concept of water management on a farm and an important step towards the solution of environmental issues.

Wildlife meadows and flower pastures

Every farm has residual areas not utilized for fodder growing or arable crops where intensive cultivation is not possible. All it usually needs is a light dressing of lime in winter, if

Little effort is required to make residual areas into flowering oases.

necessary adding some rock dust, and spraying with the biodynamic preparations when spraying the fields. After two or three years these areas will be flowering in rich abundance again. Butterflies arrive, bees find more nectar and pollen, and the birds, which are so useful to us, produce more offspring. If only grass and no herbaceous plants grow in such areas, it is advisable to apply a 2 cm layer of builder's sand to heavy soils and plant specially useful herbs such as ribwort plantain, salad burnet, caraway, eyebright, chicory, goat's-beard, yarrow, self-heal, ox-eye daisy, kidney vetch, field scabious, campion and meadow clary. September is the best time for this, as the plants take better when the soil is still warm. They will then be well established in spring and less likely to be displaced by grass. 'Pharmacies for livestock' are created in this way on rocky outcrops, marginal soil, field margins, headlands, along hedges and in orchards; they vitalize the atmosphere to lasting effect. Small applications of marl, crushed limestone and sand and an observant eye can transform such sites without much effort into flowering oases, so that the friends of the farm come to regard it as a favourite place for picnics and excursions.

The farmhouse garden

The garden is another central element in the farm organism. Both the people and the animals who live on the farm are closely connected with it. The site should be facing south, protected from cold winds and close to the homestead if possible, as it is usually the farmer's wife who takes loving care of the garden.

Protection can be enhanced by planting a hedge that contains many species and is full of life. This creates a protected micro-climate in which the soil carbon dioxide level is maintained to encourage active plant growth. The hedge provides a biotope for useful creatures such as hedgehogs, toads, birds and helpful insects.

A small body of water can contribute a great deal. If none exists naturally, it is a good idea to make an artificial pond. Dragonflies and numerous butterflies will soon come to quench their thirst, as well as bees and many song birds. If water is not available, birds in particular are apt to go for soft fruits and even stone fruits and pome fruits to find the moisture they need, especially during prolonged dry spells; they then become pests rather than useful friends. Ponds attract frogs and toads, grass snakes and also hedgehogs which between them account for many pests such as mice, slugs, snails and insects.

The garden should be of a size that permits it to be managed in addition to household duties. Everybody delights in the display of greenery and the rich, colourful variety of flowers from early spring till late autumn. A seat put in a protected sunny place and surrounded by flowers invites people to rest and reflect in the few moments they can spare from their work.

The farmhouse garden also provides vegetables, herbs and fruit as a basis for healthy nutrition for both animals and humans on the farm. A small greenhouse or a few cold frames make it easier to grow plants from seed for planting out in both the garden and in fields. When the seedlings have been transplanted the greenhouse and cold frames may be used for sowing more seed, rooting cuttings and growing tender crops such as salad cucumbers, melons, peppers and tomatoes.

The space allocated to open crops in the garden depends on requirements for the farm and sometimes also on a small group of loyal customers from a nearby town. Fresh vegetables in season and winter vegetables have to be produced in sufficient quantity, with the latter stored in small clamps, cleared cold frames or suitable cellar spaces. Fresh seasonal salads should be available daily.

The garden can also provide a rich variety of plants for herb fodder for animals. See also pages 219–228.

Small amounts of fresh herbs are generally available for most of the year, but herbs should also be harvested and dried once or several times a year as they are medicinal and help to maintain vitality in animals and humans when there is little sunlight in winter.

A rich and varied cropping sequence is as important in the garden as it is for field crops. Cosmic influences and rhythms need to be taken into account, for they do much to maintain and enhance the health of the soil and of plants, animals and humans.

Effective and frequent use of the biodynamic compost and field spray preparations is as vital for the gardens as it is in the fields. Farmhouse gardens benefit from the fact that horn manure and horn silica are easi-

The farmhouse garden is one of the core elements of the farm and is closely connected with the people and animals on the farm.

ly available at just the right moment even for small areas because some can always be spared when they are being stirred for field use.

All composts, the birch pit concentrate and the different plant liquors used to fertilize specific plants are regularly treated with the preparations. The composting site should be protected from wind and sun. Given the right care, it will be a source of steadily increasing garden fertility. The farmhouse garden itself is a site of activity that radiates vitality for the whole farm organism.

Technology in agriculture

From early civilization onwards, human evolution has involved the development of technology, primitive to begin with, but progressing at a steady pace. With more and more detailed knowledge of natural laws, the human race has been able to make the world of nature increasingly serve its own purposes. The primary aim was to improve and enhance living conditions, but in due course advanced technology became the means of exerting increasing power. In spite of this, human beings continue to relate to and depend on the world of nature.

A major change came with the industrial age. Progress was slow to begin with. Newcomen invented the first steam engine in 1705, but it was not until 1784 that Watt patented a design for a double-acting engine with separate condenser, air pump and steam jacket for the cylinder. During the next two hundred years technological development went at breath-taking speed, mechanically following its own laws. Interest focussed on increasing production capacities requiring less and less human labour with the result that developments came to be further and further removed from the world of nature and brought the age of electronics and automation.

In place of the 'brotherhood in the life of economics' postulated by Rudolf Steiner as part of his 'three-fold social organism' in 1918 we have 'soulless competition' and management techniques that seem inhuman.

The same trend is to be seen in agriculture. Labour was reduced, and this was followed by high capital investment in the industrialization and specialization of farms (Mansholt plan – single-handed operation). The need to increase production year by year in order to meet rising costs means

- increasing expenditure on mineral fertilizers and in consequence increasing use of pesticides;
- or increasing the area farmed, which requires complex specialized machinery;
- and/or increasing livestock numbers, which means buying in large volumes of feedstuffs.

Human capacities tend to fall short when it comes to the operation of large farm machinery and need to be supported with monitors, optical detectors, guide furrows and so on.

Large livestock numbers cannot be looked after efficiently by stock people. Computers are therefore used to monitor concentrate uptake in loose housing, for example. The farmer reads the printout to see if all the cows have taken their full ration. The well-being of individual animals is only checked if the figures show that they have not done so. Farmers no longer know the individual animals because numbers are so large, and each must therefore be given a marking that is visible from a distance.

Great attention is given to human work places. Heavy tractors have fully air-conditioned cabs with the driver's seat and the position of levers designed on ergonomic principles and with radio receivers as part of the standard equipment, all to make work easier and more pleasant. At the same time the distance from the soil and the plants is quite literally increasing. The energy available and brought to bear with four-wheel drive is such that subtle differences in soil structure and quality go unnoticed.

The above is an extreme that only applies in individual cases today, yet it is on the increase. It is gradually beginning to dawn on people, however, that the industrialization of agriculture has all kinds of inherent dangers, unless the laws of life are taken into account.

Farmers who think in terms of biological wholes find that the use of technology makes additional demands. More frequent assessment of soil conditions, using the spade test, will give early warning of dangers, so that steps can be taken to remedy the situation. Less powerful machines with four-wheel drive and less pressure on the soil will often prove adequate, as will waiting for the right moment with operations, and trials with new, less rigorous methods.

Note should be taken of all at-

Unless the laws of life are taken into account, the industrialization of agriculture can bring all kinds of dangers.

tempts to be more 'biological' in farming; for there is certainly no question of doing away with technology but rather of using the methods best adapted to biological requirements. Pioneering work is being done by Ernst Weichel in Heiningen, Germany, with considerable personal engagement in the following areas:
– working the soil without turning it,
– mechanical weed control,
– processing and spreading of farmyard manure.

Milking machine manufacturers are working on improvements that meet the needs of the animals, e.g. methods using a limited vacuum to ease the stress on udders and teat tips. Both the risk of mastitis and the milking time are reduced as a result. Skilful incorporation of suitable technical equipment in a biodynamic system can both improve and reduce the work, so that more time and energy is available for the care of vital interrelationships in the farm organism.

The right selection, efficient use and servicing of modern plant and machines demand increased concentration and watchfulness. Modern technology can therefore help the evolution of human consciousness and make people able to cope better with future demands.

Finance and labour

Farmers are notoriously shy when it comes to using pen and ink, but for the development of new methods it is essential to keep accurate records for an extended period, noting down individual operations and their direct and indirect effects on the complete farm organism. This applies in the first place to production methods but then also to farm profits.

Growing interest in biodynamic farming and its increasing importance at a time of rising pollution levels make it important to provide accurate documentation also for financial and labour aspects. A number of studies have been done in the economics sector, but a great deal of information is still needed on labour programmes. Comparisons made between farms have shown that the differences between farms using the same method of agriculture tend to be greater than the differences in mean figures for different methods. Nevertheless the available data show trends – to be taken with certain reservations – that will be discussed below.

A recent study on economics and labour on biodynamic farms has largely confirmed those trends.

Comparisons have shown that differences between farms using the same method of agriculture may be greater than the differences between mean figures for different methods.

Labour

On farms largely devoted to forage crops (75% or more) and not growing special crops, labour requirements differ little between organic/biodynamic and conventional methods. The man hours required for plant production are the same if the same equipment is used and natural conditions such as mean homestead-to-field distance, and size, shape and situation (e.g. level, sloping, steep) of fields are approximately the same.

The time required for applying mineral fertilizer and pesticides is about the same as that used to apply the biodynamic preparations and any other treatments needed, e.g. nettle liquor. It is more difficult to assess the time required to produce the biodynamic preparations and sprays, as the work is at least partly done at times other than the days available for field work (normally called 'rest periods' in management planning, in contradistinction to the following periods: spring cultivation; row crop cultivation – hay harvest; cereal harvest; row crop harvest) and this work is frequently also undertaken by friends from town.

In a study done for a master's diploma (Sattler 1974), the figure arrived at for producing all the preparations was 2–3 hours/ha. The time was included under 'periods of rest', the cost under the 'fixed costs' of 15 DM/ha (approx. £5 sterling).

The situation is approximately the same for animal husbandry. The hours required are practically identical – within certain limits for stock numbers – if the equipment is the same and the training and employment of personnel approximately the same. For intermediate stacking of manure for composting add about one hour's work/animal unit/year.

It cannot be denied, however, that inner attitudes and frequently also inadequate systems (distance between housing, yards and pasture) increase the time spent on animal husbandry. The same applies to the treatment of diseases. Natural methods normally require more time, which under favourable conditions is made up for by a longer life span for the animals. If the mean age of cows is extended from 6.5 to 7.5 years, a replacement heifer will only be needed every fifth rather than every fourth year, and this is reflected in reduced costs and labour requirements.

Conditions are less favourable for mixed farms where less fodder and more special crops are grown. Increased variety means either more capital investment for expensive machinery or more labour-intensive

Table 66. Labour costs in Swiss francs/ha AA for organic/biodynamic and conventional farms. Mean values for 1979–1981.

	arable			mixed		
	bio farms	partner farms	test farms*	bio farms	partner farms	test farms*
number of farms	4	4	330	10**	10**	346
machine and traction power costs	1325	1637	1456	1331	1439	1401
salaries	957	607	567	995	656	565
wages due to family	2652	2286	3212	3570	3456	3530
total energy and labour costs	4934	4530	5235	5896	5551	5496

	cattle farms			mean of three groups		
	bio farms	partner farms	test farms*	bio farms	partner farms	test farms*
number of farms	6	6	354	(20)	(20)	(1030)
machine and traction power costs	1200	1309	1246	1285	1462	1368
salaries	470	593	536	807	619	556
wages due to family	3524	3457	3593	3249	3066	3445
total energy and labour costs	5194	5359	5375	5341	5147	5369

* Data from central statistics unit for FAT book-keeping data, main report 1981.
** excluding manager farm and its partner.

Labour requirements in organic and biodynamic farming may be expected to be the same, slightly more or a great deal more.

methods for the different crops.

In his comparative study of organic farming methods, Steinmann (1983) wrote: 'Farms concentrating mainly on forage growing and not growing special crops or using direct marketing to any appreciable degree show little difference from their partners with regard to labour requirements.

'Farms where field crops and particularly special crops such as fruit and vegetables play a significant role are likely to have higher labour requirements than their conventional partners. The reasons for this come under two headings:
'a) additional expenditure due to production methods and
'b) additional expenditure due to services.'

Additional expenditure due to services falls into four categories:
– product enhancement (producing bread, quark [low-fat soft cheese] and fruit juices);
– direct marketing, which also means increased paper work if the volume is at all appreciable;
– visits from interest groups, which may need considerable extra time for both preparation and implementation, especially on farms where such visits are frequent;
– on-farm training and lecturing and advisory activities and teaching outside the individual farm.

To sum up, it is fair to say that, depending on circumstances, labour requirements in organic and biodynam-

Table 67. ▷
Yields per ha or per cow and year on organic/biodynamic and conventional farms. Mean figures for 1979–1981.

ic farming may be expected to be the same, slightly more or a great deal more.

Financial aspects

The following passage is taken from the introduction to the above study for a master's diploma (administrative district Stuttgart, Germany, 1974):

'Modern profit-orientated management based on division of labour is totally different from management systems used a hundred years ago. The aim is no longer self-sufficiency but to achieve the highest possible profit. Entrepreneurs prepared to take risks are a key characteristic. Production is based on free market economy and is generally intended for unknown consumers.'

In biodynamic farming management is based on different principles and farmers take a different attitude. They do not see their work as a trade carried out to achieve the highest possible gain but as a true vocation that satisfies both inner and outer needs. This is based on the knowledge that
– they are producing a good variety of foods of good biological quality for a group of informed consumers most of whom are known personally;
– the soil, its plants and the animals that belong to it are being maintained and fertility is being increased;
– caring for the natural and social environment is of general benefit.

Management conditions are required that will provide the necessary conditions for these aims.

Most investigations have shown that yields on organic and biodynam-

product	unit	yield per unit			mean diff. for bio farms in %	no. of observations	
		bio farms	partner farms	test farms	of partner farms	bio/ partner	test farms
wheat	[1]) t	3.86	4.53	4.70	−15	36	4,519
	[2]) t	3.88	4.51		−14	30	
rye	[1]) t	–	–	4.50	.	.	127
	[3]) t	4.42	–		.	12	
spelt	[1]) t	4.39	4.92	4.70	−11	7	249
	[3]) t	4.31	–		.	15	
oats	[1]) t	4.21	4.97	4.90	−15	9	409
	[3]) t	3.97	–		.	18	
barley	[1]) t	3.91	4.50	4.50	−13	33	1,582
	[2]) t	3.88	4.50		−14	21	
potatoes	[1]) t	31.12	31.42	36.30	*)	29	621
	[2]) t	31.69	30.88		*)	24	
milk	litre	–	–	4,912	.	–	1,465
	[2]) litre	4,517	5,111		−12	78	
milk/ha MFA	[2]) litre	–	–	11,254	.	–	264
	litre	8,609	10,669		−19	78	

[1]) All available paired observations.

[2]) Paired observations where figures available for whole three years; the same pairs were also used to compare direct cost-free yields.

[3]) Three-year mean for organic/biodynamic farms. Partner farms did not grow those crops for the whole of the three-year period.

*) Differences in the varieties grown made comparison impossible.

ic farms are on average slightly lower than on comparable conventional farms; deviations from the mean may be considerable. In financial terms, differences between the different methods are minimal, which is mainly due to
- a good input factor/product ratio with rational use of home-produced fodder and fertilizers;
- in some respects higher profits due to better producer prices and direct sales to an established group of customers;
- reduced energy requirements due to reduced need for traction power and rational use of technology.

The tables which follow give details of a study involving 26 paired Swiss farms (organic/biodynamic or conventional) (Steinmann 1983). Farms with the same production structure are shown in three groups – each including a number of pairs; each pair consists of a conventional

'Direct cost-free yield' (DCY) is the Swiss equivalent of 'gross margin'. With field crops, yields are 10–15% higher on organic/ biodynamic farms because prices for produce are slightly higher and expenditure is less on mineral fertilizers and pesticides as well as on 'various' expenses.

item	unit (Sfr = Swiss francs*)	revenue per unit			mean diff. for bio farms in % of partner farms	no. of observations	
		bio farms	partner farms	test farms		bio/ partner	test farms
wheat	2) Sfr/t	1120	990	990	+ 13	36	4519
	3) Sfr/t	1110	990		+ 12	30	
rye	2) Sfr/t	–	–	830	.	.	127
	4) Ft/t	860	–		.	12	
spelt	2) Sfr/t	960	920	910	+ 4	7	249
	4) Sfr/t	980	–		.	15	
oats	2) Sfr/t	670	640	680	+ 5	9	409
	4) Ft/t	710	–		.	18	
barley	2) Sfr/t	680	650	660	+ 5	33	1582
	3) Sfr/t	670	640		+ 5	21	
potatoes	2) Sfr/t	380	360	310	+ 6	29	621
	3) Sfr/t	380	380		± 0	24	
milk	3) Sfr/l	0.87	0.80	–	+ 9	78	.
eggs	3) Sfr/egg	0.40	0.26	–	+ 54	36	.
pigs live weight	2) Sfr/kg	4.27	4.30	4.30	– 1	24	1198

1) Including quality premium and tax refunds but excluding incentive and hillside premiums.
2) All available paired observations.
3) Paired observations where figures available for whole three years; the same pairs were also used to compare direct cost-free yields.
4) Three-year mean for organic/biodynamic farms. Partner farms did not grow those crops for the whole of the three-year period.
*) 1 Sfr is c. £0.41 (at the time of going to press).

Table 68. △ Mean revenue¹) for produce per unit on organic/biodynamic and conventional farms. 1979–1981.

Table 69. ▷ Mean yields and DCY on organic/bio-dynamic and con-ventional farms in 1979/81.

and an organic/biodynamic (bio) farm that are comparable with regard to the following criteria:
– production structure,
– climate and Swiss soil suitability chart,
– size of farm = area available for agricultural use (AA),
– livestock land use (based on live-stock register – B.f.L. d. EDV, Berne)
– and as far as possible ownership status.

A further requirement was proper book-keeping records for 1979–1981. Conventional farms are listed as 'partner farms' in the tables. The third column shows the figures for FAT 'test farms' (FAT = Swiss national research institute for agricultural management and technology, Taenikon, Switzerland) to provide a further standard for comparison. 19 of the 26 'bio' farms are organic, seven biodynamic.
Table 66 gives the labour costs/ha

	unit	bio farms	partner farms	test farms*	bio farms	partner farms	test farms*
		wheat			**rye**		
no.of farms		10	10	1 506	4	4	127
cultivated area	ha/100	199	236	398	128	–	163
yield	t/ha	3.88	4.51	4.70	4.42	–	4.50
av. revenue/t	Sfr/t	1109.0	985.0	988.5	859.1	–	833.3
total revenue**	Sfr/ha	4,898	4,592	4,812	4,029	–	3,887
seed	Sfr/ha	308	225	269	202	–	193
bought-in fertilizer	Sfr/ha	168	302	328	128	–	257
pesticides	Sfr/ha	3	105	136	–	–	105
various costs	Sfr/ha	152	258	223	143	–	251
total direct cost	Sfr/ha	631	890	956	473	–	806
direct cost-free yield	Sfr/ha	4,267	3,702	3,856	3,556	–	3,081
		spelt			**barley**		
no.of farms		5	4	249	7	7	1,582
cultivated area	ha/100	118	–	146	90	91	172
yield	t/ha	4.31	–	4.70	3.88	4.50	4.50
av. revenue/t	Sfr/t	982.4	–	909.2	673.0	643.0	660
total revenue**	Sfr/ha	4,586	–	4,645	3,753	3,861	4,104
seed	Sfr/ha	257	–	276	216	167	174
bought-in fertilizer	Sfr/ha	60	–	272	77	213	258
pesticides	Sfr/ha	–	–	135	–	89	100
various costs	Sfr/ha	263	–	270	69	240	137
total direct cost	Sfr/ha	580	–	953	362	709	669
direct cost-free yield	Sfr/ha	4,006	–	3,692	3,391	3,152	3,435
		oats			**potatoes**		
no.of farms		6	–	409	8	8	621
cultivated area	ha/100	126	–	129	120	140	209
yield	t/ha	3.97	–	4.90	31.69	30.88	36.30
av. revenue/t	Sfr/t	706.0	–	683.1	378.1	377.7	306.3
total revenue**	Sfr/ha	3,946	–	4,461	12,404	11,938	11,288
seed	Sfr/ha	202	–	181	1,602	1,907	1,697
bought-in fertilizer	Sfr/ha	30	–	247	242	419	476
pesticides	Sfr/ha	26	–	78	91	465	449
various costs	Sfr/ha	90	–	182	90	191	252
total direct cost	Sfr/ha	348	–	688	2,025	2,982	2,874
direct cost-free yield	Sfr/ha	3,598	–	3,773	10,379	8,956	8,414

* Figures from central statistics of FAT, main report 1981.
** Including premiums and compensation.

	unit	bio farms	partner farms	test farms*
no. of farms	–	26	26	1465
stock numbers	cattle unit (CU)	22.3	24.9	26.5
percentage of cows	%	74	69	69
milk production	litre/cow	4517	5111	4912
av. price milk	1/100 Sfr/litre	87	80	no data
revenue: milk**	Sfr/CU	2572	2461	2428
other	Sfr/CU	739	935	830
total revenue	Sfr/CU	3311	3396	3258
costs: suppl. feed	Sfr/CU	308	370	431
vet	Sfr/CU	70	73	76
other	Sfr/CU	120	94	91
total direct costs	Sfr/CU	498	537	598
direct cost-free yield	Sfr/CU	2813	2859	2660

*   Figures from central statistics of FAT, report from costing dept. 1981. Group: all farms in the valley region with at least 3 cows and 5 CU.

** Milk for calves not included in calculations.

For cattle farming, the 'direct cost-free sum' is about the same for all groups.

Table 70. Cattle farming yields and DCY of organic/biodynamic and conventional farms. Mean values for 1979–1981.

of AA as a mean figure for three years. The differences are minimal, with bio farms needing about 200 Swiss francs more than the conventional and 20 Sfr less than the test farms.

Table 67 shows that yields of field crops (potatoes) were 0–15% less and milk yields 12% less per cow and 19% less per hectare of fodder grown.

Table 68. The prices charged by conventional producers are considerably higher in Switzerland than they are in Germany, so that the difference in revenue is minimal, with prices just under 6% higher for bio products. Eggs are the exception. The prices conventional producers charge for bread grain in Switzerland are higher than the price of organic/biodynamically grown wheat in Germany.

Table 73 offers a good illustration of the overall situation. Labour income per hectare AA is highest for mixed bio farms (4113 Sfr), 255 Sfr more than the second highest figure, which is for conventional cattle-raising farms. The average for all bio farms is 11 Sfr above the figures for conventional farms and 75 Sfr less than for test farms.

The price difference is much greater in Germany, and assuming all else to be equal, the figures would be considerably more in favour of bio farms. It is evident, therefore, that a change to alternative methods is justifiable.

Table 74 shows that the total annual family income was 2500 Sfr higher on average for all bio farms and almost 400 Sfr higher than for all test

	unit	bio farms	partner farms	test farms*
no. of farms	–	26	26	264
main fodder growing area/farm	ha/100	1,145	1,149	1,002
suppl. fodder growing area/farm	ha/100	107	84	no data
adjusted CU	CU	21.72	24.17	24.24
MFA/CU	ha/100	53	48	41
milk/ha cow MFA	litre	8,609	10,669	11,254
revenue	Sfr/ha	6,654	7,680	8,289
bought-in fertilizer	Sfr/ha	60	164	213
pesticides	Sfr/ha	10	19	
other costs fodder growing	Sfr/ha	128	166	253
roughage and summering	Sfr/ha	198	245	306
cost of livestock husbandry	Sfr/ha	995	1,260	1,528
total direct costs	Sfr/ha	1,391	1,854	2,300
DCY fodder crops livestock	Sfr/ha	5,263	5,826	5,989

* Figures from central statistics of FAT, costing report 1981. Mixed farms, valley zone, 15–20 ha AA.

Relative to fodder growing area, bio farm yields are about 10% lower. With more extensive methods, the fodder growing area requirement is slightly higher; less expenditure on fertilizers and other livestock costs are not enough to cover the difference.

Table 71. △ Livestock and fodder yields and DCY per ha of main crop fodder on organic/biodynamic and conventional farms. Mean figures for 1979–1981.

	unit	poultry-keeping bio farms	poultry-keeping partner farms
no. of farms		12	7
no. of hens/farm		38	21
eggs laid/hen and year		203	201
mean revenue	1/100 Sfr/egg	40	26
yield	Sfr	75	48
feed	Sfr	42	44
other costs	Sfr	–	–
total direct costs	Sfr	42	44
direct cost-free yield	Sfr	33	4

With performance the same, but revenue/egg 54% higher, direct cost-free yield is eight times as high for bio farms.

◁ **Table 72.** Laying performance and DCY/hen on bio and conventional farms. Mean figures for 1979–1981.

Table 73.
Totals in Sfr/ha AA
for organic/biody-
namic and conven-
tional farms. Mean
figures for
1979–1981.

	arable farms		
	bio farms	partner farms	test farms*
no. of farms	4	4	330
gross profit from crops	2229	3362	3646
of these: cereals	890	1443	1156
potatoes	275	639	991
vegetables	90	–	105
other field crops	185	936	999
tree fruits, soft fruit	566	138	198
woodland	97	127	82
premiums for cultivation and slopes	126	79	115
gross profit from livestock	5265	5045	4469
of these: milk & milk products	3373	2504	2605
other revenue from cattle	752	1626	1221
pigs	899	907	589
poultry	143	3	28
other revenue from livestock	98	5	26
other farm profits	537	503	552
of these: rent for buildings	416	207	281
total gross profits/ha AA	8031	8910	8667
expenditure on crop growing	381	886	1014
of this: commercial fertilizers	90	317	319
pesticides	5	136	157
total cost of livestock	1289	1471	1063
of this: suppl. feed	885	1087	746
total costs machine and tractioh power	1325	1637	1456
total general operating costs	295	278	248
difference = farm income before deducting estate charges/ha AA	4741	4638	4886
deduct: estate charges	549	465	421
interest	1020	1056	1005
difference = labour income/ha AA	3172	3117	3460
indices: farm income before deducting estate charges/working day	114.49	129.38	126.68
labour income/working day	76.62	86.95	89.64

* Figures from central
statistics of FAT,
main report 1981.

mixed farms			cattle farms			mean for the three groups		
bio farms	partner farms	test farms*	bio farms	partner farms	test farms*	bio farms	partner farms	test farms*
11	11	346	6	6	354	(21)	(21)	(1030)
2288	1983	2192	1797	813	1124	2105	2053	2321
612	515	606	244	67	157	582	675	640
595	487	625	274	59	149	382	395	588
566	49	68	166	66	24	274	38	66
84	310	404	142	72	165	137	440	523
137	411	209	915	406	431	539	318	279
149	86	148	25	94	135	90	102	122
145	125	132	31	49	63	101	85	103
6224	6051	6344	5189	7449	7250	5559	6182	6021
3343	3907	3725	3892	5004	4716	3536	3805	3682
1133	1437	1518	978	2166	1529	954	1743	1423
1642	658	1040	186	224	957	909	596	862
27	26	30	134	28	24	101	20	27
79	23	31	-1	27	24	59	18	27
362	329	284	557	397	617	604	473	590
362	239	284	223	227	306	334	224	290
9230	8555	9138	7543	8659	8991	8268	8708	8932
409	674	748	307	435	448	366	665	737
85	205	245	78	139	176	84	220	247
18	91	102	25	50	60	16	92	106
1743	1349	1640	952	1340	1781	1328	1387	1495
1404	873	1195	462	702	1262	917	887	1068
1283	1373	1401	1200	1309	1246	1269	1440	1367
256	225	241	254	278	245	268	260	245
5539	4934	5108	4830	5297	5271	5037	4956	5088
479	456	476	572	424	559	533	448	485
947	1010	1033	1068	1015	1070	1012	1027	1036
4113	3468	3599	3190	3858	3642	3492	3481	3567
96.06	115.47	120.16	115.43	123.35	126.92	108.66	122.73	124.59
71.33	81.16	84.68	76.24	89.83	87.55	75.34	86.87	87.32

farms. Savings are slightly less because bio families are one consumer unit larger on average. In spite of slightly lower expenditure per consumer unit (ca. 1100 Sfr) they do not quite achieve the savings of comparable farms.

Summing up, it can be said that under prevailing conditions Swiss bio farmers can match the achievements of comparable conventional colleagues.

Table 75 compares the three-year average, maximum and minimum figures for 14 conventional farms that are part of the local agricultural association in Heidenheim (Germany) with the three-year averages of Talhof farm in Heidenheim. The area available for agricultural use (AA) is greatest for the Talhof farm, but that includes 20% of areas with very shallow soil that have only been taken into cultivation for graz-

Table 74.
Figures for organic/biodynamic and conventional farms. Mean figures for 1979–1981.

	arable farms			mixed farms		
	bio farms	partner farms	test farms*	bio farms	partner farms	test farms*
no. of farms	4	4	330	10**	10**	346
absolute figures	Sfr	Sfr	Sfr	Sfr	Sfr	Sfr
farming income	53,267	58,860	52,953	54,838	49,594	53,484
subsidiary income	14,159	4,229	5,636	6,969	5,813	5,547
total income	67,426	63,089	58,589	61,807	55,407	59,031
financial requirements of family	52,109	46,200	40,827	43,249	39,963	40,567
savings	15,317	16,889	17,762	18,558	15,444	18,464

	cattle farms			mean for the three groups		
	bio farms	partner farms	test farms*	bio farms	partner farms	test farms*
no. of farms	6	6	354	(20)	(20)	(1,030)
absolute figures	Sfr	Sfr	Sfr	Sfr	Sfr	Sfr
farming income	55,147	59,004	52,373	54,417	55,819	52,937
subsidiary income	2,708	2,298	5,185	7,945	4,113	5,456
total income	57,855	61,302	57,558	62,362	59,932	58,393
financial requirements of family	42,872	43,236	39,304	46,077	43,133	40,233
savings	14,983	18,066	18,254	16,285	16,799	18,160

* Figures from central statistics of FAT, main report 1981.
** Excluding manager's farm and partners.

	14 convtl farms	Talhof biodynamic	maximum figs for the 14 farms	minimum
size of farm in ha farmland	41.50	47.29	54.05	16.28
yield in DM/ha	5201	4293	7540	2522
expenses DM/ha	3478	2434	6566	1845
expenses in % of yield	66.9	56.7	88	47 T
gross profits dM/ha	1733	2050	3450	413
net gain in DM/ha	1461	1825	2942	164
gross margin cereals in DM/ha	1501	2615	3331 T	828
gross margin/dairy cow in DM	2058	4398	5083 T	1194
gross margin other cattle in DM/animal	525	466	1135	61
gross margin in DM/man hour	14.47	26.92	28.47 T	6.63
gross margin in DM/ha farmland	2567	3136	4368	1136

ing sheep in the last thirty years. The 14 conventional farms show considerable variation in natural conditions as this is an area where rich, deep valley floor soils with a good climate lie next to shallow, stony weathered soil exposed to a harsh climate. Talhof farm has extremely unfavourable conditions in a long, narrow valley with a very cold microclimate. The fields are mostly on the valley slopes, with about 15 km of shade from woodlands. In spite of this the figures are far from bad and in fact very good where it matters most.

Table 76 compares gross margins (GM) as follows:
1) Talhof winter wheat (biodynamic), food quality for direct sale, the rest for fodder.
2) Talhof mean figure for all combine-harvested produce. Total wheat sales figures include all species, including peas (counted among cereals for book-keeping), oats and fodder barley.
3) On one of the 14 conventional farms, winter wheat was grown under better conditions. The farm

in question is a mixed cereal and dairy farm.

Notes on the above
1) High yield for the site concerned. Direct sales mean high return. GM/ha and man hour very high in spite of variable costs (VC) due to marketing costs (cleaning, sacks, special storage, work hours, etc.).
2) Mean yield for the site (combined figure for winter wheat, spring wheat, oats, naked barley – 20% less in quantity – and peas) and good financial return. Low VC resulted in 50% above average GM (see Table 76).
3) Mean yield for livestock farm in good site with high expenditure on commercial fertilizer and pesticides. GM/ha and GM/man hour are almost the same as for 2).

Summing up, it may be said that good yields with a high level of direct sales can give a 50% above average GM for all cereals grown on a biodynamic farm.
Conventional farms require relatively large amounts of agrochemicals to

Table 75.
5-year averages from 14 farms of the local agricultural association in Heidenheim (Germany) compared with those of Talhof farm (1982–1986). T = Talhof. [DM = Deutschmark = c. £0.33 at time of going to press]

	1) wheat - biodynamic		
	t/ha	DM/t	DM/ha
yield of grain for human consumption	4	1500	6000
yield of fodder grain	1	440	440
marketed crops, not cleaned			
total yields	–	–	6440
seed - own	0.25	1500	375
seed - bought in			
fertilizers			
pesticides			
insurance			40
drying			40
own machines			240
processing for market			250
total variable costs			945
gross margin			5945
time			total man hours
SC			3
RCH			2
CH			13
RT			12
other			5
total labour required			35
GM/man hours in DM			157.00

Calculating gross margin: SC = spring cultivations
1) wheat - biodynamic   RCH = row crops, hay harvest
2) mean for all cereals - biod.   CH = cereal harvest
3) wheat - conventional   RT = row crops harvest

achieve the same result. The situation is approximately the same for roots and tubers, e.g. potatoes, carrots and beetroot, compared to conventionally grown sugar beet.

The gross product diagram (Fig. 82) may help to explain the figures given in Table 77.

The true fixed-term gains have to

– cover the financial needs of the family,
– build up capital for major investments,
– provide for repayment instalments to be paid on time, without posing a threat to normal running of the farm and
– build up reserves for payment in

2) cereals - biodynamic			3) wheat - conventional		
t/ha	DM/t	DM/ha	t/ha	DM/t	DM/ha
1.1	1500	1650			
2.8	440	1232			
			6.5	500	3250
–	–	2882	–	–	3250
0.15	1500	225	0.1	600	60
0.10	1000	100	0.1	1000	100
					500
					175
		40			40
		40			50
		215			180
		100			–
		720			1105
		2162			2145

total man hours	total man hours
3	3
2	2
13	13
12	12
2	1
32	31
67.50	69.20

settlement to heirs, provision for old age and finance for extraordinary risk situations.

A financially sound farm should achieve profitability of over 100%. Due to price rises and technological advances, depreciation does not match the sum needed to replace old machinery and plant after ten years. It is therefore necessary to have sufficient capital available to avoid serious debt.

Comparison of the figures given for the 'agricultural association' in Table 75 and the 'conventional group' from Baden-Wuerttemberg in Table 78 shows that truly comparable

No.	yield		fertilizer	pesticides	processing for market	total variable costs	GM in DM		man h/ha
	t	DM					/ha	man h	
1	5.0	6440	–	–	250	945	5495	157.00	35
2	3.9	2882	–	–	100	720	2162	67.50	32
3	6.5	3250	500	175	–	1105	2145	69.26	31

Table 77. Key figures from Table 76.

partners must be found to establish a clear picture concerning the economic viability of different farming methods. Apart from site conditions, the farming system is of crucial importance. The conventional farms in Table 78 are fodder-growing and dairy farms from the lesser Swabian Alb and the right partners for Talhof farm. The 14 conventional farms in Table 75 include a number of different systems and are therefore less suitable for comparison.

Some of the key figures in Table 78 merit a closer look:
– The true fixed-term gains per hectare AA are 1.91 times higher for the Talhof farm than for the conventional group and 2.81 times higher for the Steighof farm;
– capital build-up per hectare AA is 5.94 and 3.46 times as high respectively;
– gross margin per man hour is 2.0 and 2.22 times as high respectively, and
– profitability is 170 and 135% respectively compared to 56%. According to the average figure, the conventional farms are in danger of becoming non-viable unless they are able to make up the deficit from subsidiary income.

The biodynamic farms have done well despite poor site conditions. The main reasons for this are as follows:
– *Consistent* application of the biodynamic method for many decades, making intensive use of dynamic measures.
– Operations done as far as possible on favourable dates in the cosmic calendar, taking *all* important production factors into account.
– Careful management of their own means of production and necessary

Fig. 82. Diagram to show structure of gross margin.

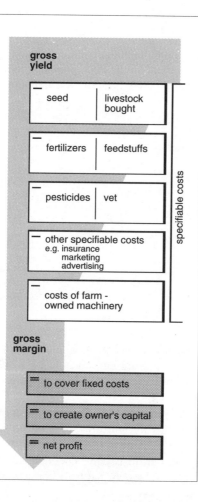

Table 78. ▷ Key figures from the book-keeping records of Talhof and Steighof farms compared to mean figures for Baden-Wuerttemberg Group 14 (Lesser Alb). Mean figures for 1983–1986.

		Talhof	Steighof	conventional group
		biodynamic		
agricultural land area	AL ha	46.20	31.91	33.07
unwaged families	man power	0.95	1.51	1.65
arable land	ha	24.23	21.83	
arable land	in % AL	52.20	68.41	37.18
permanent grassland	ha	21.97	10.08	
permanent grassland	in % AL	47.80	31.59	62.75
livestock nos. absolute	in CU	43.90	31.93	
livestock CU	/100 ha	94.60	100.70	146.20
assets	DM/ha AL	12,966	27,430	17,822
owner's capital	DM/ha AL	12,580	22,693	12,680
investments buildings/machines	DM/ha AL	38	678	901
specific expenditure	DM/ha AL	2,348	3,469	3,200
specific revenue	DM/ha AL	4,220	5,437	4,180
expenditure in % of revenue	%	56	64	77
total profit	DM	87,632	81,979	32,133
true fixed-term gains	DM/ha AL	1,872	2,750	980
profit	DM/fam.MP	92,244	58,163	19,533
change in own capital	DM	78,168	31,509	9,429
profitability	%	170.1	135.2	55.5
area for cereals	ha	9.48	8.69	
cereals	% of area	39.1	39.75	59.25
silage maize	ha	0.83	–	
silage maize	% of area	3.4	–	15.75
leys	ha	11.18	8.87	
leys	% of area	46.20	40.8	18.00
combine-	ha			
harvested crops	% of area	11.43	8.83	
combine-	ha			
harvested crops	% of area	47.13	41.10	62.18
row crops	ha	0.71	2.39	
row crops	% of area	2.95	10.95	1.88
annual average livestock				
young & fattening stock	n	27	24	36
dairy cows	n	27	15	24
yield cereals	t/ha	3.95	2.81	4.17
calves reared	n/cow	1.18	1.17	1.0
milk yield	kg/cow	4,916	3,329	4,133
main fodder crop area	0.01 ha/CU	79.57	65.9	58.08
expenditure fertilizers	DM/ha AL	6	74	271
special expenditure soil improvement	DM/ha AL	106	447	385
livestock bought	DM/ha AL	34	149	253
feedstuff bought	DM/ha AL	168	245	665
special expenditure livestock husbandry	DM/ha AL	393	450	1,075
machine maintenance	DM/ha AL	383	275	206
machine depreciation	DM/ha AL	340	283	335

		Talhof	Steighof	conventional group
		biodynamic		
exp. labour aids	DM/ha AL	822	773	788
maintenance buildings	DM/ha AL	44	57	174
depreciation buildings	DM/ha AL	141	280	183
rent, interest	DM/ha AL	43	142	236
revenue cattle	DM/ha AL	1,103	991	1,141
revenue milk	DM/ha AL	2,443	877	1,957
revenue animal products	DM/ha AL	3,639	2,083	3,490
farm consumption	DM/ha AL			
feedstuff	DM/ha AL	737	419	380
cereals realized	StGM* DM.ha	2,747	2,247	1,161
potatoes realized	StGM DM.ha	7,968	4,775	3,004
silage maize realized	StGM DM.ha	−600	−	−1,151
leys realized	StGM DM.ha	−475	−525	−499
permanent grassland realized	StGM DM.ha	−220	−261	−410
dairy cows realized	StGM DM.ha	4,459	2,034	2,020
young/fattening stock realized	StGM DM.ha	382	467	428
laying hens realized	StGM DM/100 units	1,985	2,590	1,136
concentrates	DM/cow	−489	−689	−264
variable costs	DM/kSE	−157	−145	−159
labour required	man h/1000 kSE	20.83	14.87	10.90
standard GM realized	DM	153,866	130,367	65,963
standard GM theoretical	DM	68,952	110,047	65,635
ratio realized:theor.	%	223.8	117.55	100.6
labour requirement	man h/ha AL	123	136	144
GM	DM/man h	27.00	30.04	13.65

*stGM = standard gross margin

Table 78. cont.

outside energy supplies.
- Careful husbanding of high-performance healthy plant varieties and breeding stock.
- Ongoing review of the established management system in the light of new research and practical information.
- Last but not least our faithful customers from far and near.

It has to be admitted that the manager of Talhof farm has only been giving serious consideration to soil and fodder tests and analyses and to management data in the last two decades. In his younger years as a farmer he felt that practical experi-ence, the necessary intuition and energy and initiative would be enough to help a farm to develop its own individual agricultural nature.

Whilst this is no doubt possible, the goal will be achieved more directly and safely if due account is taken of analytical and bookkeeping data.

Biodynamic farmers will gain much from effective use of systems analysis. Comparison with the data of comparable conventional partners will show that biodynamic agriculture has its justification not only for environmental and ideal reasons but also in financial terms.

Mineral balances

Just as the books have to be balanced, with both income and expenditure accounted for, so it is also possible to produce a balance sheet for the physical substances on the farm.

Justus von Liebig analysed plants and soil samples to see what minerals plants were taking up from the soil – including nitrogen, phosphorus, potassium and calcium. Part of these leave the farm when produce is sold, whilst part returns to the soil with harvest residues and in farmyard manure.

Exact balances can only be established for closed systems, e.g. in a lysimeter or in experiments using potted plants. The farm organism is bound up with the atmosphere (nitrogen fixation), the soil and the weathering of rocks, the water and many other things. It is therefore not possible to determine exactly the how much of an element is taken up from the air and the soil or lost by leaching into the ground water. The example of a nitrogen balance which is shown below is based on rough estimates of gains through fixation by legumes and from precipitations and free living organisms and losses due to leaching (farm no. 4 profiled at the beginning of the book).

In this cropping sequence with a high percentage of legumes (45%), gains and losses are well balanced with 131 kg/ha/year taken out of and 141 kg/ha/year coming into the soil.

Table 79.
Nitrogen balance,
farm no. 4
(see Farm profiles).

crop kg/ha	output	leached	ferti-lizer	precipita-tion	legumes	free bacteria
oats	60	20	24	10		10
row crops	130	40	150	10		15
wheat	70	20	24	10		10
legume mixtures	80	10	100	10	50	10
row crops	130	40	150	10		15
wheat	70	20	24	10		10
oats/barley/undersown	80	10	100	10	50	10
sainfoin	640	20	248	40	400	40
total - 11 years	1260	180	820	110	500	120
	output 1440				input 1550	
kg N/ha/year	131				141	

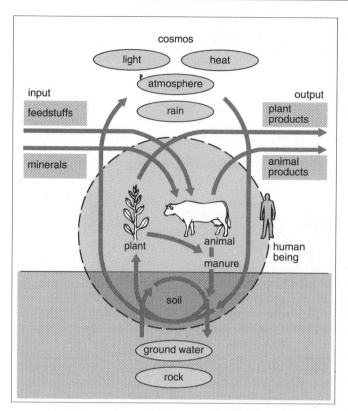

cosmos

light   heat

atmosphere

input   rain   output

feedstuffs   plant products

minerals   animal products

plant   animal   human being

manure

soil

ground water

rock

Fig. 83. Interchanges between farm and environment.

Fertilizers only provide 65%. This type of balance can only give a rough idea, as information on the different factors is limited.

Another way of getting a picture of the situation for the whole farm is to compare merely the nitrogen, phosphorus and potassium that is bought in and leaves the farm with the sale of products, ignoring the exchanges that occur within the system and in the atmosphere and the soil.

The statistics given in Fig. 84 are based on estimates from the German Federal Office of Statistics, on tables giving concentrations of constituents and on farming reports.

In Sweden and Germany input (bought-in fertilizers and feedstuffs) is greatly in excess of output (sale of products). The figures have been checked by H. Vetter (1982) who ar-

rived at essentially the same results.

The three biodynamic farms featured in Fig. 85 had higher nitrogen and potassium outputs than inputs, whilst the figures for phosphorus are more or less in balance. It is evident that adequate nitrogen is available from natural compounds. Phosphorus and potassium can be dissolved out of deposits and brought into the mineral cycle if the soil has sufficient vitality.

Careful management of the soil and green cover (plants growing in the soil throughout the year, as far as possible, i.e. also outside the main growth period) can reduce leaching of nitrates, potassium and calcium from humic soil with a good crumb structure.

Excessive use of mineral fertilizers ultimately leads to 'luxury consumption' (Scheffer & Schachtschabel 1982) and the exhaustion of dwindling resources. According to *Global 2000*, world phosphate and potassium resources will last another 50 years. Nitrogen fixation costs energy (18 million kcal/t of industrially produced fertilizer). This is reflected in the figures given for agricultural energy consumption. According to Lockeretz *et al.* (1975 and 1976), mixed farms in the USA using organic fertilizers had 8–10 % lower yields and used 56–70 % less energy than conventionally run farms. Differences in energy consumption are mainly apparent with reference to fertilizers, pesticides and soil cultivation, less so with regard to general management aspects.

Comparison of the mineral balances for the three farms in Fig. 85 and Talhof farm clearly shows the differences in local conditions and products sold (Table 80).

Farm no. 1 sells mainly meat, milk,

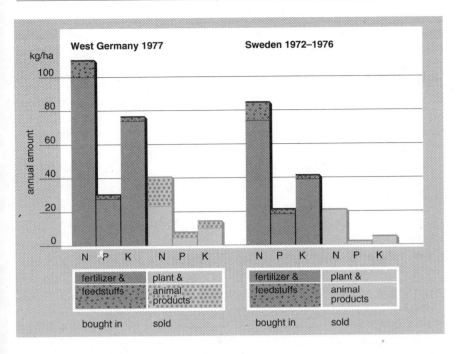

Fig. 84.
Mineral balances in Germany and Sweden (Wistinghausen 1980).

eggs and cereal grains, nos. 2 and 3 cereals and field-grown vegetables, Talhof farm milk, meat and cereal grains. Vegetables contain more potassium than cereals and animal products. Mineral output via meat and milk sales is minimal. Soil analyses from farm no. 1 show the capacity for regeneration due to building up humus levels (C x 1.72 = humus). This goes hand in hand with increasing mineral availability.

Fig. 85.
Mineral balances of three biodynamic farms (Wistinghausen 1980).

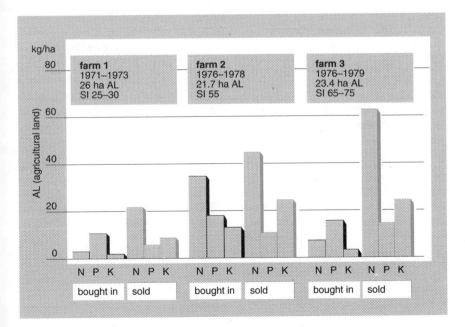

farm		N kg/ha	P kg/ha	K kg/ha
no. 1	bought in	2.8	9.2	0.6
	sold	22.2	3.6	8.1
		−19.4	+ 5.6	− 7.5
no. 2	bought in	35.0	16.0	13.0
	sold	47.0	13.0	24.0
		−12.0	+ 9.0	−11.0
no. 3	bought in	7.0	16.0	4.0
	sold	63.0	13.0	25.0
		−56.0	+ 3.0	−21.0
Talhof	bought in	8.4	1.7	6.2
	sold	27.5	5.0	6.5
		−19.1	− 3.3	− 0.3

Nos. 1–3 from E. v. Wistinghausen (1980), Talhof from Kaffka (1984).

Table 80. N, P and K balances of four biodynamic farms

At Talhof farm, soil carbon levels rose by 0.86% between 1972 and 1982.

year	arable	meadow	pasture	
1972	2.36	3.89	3.94	% C
1982	2.99	4.91	4.87	% C

Table 81. Rising humus level and mineral availability on farm no. 4 (see Farm profiles).

On a farm, as in any other organism, a vast number of substances are constantly exchanged. They provide the basis for the life processes on earth. Chemical analysis shows what happens in the area where these substances are weighable, and that is the only way we have of balancing the books for mineral metabolism. It does not, of course, provide direct insight into the actual life processes. What it does show is that biodynamic farming is a way of husbanding the forces and substances that the earth provides.

year	pH	C %	N %	C/N	P_2O_5 mg/100 g	K_2O soil	Mg
1974	7.0	2.32	0.308	7.5	5.8	15.4	15.4
1980	6.8	3.88	0.380	10.2	6.4	18.8	28.4

pH = (KCl); P_2O_5, K_2O, Mg = (CAL), mean for five fields.

Nitrate pollution of ground water due to storage and use of fertilizers

The maximum permissible nitrate concentration in drinking (ground) water has been reduced to 50 mg/l, and the question arises as to whether biodynamic farms are contributing to the pollution. With a livestock concentration of c. 0.8–1.3 CU/ha AL, the level of nitrogen produced is extremely low at 35–55 kg/ha/year. It is evident from the previous chapter that nitrogen output is much higher than nitrogen input on biodynamic farms. The difference between input and output in Table 80 (page 308) is 19–56 kg/ha. It may therefore be assumed that there is no serious leaching into the ground water. On farm no. 14 it is estimated that leaching is no more than 16 kg/ha/year.

According to the data available, correctly sited and managed *composting sites* offer no risk of nitrate pollution. On permeable soils, a layer of bentonite under the heap will combine with mucilage from the manure to form a layer that is practically impermeable to dung liquor. Approximately 80% of the nitrogen in manure is organically fixed, leaving only 20% in form of nitrate N or ammonia N. Analysis of our dung storage sites therefore always shows extremely low nitrate concentrations. With *farmyard manure* composted on sandy soil (0.8 kg of bentonite/m^2 spread before making the heap), nitrogen loss was 1.9 kg/t of manure. Only 1.4% of this, i.e. 27 g of nitrogen/t, leached into the soil in form of nitrates (c. 1 l/m^2 of composting site).

Marketing aspects

Summing up the question as to whether organic farming is an individual or a general issue, Diercks (1983) comments as follows: 'In the final instance it would be for consumers and producers themselves to decide the rate and degree of change to organic farming methods. Unless of course there is a complete change in government agricultural policy, so that farmers are relieved of the growing economic pressure that is the sole reason for optimum use of modern chemicals and technology.'

Consumers with a genuine interest in biodynamic agriculture made this decision decades ago. Demeter consumer organizations are actively promoting the method by helping to provide funds for advisory, research and training facilities.

Standards for biodynamically produced foods are guaranteed by the Demeter symbol. Farms that are still in the process of conversion may use the Biodyn* label.

Farms and market gardens enter into a contract with the Demeter Association (in the UK certification is handled by the Demeter Standards Committee of the Bio-Dynamic Agricultural Association) and are then entitled to use the Demeter and Biodyn* trademarks. Farming methods must follow the Demeter guidelines, and in Germany farms must be officially approved by a representative each of the Biodynamic Research Group (Forschungsring fuer Biologisch-Dynamische Wirtschaftsweise) and the regional farmers' group.

In Germany, the Biodynamic Research Group includes farmers, scientists, advisers, experts from various spheres of life, and regional producer groups. It provides a forum for discussion of farming and market gardening methods and establishes the guidelines for this and for processing and marketing.

The route that Demeter products take from the producer through processing and marketing to the consumer is also subject to contracts and guarantees. The Demeter quality testing unit at the Institute of Biodynamic Research in Darmstadt carries out regular quality tests and has products analysed for residues.

Processing of Demeter foods involves methods designed to preserve quality, with special attention given to nutritive value.

The many different tasks (trademark protection, advice, quality control, general information) are partly financed by a protection charge that is levied at one point along the route for every Demeter product. The current charge for farmgate sales is 2% of the sale price and buyers should be able to recognize it for what it is. The producer remits the charge to the

The Demeter trademark is used by market gardeners and farmers who satisfy the requirements of the Demeter guidelines; the Biodyn* trademark is used by those who are converting to biodynamic management and following the guidelines laid down for this.

* at the time of going to press in the UK, the Biodyn trademark has recently been superseded by the designation 'Biodynamic in conversion'.

Income from agricultural products must be such that farmers can continue to produce foods of the highest quality in future.

Demeter Association to support its work.

The 'growing economic pressure' (Diercks) and low profitability (56% for the whole group of conventionally managed farms shown in Table 78) are also affecting market gardens and farms run on biological lines. This is one reason why it is important that the products of biodynamic farms go wherever possible to the Demeter market and do not enter the general market. That is the only way in which the products can reach interested consumers, so that the farms can be supported economically.

Ongoing discussions between representatives of Demeter consumer groups, people who market and process Demeter products, and representatives of farm and market garden producers are designed to make the production and pricing of products clear and comprehensible at all levels. Such efforts increase the the contact that already exists between consumers and producers through farm-gate sales, creating a new form of relationship between city and country people and providing a basis for mutual understanding and sharing of concerns.

Every biodynamic farm should earn enough from its products to enable it to go on to produce a good variety of high quality foods in the years ahead, maintaining the health and fertility of the soil and of plants and animals without being threatened in its existence.

Conversion to biodynamic farming methods

The damage to the environment, which may be on a large scale as in the case of the dying forests or on a lesser scale in 'limited disasters' at the regional level, takes many forms – e.g. increased HCB levels in milk due to a chemical that was formerly approved for the treatment of dwarf bunt of wheat – must cause every responsible farmer to make a critical assessment of his own situation. Sooner or later the use of organic or biodynamic methods will be considered. Farmers will ask themselves if these provide a reasonable way out of the enforced specialization, the use of doubtful materials and energies and the need to achieve maximum yields at all costs.

It happens more and more often that farmers who have attended lectures, farm visits and/or introductory courses and have talked to farmers who are using these methods and have made their first experiments – perhaps in the farmhouse garden – decide to convert. Ideally every member of the family who lives and works on the farm should feel positive about this, for it will affect them all.

Once the decision has been made, it is advisable to consult an experienced farmer in the area or a trained adviser and get their help in working out a detailed schedule for the next few years.

Specialized farms are not always well suited for conversion. Exclusively arable farms with a high proportion of cereals, maize or sugar beet, farms without livestock, and those devoted mainly to livestock require long term planning, with changes made in careful stages.

The first step in conversion is a precise farm analysis. The following need to be considered:
– soil and climate,
– size of farm (division into fields, internal traffic systems),
– arable to grassland ratio,
– livestock numbers,
– existing animal houses and other buildings,
– liquid and solid manure, pit space in cubic metres,
– cropping sequence and crop ratios used to date, and
– available labour.

Planning must be on the basis of these actual data. The official farming advisory centres have many years of experience and can often give valuable aid.

To achieve the goal without facing impossible social and economic risks, it is necessary to establish clearly how to proceed in a number of specific areas:
– biodynamic preparations (storage, use, production),
– livestock husbandry (manure and

Conversion does not involve financial risks if planned with care and carried out with the help of trained advisers and experienced colleagues from the regional group.

feed requirements),
- fodder crops (legumes),
- cropping sequence and crop ratios,
- care of the soil,
- weed and pest control,
- work programme,
- marketing,
- finance, and finally a
- detailed timetable.

The time needed for conversion depends on a number of factors; generally speaking it is three years. Major factors are soil condition, livestock numbers, manure reserves, the intensity of previous management and the flexibility of the manager.

Three elements of farm organization must be given first consideration:

- the cropping sequence, long-range and as varied as possible;
- available animal dung - if necessary some may have to be bought in;
- undercrops and catch crops to provide extra forage in unfavourable years (dry or little fodder) and for green manuring.

The farmer needs to consider these three elements very thoroughly if he is to develop the system that will best suit his requirements and the given situation. The result may be something like this (Table 82):

Conversion starts when a crop printed in italics is grown. On this particular farm, all land can be farmed biodynamically by the third

Table 82. Conversion plan.

Farm-produced fertilizer	cropping sequence	undercrops and catch crops
composted manure	1) ley	
	2) ley	
dung liquor in spring	3) winter wheat	
composted manure, half quantity		green manure mixture
	4) summer grazing (no peas)	black medick & white clover undersown
composted manure	5) row crops, vegetables	
dung liquor in spring	6) wheat (or rye)	
composted manure, half quantity		green manure mixture
	7) summer grazing (with peas)	
		vetch & mustard mixture and shatted peas
composted manure	8) row crops	
dung liquor in autumn	9) winter rye	
		drill ley

1st year	2nd year	3rd year
1) ley	ley	*winter wheat*
2) ley	*winter wheat*	summer grazing
3) *winter wheat*	summer grazing	row crops
4) *summer grazing*	row crops	wheat or rye
5) row crops	wheat or rye	*summer grazing*
6) wheat or rye	summer grazing	*row crops*
7) summer grazing	*row crops*	winter rye
8) *row crops*	winter rye	ley
9) winter rye	*ley*	ley

year. Fields still farmed conventionally in the first two years are given applications of mineral fertilizer if and when required. Weed control is essentially mechanical or with a flame weeder, with herbicides used only in exceptional cases. No other chemical plant protectives should be used.

The biodynamic method can be introduced fairly quickly after fodder crops or green manuring, with full use made of the potential the new method offers.

Regular use of
– compost preparations,
– biodynamic field sprays,
– cowpat preparation, birch pit concentrate and liquid manure barrel,
– seed baths and drill fertilizer,
– improvers and conditioners
will ease the conversion process for soil, plants and animals and help to achieve the yields that are needed to avoid economic disasters.

During the first few years it may be advisable to use commercial organic fertilizers for particularly demanding crops. Care must be taken to see that these are free from compounds that might leave harmful residues in the soil and in products. Soil analysis and observation of soil and crops will show if rock dust, calcified seaweed or dolomite limestone and rock phosphate need to be added

Conversion of a farm usually takes three years.

at the dung processing stage.

Buying-in of feedstuffs needs to be reduced in stages to avoid sudden drops in performance. Hay and silage production will need special attention. It must be timely, with losses reduced to a minimum, so that all yields from livestock are essentially achieved with farm-produced basic feed.

It is generally advisable to be economical with materials and energies. If their use is carefully thought out and meets requirements exactly, expenditure is greatly reduced, which may make up for possible losses in yield.

The manager needs to be flexible, paying continuous attention to everything that goes on in the fields, stables and farmstead and adapting to the new situation. If an experienced adviser supports him faithfully in the early years, most conventionally run farms can be converted to the biodynamic method without running a financial risk.

Training

Education, training and an active mind are rated high at a time of rapid changes in technology and with constant new discoveries in all spheres of life. This applies particularly to an agricultural method such as biodynamic farming where much new territory is opening up, and where established institutions such as universities, research institutes and advice centres are only beginning to take an interest. Training and further education have therefore always been a major concern of the Biodynamic Research Group in Germany and for committed farmers.

Today, conferences and introductory courses are held annually in Germany, with the conferences particularly devoted to the sharing of experience, further education and a common effort to gain further insight. One-year training courses and accompanying courses in anthroposophy are available in a number of countries.

People working on the farms gain most of their further education at regional group meetings and national conferences; training generally takes place on the farms, with external courses to supplement it. Training places are in short supply and cannot meet the demand despite all efforts to utilize the facilities to their maximum.

A considerable proportion of young people looking for training come from cities rather than the country and often have false and nostalgic ideas about working in biodynamic agriculture. A few actually become farmers after completing the course; the others go to universities and technical colleges for further studies or into something entirely different. Many of the last category come to the farm years later, bringing their families with them, and declare that the period of work and study on the farm held special significance for their further life. Many of them will then support the work both morally and financially, and almost all of them feel real concern for the problems faced by farmers. They make an important contribution to greater understanding between town and country, consumer and producer.

Training on the farms is not limited to farming theory and practice. There is special emphasis on a broadening of horizons and on united efforts to gain understanding of the principles of anthroposophy; this provides for better understanding of the practical methods. Where circumstances permit, artistic work is also done together, making music, for example, singing, painting and modelling and celebrating the festivals of the year.

The demands made on the training farm and the community living on the farm – frequently just the farmer

The demands made on a training farm should not be underestimated. On the other hand life on the farm is enriched by the presence of young people.

and his family – should not be under-estimated. They include the following.

– Caring for the physical and mental well-being of the young people adds to the numerous duties of the farmer's wife who is looking after the household.
– The time needed for teaching and instruction makes enormous demands on the physical and mental stamina of those who train young people.
– Inevitable errors may cause losses in field crops and in the stables.
– Increased costs for repair and maintenance of machinery may be considerable (see Table 78: maintenance of machinery per hectare of AL is 2.7 times as high as for comparable conventional farms, expenditure on labour aids 25% higher).

None of these *potential* disadvantages should prevent a family from taking young people for training if the necessary preconditions exist. The effort is more than made up for by the gain in richness and variety.

Every young person brings not only personal problems into the community but also individual abilities. Some old established features and habits will gain from a fresh new look and new vitality.

More time will be available for:
– more individual care given to plants and animals,

If the preconditions are met, a farmer should accept young people for training.

– design and evaluation of experiments,
– use and evaluation of new methods and
– the practical application of the many special biodynamic measures.

Capable young people will be able to take responsibility in their second or third year, so that the farmer will be able to go outside the farm to give lectures and teach at schools, in courses and at conferences or be involved in professional and social institutions and organizations.

The greatest benefit lies in the fact that teaching and training always challenges the individual to review his personal experience, knowledge and opinions in the light of recent developments, and to add to them if necessary and perfect them. This helps individuals to develop, keeps them young and brings previously unknown capabilities to light and life. New capacities are thus brought to the farm that may contribute to the development of its individual agricultural identity.

A matter of new faculties and capacities

Modern scientific and technical advances have freed human beings from bondage to the physical world in many respects. Yet problems have also arisen where it is evident that people are no longer able to perceive the consequences of their actions and the knowledge they acquire. This applies not only to the development of the atom bomb, but to everyday life in general.

How far do people still know the origins of the things they buy, or where they go once they are thrown away? The method of agriculture presented in this book is based on principles developed by Rudolf Steiner. Its importance goes beyond farming and horticultural practice and the production of foods that meet the true needs of human beings. It is a model for a way of living and working in which theory and practice are given an orientation that will gradually enable people to take full responsbility for their actions once again.

It does mean that faculties and capacities have to be developed that enable us to relate to the natural world in a new way. These can be achieved by conscious training and may then serve as an instrument of perception.

In essence, efforts to broaden our view of the natural world on the basis of Rudolf Steiner's science of anthroposophy have to start with reflections on our own nature. If we take this line, we can contribute to the overcoming of environmental problems by

– considering the position of human beings, who perceive the world and act in it, and their potential for taking independent, responsible action;

– further developing the Goethean approach as exemplified in Goethe's theories of colour and metamorphosis. (The method is to consider phenomena in detailed fact and become aware of the process that has given rise to them. Thus the excellent beginnings that have been made in describing natural processes in the field of ecology can be taken further by life communities.)

– Taking up practical work in all kinds of different life spheres and basing them on insights gained through anthroposophy.

In working with nature, the aim is to make the sphere for which one is responsible, e.g. a farm, into a well-ordered organism. This can then develop an individual identity on the basis of given conditions on earth and in the cosmos and in line with human aims. We work to enable the development of a cohesive living entity – the way nature does as well – with human involvement giving it the

Anthroposophy is a science of the spirit that broadens the prevailing one-sided scientific view, providing new approaches that make it come alive and make it more complete.

orientation to become an integral whole.

The opposing tendencies towards uniformity and differentiation will then move towards a harmonious balance.

– Specialization on the farm will be kept within limits that are compatible with the quality of life referred to above;
– differentiation will be taken as far as possible, so that enhanced productivity arises from that quality of life.

A common objection is that all this is based on a philosophy that limits human freedom and must of course be rejected, though individual efforts are certainly worth acknowledging. This opinion has arisen from the accepted view of which people are not even aware. It is assumed – only brief mention can be made of this – that the only way of achieving valid knowledge is to follow the ideal of modern science and assume the attitude of an observer who looks from the outside at a world that is complete without him, and that this is not a 'philosophy'.

The anthroposophical road to knowledge leads to the realization that this is not the only way of looking at things. Different ways of observing the world complement each other, revealing not only objective but also essential spiritual reality. This alone can help people to act out of responsibility and work towards a further development of nature that is in accord with the spirit.

Dr Jochen Bockemuehl

Head of the Science Section of the School of Spiritual Science at the Goetheanum in Dornach, Switzerland.

Literature

In the literature list below, those references for which English translations exist are given in their English versions. A supplementary reading list of English-language material will be found on p.333

Abele, U.: Vergleichende Untersuchungen zum konventionellen und biologisch-dynamischen Pflanzenbau unter besonderer Beruecksichtigung von Saatzeit und Entitaeten. Inaugural-Dissertation. Fachbereich: Angewandte Biologie. Justus-Liebig-Universitaet, Giessen 1973.

Abele, U.: Abschlussbericht. Untersuchung des Rotteverlaufes von Guelle bei verschiedener Behandlung. Institut fuer biologisch-dynamische Forschung, Darmstadt 1976.

Abele, U.: Ertragssteigerung durch Fluessigmistbehandlung. KTBL-Schrift 224, Muenster-Hiltrup 1978.

Ahrens, E., und Mitarbeiter: Significance of Fertilization of the Post-Harvest Condition of Vegetables, Especially Spinach. Environmentally Sound Agriculture, Ed. W. Lockeretz Praeger, New York 1983.

Amberger, A.: Pflanzenernaehrung. UTB. Verlag Eugen Ulmer, Stuttgart 1978.

Andreae, U.: Ethologische Beurteilung der Aufstallungssysteme in der Rindermast. 1. Weltkongress fuer angewandte Ethologie der landwirtschaftlichen Grosstiere, 1978.

Appel, J.: Unkrautregulierung ohne Herbizide. Schriftenreihe Lebendige Erde, Darmstadt 1979.

Armann, K., und Pettersson, B.: Alternativa odlingsformer, Biodynamisk odling. LTS Foerlag, Stockholm 1979.

Bartsch, H., und Dreidax, F.: Der lebendige Duenger. Muellersche Verlagsbuchhandlung, Planegg vor Muenchen 1941.

Bauer, M.: Verbesserung der Trachtsituation fuer Bienenvoelker in der Feldflur. Monatsschrift Bienenpflege, Stuttgart, Januar 1985.

Berger, F.: Samenbau von Luzerne und Rotklee. Die Deutsche Landwirtschaft, Heft 4, 347–351, 1953.

Bilstein, U.: Lexikon der neuzeitlichen Landwirtschaft. Feld und Wald, 1974.

Biologisch-Dynamischer Landbau 1945 bis 1949, Neuaufbau. Schriftenreihe Lebendige Erde, Darmstadt 1949.

Biologisch-Dynamischer Land- und Gartenbau. Schriftenreihe Leb. Erde, Darmstadt, Band I/II 1973, Band III 1980.

Blen, H.: Stroemungstechnische Beitraege zum Windschutzproblem. Landtechnische Forschung, Heft 3, 1953.

Bockemuehl, J.: Vom Leben des Komposthaufens. Elemente der Naturwissenschaft. Dornach 1981, 2. Aufl.

Bogner, H., und Ritter, H. C.: Tierproduktion. Eugen Ulmer, Stuttgart 1976.

Boguslawski, E. von: Ackerbau. Grundlagen der Pflanzenproduktion. DLG-Verlag, Frankfurt/Main 1981.

Boerner, H.: Pflanzenkrankheiten und Pflanzenschutz. UTB. Verlag Eugen Ulmer, Stuttgart 1983, 5. Aufl.

Boros, G.: Heil- und Teepflanzen. Verlag Eugen Ulmer, Stuttgart 1980, 3. Aufl.

Boros, G.: Unsere Kuechen- und Gewuerzkraeuter. Verlag Eugen Ulmer, Stuttgart 1981, 4. Aufl.

Bringmann, L., und Kaiser, H.: Maisstreifen als Windschutz. Meteorologische Untersuchungen und Ertragsfeststellungen auf Gut Grafenthal. Zeitschrift fuer Acker- und Pflanzenbau, Band 99, Heft 3, 321–334, 1955.

Brockhaus, Der Neue. Brockhaus Verlag, Wiesbaden 1952.

Brockhaus, Der Neue. Brockhaus Verlag, Wiesbaden 1958.

Bruenner, F., und Schoellhorn, J.: Bewirtschaftung von Wiesen und Weiden. Verlag Eugen Ulmer, Stuttgart 1972.

Buhl, D., Weidner, H., und Zogg, M.: Krankheiten und Schaedlinge an Getreide und Mais. Verlag Eugen Ulmer, Stuttgart 1975.

Bundessortenamt. Beschreibende Sortenliste 1981 fuer Getreide, Mais, Oelfruechte, Leguminosen, Hackfruechte ausser Kartoffeln, Graeser, Klee, Luzerne.

Camenzind, Th.: Handbuch der Rindviehzucht und -pflege. Friedrich Andrist Fachbuch-Verlag, Giessen 1949.

Cloos, W.: Lebensstufen der Erde. Verlag Die Kommenden, Freiburg 1983.

Darwin, C.: The Power of Movement in Plants. John Murray, London 1880.

Deutsch, A.: Pflanzenproduktion. Leopold Stocker Verlag, Graz 1972.

Diercks, R.: Alternativen im Landbau. Verlag Eugen Ulmer, Stuttgart 1983.

Ehlers, M.: Baum und Strauch in der Gestaltung der Deutschen Landschaft. Verlag Paul Parey, Hamburg/Berlin 1960.

Ellenberg, H.: Vegetation Mitteleuropas mit den Alpen. Verlag Eugen Ulmer, Stuttgart 1982, 3. Aufl.

Elliot, R. H.: The Clifton Park- System of Farming and Laying down Land to Grass. Faber and Faber Ltd., London 1948, 6. Aufl.

Faustzahlen fuer die Landwirtschaft. Ruhrstickstoff Bochum, 1980, 9. Aufl.

Feuerlein, W.: Geraete zur Bodenbearbeitung. Verlag Eugen Ulmer, Stuttgart 1971, 2. Aufl.

Finck, A.: Pflanzenernaehrung in Stichworten. Verlag Ferdinand Hirt, Kiel 1976.

Fischbeck, G., Heylandt, K.-H., und Knauer, N.: Spezieller Pflanzenbau. UTB. Verlag Eugen Ulmer, Stuttgart 1982, 2. Aufl.

Fruwirth, C.: Landwirtschaftlich wichtige Huelsenfruchter. Verlag Paul Parey, Hamburg/Berlin 1936.

Gamperl, H.: Flurbereinigung und Naturschutz. BLV, Muenchen 1952.

Geiger, R.: Der kuenstliche Windschutz als meteorologisches Problem. Erdkunde Band V, Heft 2, Bonn 1951.

Goethe, J. W. von: Metamorphose der Pflanzen. Weimar 1891. Verlag Freies Geistesleben, Stuttgart 1966.

Goetz, A., und Konrad, J.: Landwirtschaftliches Lehrbuch, Band 1 Pflanzenbau. Verlag Eugen Ulmer, Stuttgart 1978, 5. Aufl.

Grohmann, G.: The Plant. Vol. 1. English by Katherine Castelliz. Rudolf Steiner Press, London 1974.

Hanf, M.: Unkraeuter Europas. Klambt-Druck, Speyer 1982.

Harms, J.: Zoobiologie fuer Mediziner und Landwirte. Verlag Gustav Fischer, Jena 1946.

Hartenstein, E.: Tausend Jahre wie ein Tag. Prisma Verlag, Guetersloh 1960.

Hayward, H. E., und Spurr, W. B.: Effects of osmotic concentration of substrate on the entry of water into corn roots. Bot. Gaz. 105, 152–164, 1943.

Heinze, H.: Aus der Entwicklung der Qualitaetsforschung im Institut fuer biologisch-dynamische Forschung. Zeitschrift Lebendige Erde, 42–46 und 139–143, Darmstadt 1978.

Heynitz, K. von, und Merckens, G.: Das biologische Gartenbuch. Verlag Eugen Ulmer, Stuttgart 1981, 2. Aufl.

Heynitz, K. von: Kompost im Garten. Verlag Eugen Ulmer, Stuttgart 1983.

Hoerner, W.: Zeit und Rhythmus. Verlag Urachhaus, Stuttgart 1978.

Hoffmann, G.-M., und Schmutterer, H.: Parasitaere Krankheiten und Schaedlinge an landwirtschaftlichen Kulturpflanzen. Verlag Eugen Ulmer, Stuttgart 1983.

Hoffmann, M.: Abflammtechnik. KTBL-Schrift 243, Darmstadt 1980.

Holzner, W.: Ackerunkraeuter. Leopold Stocker Verlag, Graz 1981 .

Huebner, R.: Der Same in der Landwirtschaft. Neumann-Verlag, Radebeul und Dresden 1955.

Iwersen, J.: Windschutz in Schleswig-Holstein. Gottorfer Schriften, Band II, Schleswig 1953.

Jahrbuch der Gefluegelwirtschaft 1952. Verlag Eugen Ulmer, Stuttgart.

Johannsen. I., Rendel, J., und Gravert, H. O.: Haustiergenetik und Tierzuechtung. Verlag Paul Parey, Hamburg/Berlin 1966.

Kaffka, S.: Dairy farm management and energy use efficiency. Thesis of Cornell University, Ithaca, New York 1984.

Kahnt, G.: Ackerbau ohne Pflug. Verlag Eugen Ulmer, Stuttgart 1976.

Kaiser, H.: Die Anwendung des Reynoldschen Aehnlichkeitsgesetzes auf Stroemungswiderstaende. Meteorologische Rundschau, Heft 6, 121, 1953.

Kiel, W.: Acker- und Pflanzenbau. Deutscher Bauernverlag, Berlin 1954.

Kirchner, H.-A.: Grundriss der Phytopathologie und des Pflanzenschutzes. VEB Gustav Fischer Verlag, Jena 1975.

Klapp, E.: Futterbau und Gruenlandnutzung. Verlag Paul Parey, Hamburg/Berlin 1951.

Klapp, E.: Taschenbuch der Graeser. Verlag Paul Parey, Hamburg/Berlin 1952.

Knapp, R.: Experimentelle Soziologie und gegenseitige Beeinflussung der Pflanzen. Verlag Eugen Ulmer, Stuttgart 1967.

Knapp, R.: Einfuehrung in die Pflanzensoziologie. Eugen Ulmer, Stuttgart 1971.

Koch, W., und Hurle, K.: Grundlagen der Unkrautbekaempfung. Verlag Eugen Ulmer, Stuttgart 1978.

Koennecke, G.: Pflanzenbauliche Grundsatzfragen der Fruchtfolgegestaltung. Die Deutsche Landwirtschaft, Heft 7, 1961.

Koepf, H. H., Pettersson, B. D., and Schaumann, W. Bio-Dynamic Agriculture. Anthroposophic Press, Spring Valley, New York 1976.

Koepf, H.: Landbau natur- und menschengemaess. Verlag Freies Geistesleben, Stuttgart 1980.

Kolisko, E.: Die zwoelf Gruppen des Tierreiches. Gaea Sophia Band V, Verlag Emil Weises. Dresden 1930.

Kraeusslich, H.: Rinderzucht. Verlag Eugen Ulmer, Stuttgart 1981, 6. Aufl.

Kraus, C.: Zur Kenntnis der Verbreitung der Wurzeln in Bestaenden von Rein- und Mischsaaten. Fruehling Landw. Zeitung, Heft 10, 337–412, 1914.

Kreutz, W.: Der Windschutz. Ardea-Verlag, Dortmund 1952.

Kuenzel, M.: Ueber den Nutzen von Saatbaedern. Neuaufbau Biologisch-Dynamischer Landbau 1945–1949. Schriftenreihe Lebendige Erde, Stuttgart 1949.

Kuhlewind, C.: Der Windschutz als Mittel der Landeskultur. DLG-Mitteilungen Nr. 50, 1953.

Kuhlewind, C.: Die Windschutzplanung fuer die Neusiedlung Vosseneck. Ministerium fuer Ernaehrung, Landwirtschaft und Forsten und Wiederaufbau, Nordrhein-Westfalen 1951 .

Kuhlewind, C., Bringmann, L., und Blenk, H.: Richtlinien fuer Windschutz. Teil 1 und 2, Duesseldorf 1955, DLG-Verlag, Frankfurt/Main.

Kuratorium fuer Technik und Bauwesen in der Landwirtschaft (KTBL): Datensammlung fuer die Betriebsplanung in der Landwirtschaft. Landwirtschaftsverlag, Muenster-Hiltrup 1981, 7. Aufl.

Kutschera, L.: Wurzelatlas mitteleuropaeischer Ackerunkraeuter und Kulturpflanzen. DLG-Verlag, Frankfurt/M. 1960.

Laatsch, W.: Dynamik der mitteleuropaeischen Mineralboeden. Verlag T. Steinkopff, Dresden und Leipzig 1954.

Larcher, W.: Oekologie der Pflanzen. UTB. Verlag Eugen Ulmer, Stuttgart 1984.

Liebig, J. von: Ueber den Materialismus. Chemische Briefe, Leipzig 1865. Neu herausgegeben in Schriftenreihe Lebendige Erde, Darmstadt 1959.

Lockeretz, W., et al.: A Comparison of the Production, Economic Returns and Energy Intensiveness. CBNS Washington University, Saint Louis 1975.

Magerstedt, A. F.: Der Feld-, Garten- und Wiesenbau der Roemer. Dr. Martin Saendig oHG, Walluf bei Wiesbaden 1972.

Mangelsdorf, P.C., et al.: Do-mestication of Corn. In Caldwell, J. R. (ed.): New Roads to Yesterday. Basic Books, New York 1966.

Moll, W.: Taschenbuch fuer Umweltschutz III. Nr. 901, UTB. Verlag Ernst Reinhardt, Muenchen und Basel 1982.

Mueller, R.: Sonnenforschung im Internationalen Geophysikalischen Jahr. Muenchen 1958.

Nachtsheim, H., und Stengel, H.: Vom Wildtier zum Haustier. Verlag Paul Parey Hamburg/Berlin 1977.

Naegeli, W.: Untersuchungen ueber die Windverhaeltnisse im Bereich von Windschutzanlagen. Mitteilungen der Schweizerischen Anstalt fuer das forstliche Versuchswesen, Heft 1, 1943.

Naegeli, W.: Weitere Untersuchungen ueber die Windverhältnisse im Bereich von Windschutzstreifen. Mitteilungen der Schweizerischen Anstalt fuer das forstliche Versuchswesen, Heft 2, 1946.

Naegeli, W.: Untersuchungen ueber die Windverhaeltnisse im Bereich von Schilfwaenden. Mitteilungen der Schweizerischen Anstalt fuer das forstliche Versuchswesen, Heft 2, 1953.

Oberdorf, F.: Wirtschaftliche Pflanzengemeinschaft im Ackerbau. Deutscher Bauernverlag, Berlin 1953.

Padel, S.: Anforderungen an Sorten im biologischen Getreidebau. IFOAM, Heft 48, 1. Quartal 1984.

Pettersson, B., und Wistinghausen, E. von: Bodenuntersuchungen zu einem langjaehrigen Feldversuch in Jaerna, Schweden. Forschungsring fuer biologisch-dynamische Wirtschaftsweise, Darmstadt 1977

Planck, M.: Der Kausalbegriff in der Physik. Determinismus und Indeterminismus. Scheinprobleme der Wissenschaft. Johann Ambrosius Barth Verlag, Leipzig 1953.

Plinius secundus d. Ae., C.: Naturkunde. Buch 2: Kosmologie, Buch 11: Zoologie, Buch 12–19: Botanik. Heimeran Verlag, Muenchen 1976.

Popow, J. S.: Ernaehrung landwirtschaftlicher Nutztiere. Deutscher Landwirtschaftsverlag, Berlin 1960.

Preuschen, G.: Unkrautbekaempfung durch Abflammen. DLG-Mitteilungen, Heft 22, 841, 1968.

Regierungspraesidium Stuttgart (Hrsg.): Einfuehrung in die Wirtschaftslehre. Meisterpruef.-Vorbereitungskurs 1974.

Reisch, E., und Zeddies, I.: Einfuehrung in die landwirtschaftliche Betriebslehre. Band 2: Spezieller Teil. Verlag Eugen Ulmer, Stuttgart 1977.

Remer, N.: Gesundheit und Leistung bei Haustieren. Demeter-Schriftenreihe Band 5. Muellersche Verlagsbuchhandlung, Dresden 1940.

Remer, N.: Bodenstaendige Dauerfruchtbarkeit. Schriftenreihe Lebendige Erde, Stuttgart 1954.

Remer, N.: Lebensgesetze im Landbau. Philosophisch-Anthroposophischer Verlag am Goetheanum, Dornach/Schweiz 1968.

Remer, N.: Organischer Duenger. Selbstverlag N. Remer, Amelinghausen 1978.

Renius, W.: Untersaaten im Gruenduengungs-Zwischenfruchtbau. Lebendige Erde 65–68, Darmstadt 1978.

Renius, W.: Warum und wie Herbst-Graseinsaat im Futterzwischenfruchtbau und Gruenduengungsanbau. Zeitschrift Lebendige Erde 98–101, Darmstadt 1978.

Renzenbrink, U: Die sieben Getreide. Rudolf Geering Verlag, Dornach/Schweiz 1981.

Rickert, M.: Der Landhaushalt. Verlag Paul Parey, Hamburg/Berlin 1952.

Roy, H. L. le: Elemente der Tierzucht. BLV, Muenchen 1966.

Ruebensam, E., und Rauhe, K: Ackerbau. Deutscher Landwirtschaftsverlag, Berlin 1964.

Sattler, F.: Meisterarbeit 1973: Die kuenftige Organisation des Talhofes nach Verkleinerung der landwirtschaftlichen Nutzflaeche. Unveroeffentlicht.

Sattler, F.: Von der Entwicklung des Talhofes. Zeitschrift Lebendige Erde, Sonderdruck, Darmstadt 1977.

Sauerlandt, W., und Tietjen, C.: Humuswirtschaft des Ackers. DLG-Verlag, Frankfurt/Main 1970.

Schaumann, W.: Die Bildung der Pflanzenqualitaet als Ergebnis der Wirkung von Erde und Sonne. Zeitschrift Lebendige Erde, Heft 4, Darmstadt 1972.

Schaumann, W.: Kann die Landwirtschaft auf den Weg gebracht werden, immer weniger synthetisch-chemische Mittel anzuwenden? Zeitschrift Lebendige Erde, Sonderdruck, Darmstadt 1980.

Schechtner, G.: Aktuelle Fragen der Wirtschaftsduengeranwendung auf dem Gruenland. 5. Arbeitstag "Guellerei". Bundesvers.-Anstalt, Gumpenstein 1969.

Scheerer, G.: Fruchttragende Hecken. Gartenverlag GmbH, Berlin-Kl. Machnow 1951.

Scheffer, F., und Schachtschabel, P.: Lehrbuch der Bodenkunde. Verlag Ferdinand Enke, Stuttgart 1982, 11. Aufl.

Schieblich, J.: Saatguterzeugung bei Futterpflanzen. Deutscher Bauernverlag, Berlin 1959.

Schiemann, E.: Weizen, Roggen, Gerste. Systematik, Geschichte und Verwendung. Verlag G. Fischer, Jena 1948.

Schlichting, E., und Blume, H. P.: Bodenkundliches Praktikum. Verlag Paul Parey, Berlin/Hamburg 1966.

Schroeder, D.: Bodenkunde in Stichworten. Verlag Ferdinand Hirt, Kiel 1978, 3. Aufl.

Schumacher, W.: Lehrbuch der Botanik. 2. Teil Physiologie. Gustav Fischer Verlag, Stuttgart 1958.

Schuphan, W.: Mensch und Nahrungspflanze. Hrsg.: Eden-Stiftung Bad Soden/Ts., Dr. W. Junk, b. v. Verlag, Den Haag 1976.

Schwarz, M. K.: Der Gaertnerhof im Gefuege der Landschaft. Verlag Boden und Gesundheit, Langenburg 1974.

Sekera, M.: Gesunder und kranker Boden. Leopold Stocker Verlag, Graz, 1958.

Spielberger, U., und Schaette, R.: Biologische Stallapotheke. Verlag Lebendige Erde, Darmstadt 1983.

Spiess, H.: Ueber die Wirkungen der biologisch-dynamischen Praeparate Hornmist und Hornkiesel auf Ertrag und Qualität einiger Kulturpflanzen. Lebendige Erde, Heft 4/5, Darmstadt 1979.

Spiess, H., und Junker, H.: Bekaempfung des Weizensteinbrandes (Tilletia caries) im biologisch-dynamischen Anbau. Zeitschrift Lebendige Erde 5, 220–227, Darmstadt 1986.

Standop, E.. Die Form der wissenschaftlichen Arbeit. UTB. Verlag Quelle und Meyer, Heidelberg 1981.

Statistisches Jahrbuch 1978 fuer die Bundesrepublik Deutschland. Kohlhammer-Verlag, Stuttgart.

Steckhan, H.: Bodenabtrag durch Wind in Niedersachsen. Neues Archiv fuer Niedersachsen, Heft 17, Bremen 1950.

Steiner, R.: Occult Science: An Outline. English by G. and M. Adams. Rudolf

Steiner Press, London 1979.

Steiner, R.: The Agriculture Course. English by G. Adams. Bio-Dynamic Agricultural Association, London 1974.

Steiner, R.: The Social Future. English by H.B. Monges. Anthroposophic Press, Hudson, New York 1972.

Steiner, R.: Natur- und Geistwesen. Gesamtausgabe Nr. 98. Rudolf-Steiner-Verlag, Dornach 1983.

Steinmann, R.: Der biologische Landbau – ein betriebswirtschaftlicher Vergleich. FAT-Schriftenreihe, Heft 19. Eidgenoessische Forschungsanstalt fuer Betriebswirtschaft und Technik, Taenikon 1983.

Tierschutzgesetz der Bundesrepublik Deutschland 1972.

Thun, M. and K.: Working with the Stars. A Bio-Dynamic Sowing and Planting Calendar. Lanthorn Press, East Grinstead, published annually.

Thun, M.: Unkraut. Selbstverlag, Biedenkopf 1980.

Thun, M., und Heinze, H.: Anbauversuche und Zusammenhaenge zwischen Mondstellung im Tierkreis und Kulturpflanzen, Band 1 und 2. Schriftenreihe Lebendige Erde, Darmstadt 1973.

Tokin, B.: Phytonzide. VEB-Verlag, Volk und Gesundheit, Berlin 1956.

Trolldenier, C.: Bodenbiologie. Die Bodenorganismen im Haushalt der Natur. Franckh'sche Verlagshandlung, Stuttgart 1971.

Vetter, H., und Klasink, A.: Grenzen fuer die Anwendung hoher Fluessigmistgaben aus Mist und Guelle. DLG-Verlag, Frankfurt/Main 1973.

Voisin, A.: Die Weidetetanie. BLV, Muenchen 1963.

Vreede, E.: Anthroposophie und Astronomie. Novalis-Verlag, Freiburg/Br. 1954.

Wachsmuth, G.: Erde und Mensch. Philosophisch-Anthroposophischer Verlag, Dornach 1965. 3. Aufl.

Wala: Praeparate fuer die Tierheilkunde. Wala-Heilmittel GmbH, Eckwaelden, ohne Jahr, 2. Aufl.

Weichel, E.: Neue Verfahren und Geraete zur oekologisch orientierten Bodenbearbeitung. Stiftung Oekologischer Landbau. C. F. Mueller, Karlsruhe 1980.

Wenner, H. L., und Mitarbeiter: Landtechnik und Bauwesen. Die Landwirtschaft Band 3. Landwirtschaftsverlag GmbH, Muenster-Hiltrup 1973.

Werr, J.: Tierzucht und Tiermedizin. Schriftenreihe Lebendige Erde, Stuttgart 1953.

Wildermuth, H.: Natur als Aufgabe. Schweizerischer Bund fuer Naturschutz 1980.

Wiljams, W. R.: Das Trawolpolnajasystem der Landwirtschaft. Uebers. von G. Jury. Berlin 1958.

Willmann, K. T.: Das Leben und Wirken der Wuermer im Gartenland. Zeitschrift Lebendige Erde, Darmstadt, 226–230, 1974; 17–23, 1976.

Wistinghausen, A. von: Vergleichende Ertrags- und Qualitaetsuntersuchungen in Zusammenarbeit mit der Landwirtschaftskammer Berlin. Zeitschrift Lebendige Erde, 16, Darmstadt 1973.

Wistinghausen, A. von: Erinnerungen an den Anfang der biologisch-dynamischen Wirtschaftsweise. Verlag Lebendige Erde, Darmstadt 1982.

Wistinghausen, A. von: Leguminosen. Eine Pflanzenfamilie hilft der biologisch-dynamischen Landwirtschaft. Schriftenreihe Lebendige Erde, Darmstadt 1985.

Wistinghausen, E. von: Die Qualitaet von Moehren, Rote Bete und Weizen in Beziehung zu ihren Standortverhaeltnissen und Bodenbedingungen. Zeitschrift Lebendige Erde, Heft 3, Sonderdruck, Darmstadt 1976.

Wistinghausen, E. von: Der Boden ein lebendiges Organ. Zeitschrift Lebendige Erde, Sonderdruck, Darmstadt 1978.

Wistinghausen, E. von: Was ist Qualitaet? Wie entsteht sie und wie ist sie nachzuweisen? Schriftenreihe Lebendige Erde, Darmstadt 1979.

Wistinghausen, E. von: Untersuchungen zur Qualitaetsfindung am Beispiel der Moehre im Feldversuch. Elemente der Naturwissenschaften, Dornach 1/1979.

Wistinghausen, E. von: Einfuhr und Ausfuhr von Stoffen im landwirtschaftlichen Betrieb. Zeitschrift Lebendige Erde, Heft I, 53, 1980. Schriftenreihe des BMELF 1982, Alternativen im Landbau, Angewandte Wissenschaft, Heft 263.

Wistinghausen, E. von: Duengung und biologisch-dynamische Praeparate. Schriftenreihe Lebendige Erde, Darmstadt 1984.

Woelfle, M.: Waldbau und Forstmeteorologie BLV, Muenchen 1950.

Zander. Handwoerterbuch der Pflanzennamen. Neubearbeitet von F. Encke, G. Buchheim, S. Seybold. Verlag Eugen Ulmer, Stuttgart 1984, 13. Aufl.

Index

Colour Plates
(facing pages 80, 81, 96, 97, 192, 193, 208, 209)

M. Bauer, Tuebingen: plate 36.
M. Hollerbach, Bad Vilbel: plate 23.
F. Sattler, Heidenheim: plates 1, 2, 5, 6, 7, 8, 10, 11, 12, 13,
14, 15, 16, 17, 18, 19, 20, 21, 22, 24, 25, 26, 27, 28, 29, 30,
31, 34.
H. Schrempp, Breisach: plates 32, 33.
E. v. Wistinghausen, Darmstadt: plates 3, 4, 9, 35.

Additional Reading list

Baker, C.T.G.: Understanding the Honeybee. Bio-Dynamic Agricultural Association, Stourbridge 1981.

Castelliz, K.: Life to the Land. Lanthorn Press, East Grinstead 1980 .

Cloos, W.: The Living Earth. Lanthorn Press, East Grinstead 1977. (Translation of an earlier edition than that cited in the main literature list).

Corrin, G.: Handbook on Composting and the Bio-Dynamic Preparations. Bio-Dynamic Agricultural Association, London 1960.

Groh, T. and McFadden, S.: Farms of Tomorrow: Community Supported Farms and Farm Supported Communities. Bio-Dynamic Literature, Kimberton 1990.

Grotzke, H.: Bio-Dynamic Greenhouse Management. Bio-Dynamic Literature, Kimberton 1990.

Kimberton Hills Agricultural Calendar. Kimberton Hills, Kimberton published annually.

Koepf, H.H.: Compost. Bio-Dynamic Literature, Kimberton 1990.

Koepf, H.H.: The Bio-Dynamic Farm. Anthroposophic Press, New York 1989.

Koepf, H.H.: Bio-Dynamic Sprays. Bio-Dynamic Literature, Kimberton 1981.

Kolisko E. and Kolisko, L.: Agriculture of Tomorrow. Kolisko Archive Publications, Ringwood 1982.

New Zealand Bio-Dynamic Association: Bio-Dynamics. Random House, Auckland 1989.

Pfeiffer, E.: Bio-Dynamic Treatment of Fruit Trees, Berries and Shrubs. Bio-Dynamic Farming and Gardening Association, Stroudsberg 1976.

Pfeiffer, E.: Bio-Dynamic Gardening and Farming (3 volumes). Mercury Press, Spring Valley, New York 1983-84.

Pfeiffer, E.: The Earth's Face. Lanthorn Press, East Grinstead 1988.

Pfeiffer, E.: Soil Fertility, Renewal and Preservation. Lanthorn Press, East Grinstead 1983.

Pfeiffer, E. and Riese, E.: Grow a Garden and be Self-sufficient. Mercury Press, Spring Valley, New York 1985.

Philbrick, H. and Gregg, R.B.: Companion Plants. Broadcast Books, Shaftesbury 1991.

Pliny, the Elder: Natural History: A Selection. Penguin Books, Harmondsworth 1991. (The only accessible English translation, unfortunately less complete than that cited in the main literature list).

Podolinsky, A.: Bio-Dynamic Agriculture. Introductory Lectures (2 volumes). Gavemer Foundation Publications, Sydney 1985.

Remer, N.: The Laws of Life in Agriculture. Bio-Dynamic Farming and Gardening Association, Kimberton (in press).

Soper, J. Studying the Agriculture Course. Bio-Dynamic Agricultural Association, London 1976.

Soper, J.: Bio-Dynamic Gardening. Bio-Dynamic Agricultural Association, Stourbridge 1983.

Storl, W.D.: Culture and Horticulture. Bio-Dynamic Literature, Kimberton 1979.

Thun, M.: Work on the Land and the Constellations. Lanthorn Press, East Grinstead 1990.